S324 ANIMAL PHYSIOLOGY BOOK 3
SCIENCE: A THIRD LEVEL COURSE

D0315844

Size and Action

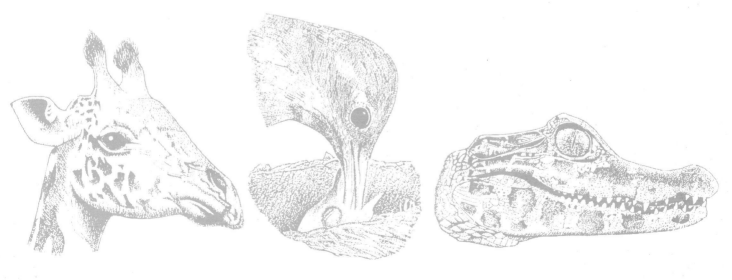

ANIMAL PHYSIOLOGY BOOK 3 BY CAROLINE POND

THE S324 COURSE TEAM

COURSE TEAM CHAIR

David Robinson

COURSE MANAGER

Colin Walker

AUTHOR FOR BOOK 3

Caroline Pond

OTHER CONTRIBUTORS TO THE COURSE

Anthony Cassidy
Bob Cordell
Marion Hall
Robin Harding
Tim Halliday
Jean Holley
Richard Holmes
Colin Jones (University of Oxford)
Stewart Richards (Wye College)
Jonathan Rosewell
Jennie Simmons
Ted Taylor and Nia Whiteley
(The University of Birmingham)
Alison Tedstone (London School of
Hygiene and Tropical Medicine)
Jeff Thomas

DESIGN

Debbie Crouch

ILLUSTRATION

Janis Gilbert

EDITORS

Perry Morley
Joanna Munnelly
Bina Sharma

INDEX

Jean Macqueen

BBC

Hendrik Ball
Sandra Budin
Andrew Crilly
Mike Gunton
David Jackson
Aileen Llewellyn
Barrie Whatley

COURSE SECRETARY

Yvonne Royals

ASSESSORS FOR BOOK 3

Dr Michael Cullen (Muscular Dystrophy Laboratories,
Newcastle upon Tyne)
Professor John Currey (University of York)
Professor Paul Racey (University of Aberdeen)
Professor A. J. F. Webster (University of Bristol)

This book is dedicated to Dr Richard Holmes, who died suddenly on 23 September 1994, during the final stages of its preparation. Richard Holmes was closely associated with S324 *Animal Physiology*, and its predecessor S321, from its beginnings in 1974. The course owes much to his inspiration and guidance.

The Open University
Walton Hall, Milton Keynes
MK7 6AA
First published 1995

Copyright © 1995 The Open University

All rights reserved. No part of this publication may be reproduced, stored in a retrieval system or transmitted, in any form or by any means, without written permission from the publisher or a licence from the Copyright Licensing Agency Limited. Details of such licences (for reprographic reproduction) may be obtained from the Copyright Licensing Agency Limited of 90 Tottenham Court Road, London, WC1P 9HE.

Edited, designed and typeset by the Open University

Printed in the United Kingdom by Henry Ling Ltd, at the Dorset Press, Dorchester, Dorset

ISBN 0 7492 5137 9

This text forms part of an Open University Third Level Course. If you would like a copy of *Studying with the Open University*, please write to the Central Enquiry Service, PO Box 200, The Open University, Walton Hall, Milton Keynes, MK7 6YZ. If you have not already enrolled on the Course and would like to buy this or other Open University material, please write to Open University Educational Enterprises Ltd, 12 Cofferidge Close, Stony Stratford, Milton Keynes, MK11 1BY, United Kingdom.

1.1

CONTENTS

CHAPTER I   WHOLE-BODY GROWTH

1.1 Introduction

The first four chapters of Book 3 are about changes in the size, composition and physiological capacities of the body during an organism's lifetime. With few exceptions (such as metamorphosis in certain insects), the ordinary life functions continue while growth is in progress but, unlike other life processes such as respiration and excretion, becoming larger is not essential to the life of any particular cell or organism. Some cells or organisms can live for many years without any noticeable growth taking place, but can become larger very rapidly in the appropriate environment or physiological circumstances.

Many different factors influence when and how fast animals grow: nutrition, competing demands on physiological resources such as reproduction or exercise and endogenous factors such as hormones. Because so many different kinds of cells and organs are involved in growth, it is very difficult to isolate, and thus experiment with, single factors that influence the process. Thus research identifies more and more factors that can be shown to influence growth processes, but none proves to be in overall 'command' of the growth of a single tissue or organ. As discussed in Chapter 4, there could be sound physiological reasons for such a multitude of regulators with apparently overlapping functions.

The continuous turnover of the body fabric and the repair of injured or poisoned tissues are integral to the life of all cellular organisms at all stages of the life cycle. Living organisms are engaged in constant turnover of energy and nutrients, much of which are used for movement and to sustain life. Degenerative disease, injury or the need for rapid enlargement may require the diversion of a portion, sometimes a very large portion, of the available energy and nutrients towards tissue growth and repair. The mechanisms of growth and repair are intimately linked and are discussed together in Chapter 2.

Different organs and parts of the body may grow at different rates, with the result that the shape and composition, as well as the size, of the body change with time. The implications of such changes in the relative sizes of body parts and rates of biochemical processes are the theme of Chapter 3.

With time, all organisms become older and most grow larger, but the association between age and capacity for growth differs greatly between species. In many insects and small vertebrates (e.g. some small mammals and birds), the age at which growth stops is fixed, sometimes to the nearest day, but in many other groups, such as tortoises, most fish and many soft-bodied invertebrates, it is very variable. There is no fixed relationship between size and age: healthy individuals of similar age can differ greatly in size, depending upon the conditions under which they have been living. One important factor that curtails growth is the onset of sexual maturity when the organism starts to divert resources from its own somatic growth to reproduction. Although ageing necessarily accompanies growth, and often affects the organism's capacity for enlargement and repair, it is a distinct process that is addressed in Chapter 4.

Among the chief consequences of becoming larger and older are changes in the capacity for movement and their implications for locomotion, feeding and reproductive capacity. The second half of the book is about the structure and function of the musculature and skeleton and how they work together to produce locomotion. Repair and replacement are particularly important for tissues that are exposed to continual wear or to large forces, such as those incurred during movement, for example, the skin, the lining of the gut, and the muscles and skeleton. So concepts developed in the first half of the book are used to explore some mechanisms by which these tissues maintain their integrity in the face of frequent damage, and to explain what happens to their function when repair and replacement fail.

1.1.1   The measurement and analysis of growth

The study of growth involves first, the description of the phenomenon of growth, such as changes in mass, length or other dimension; second, the study of the mechanisms that underlie the gross changes; and third, how these mechanisms are controlled by endogenous factors arising from the organism itself or by environmental factors. Studies designed to document the course of normal growth must avoid using invasive or destructive methods likely to affect any future growth. It is usually possible to measure both the total body mass and the linear dimensions of living organisms very accurately without doing them any damage. For long, narrow animals such as fish, lizards, snakes and people, body length (which in people means standing height) can be quantified easily and accurately and is a sensitive measure of changes in total body size.

Professor James Tanner and his colleagues began their study of growth in children in the 1950s by measuring these simple parameters in a group of London schoolchildren. Figure 1.1 shows some of the data expressed as a simple relationship between standing height and age in boys and girls. Satisfactory though Figure 1.1 might be as a description of events, it cannot tell us much about the biological processes that produce and control growth. A step towards clarifying such factors can be taken by replotting the same data in the way shown in Figure 1.2. This Figure shows the interaction of age and growth velocity: the annual increment in height of the children as a function of age.

■   Examine Figures 1.1 and 1.2 carefully and answer the following questions:

(a)   What is the difference in height between girls and boys aged from birth to 10 y?

(b)   What is the difference in the growth velocity of boys and girls between birth and 10 y?

(c)   State three ways in which the adolescent growth spurt differs between boys and girls.

(a)   Boys are slightly taller throughout this period, but the difference is less than 5%.

(b)   Girls grow slightly faster than boys between the ages of 1 and 4 y, then at about the same rate as boys. After the age of 8 y, girls start to grow much more rapidly than boys of the same age.

(c)   The adolescent growth spurt starts at an earlier age in girls, but the maximum growth velocity achieved is lower, and the growth spurt lasts for a shorter total time than in boys.

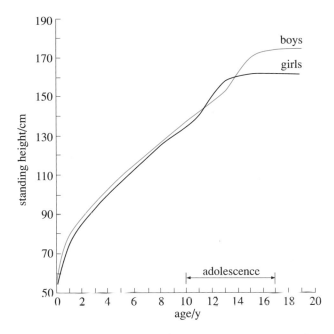

Figure 1.1   Average standing height of London boys and girls as a function of age.

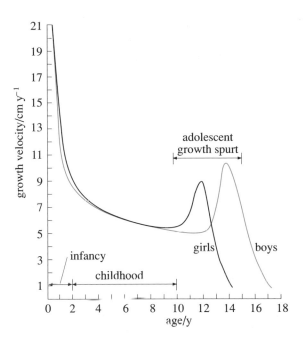

Figure 1.2   Growth velocity of boys and girls as a function of age. These data are the same as those used for Figure 1.1.

This mathematical manipulation of these data has directed the investigators' attention towards the essential properties of the mechanism(s) that determine(s) growth velocity: a factor operating in girls at about the age of 8.5 y and in boys at the age of 12 y promotes, or permits, a sudden increase in the growth velocity. Faster growth in height continues for longer in boys than in girls, with the result that young men are taller than young women when growth in height stops.

Growth in height is only one aspect of body development. In organisms that retain more or less constant body density and body shape, growth in mass would be expected to be related to linear dimensions cubed. If a body is assumed to be mathematically similar to a square or a sphere, then a single linear dimension, such as length of the side of a cube or the radius of a sphere, is proportional to $(area)^{1/2}$ and to $(volume)^{1/3}$. If the density of a body is constant, mass is directly proportional to volume.

The cubic relationship between height (a linear dimension) and mass is only approximately true for the many animals, including humans, whose body shape and body proportions do not remain constant throughout life. As most people know to their dismay, growth in mass can, and very often does, continue long after growth in height ends and the relationship between height and body mass can vary greatly between individuals.

The various measures of growth processes should also be viewed in relation to the size of the growing organism. Assuming that each tissue or cell does its share of accumulating and synthesizing the materials for growth, larger organisms would be expected to be capable of higher rates of growth. In other words, older children might be expected to grow faster simply because they have become larger. In fact, as you can see from Figure 1.2, this expectation is not borne out:

the most rapid growth is observed in the youngest infants. The very rapid growth in 'height' of neonates should therefore be seen as even more impressive compared to the growth velocities observed later in life, because infants are smaller and hence have less tissue 'with which to grow'. Clearly the tissues of neonates are devoting a much greater proportion of their metabolic resources to growth than those of more mature individuals.

1.2 Experimental approaches to the study of growth

The energy and chemical substrates needed to support growth can account for a very substantial fraction of the organism's total intake of energy and nutrients. Experiments in which a growing organism is deprived of a single component of its diet can both pin-point nutrients that are essential to growth and draw attention to endogenous mechanisms of growth regulation. Although spectacular and sometimes grotesque changes in body shape and size can be produced quite easily by extreme manipulation of diet or environment during growth, experimental manipulation must be carefully planned if it is to reveal natural mechanisms of growth. In mammals and birds, growth after birth is both easier to document and easier to experiment upon, so this topic is treated first.

1.2.1 Nutrition and growth

In most animals, the same food that sustains normal life in the non-growing organism also supports growth; few foods, if any, can be uniquely designated 'growth foods'. Nutritional experiments, therefore, are of two main kinds: an animal may be given a nutritionally adequate diet in restricted quantities, or be given a diet in which essential components such as vitamins or minerals are reduced or eliminated. Experiments in which the quantity but not the composition of the diet is varied shed some light upon the organism's ability to retard or accelerate its growth rate; those in which particular nutrients are lacking can show how the organism orders its 'priorities' for the growth of certain tissues or anatomical parts.

Humans and domestic animals, particularly animals bred for meat, are among the few species whose growth on different diets has been intensively studied. Figure 1.3 shows some data for the growth of children in Sweden in 1883, 1938 and 1968. Almost everyone is aware of the enormous improvements in the palatability and digestibility of the Western diet since the beginning of the 20th century. Improvements in food technology mean that, from birth onwards, people can eat greater quantities of more nutritious, less contaminated food for less effort than a generation ago. Immunization, better hygiene and antibiotic drugs have greatly reduced the incidence and severity of infectious diseases such as mumps and measles, which as recently as the 1950s were very common in childhood, and often severe enough curtail growth for several months.

■   Identify and explain three changes in growth pattern that have taken place between 1883 and 1968.

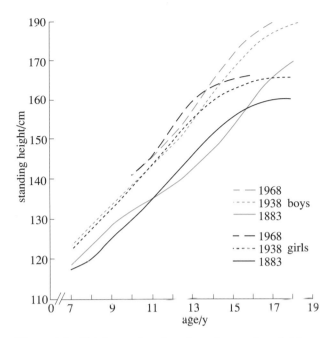

Figure 1.3   Height as a function of age for samples of girls and boys in Sweden in 1883, 1938 and 1968.

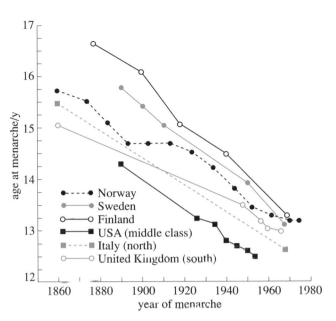

Figure 1.4   Change in age of menarche of girls living in different countries.

First, both sexes were taller when growth stopped in 1968 than in 1883. Second, the peak growth velocity was higher (the slope of the curve steeper) in 1968 than in 1883. Third, children continued to grow at an older age in 1883 compared with 1968, i.e. girls of 16 y and boys of 18 y were still growing in 1883, but in 1968 girls had almost reached their adult height at age 15 y and boys at age 17 y.

These data show that improved nutrition has resulted in taller people, but they are not as tall as would be expected if the people eating the better diets in 1938 and 1968 did not also stop growing at an earlier age than in 1883. Both growth rate and the age at which growth takes place are affected by the improvements in nutrition and health. A similar conclusion is reached from studies of growth on meagre diets. Since the time of the French Revolution, it has been noted that boys recruited into the army at the age of 18 or 19 y often grow significantly up to the age of 22 y on the richer, more plentiful army diet. However, civilian boys of the same age, who remain on the poorer diet, hardly grow at all and hence become shorter adults. Such boys who have been growing more slowly than the 'optimum' rate retain the ability to grow to a later age than 20th-century teenagers whose richer diet enables them to reach full stature at a younger age. In humans, as in most mammals, the capacity for growth is not retained indefinitely and comes to an end at or shortly after attainment of sexual maturity, even if the individual has not reached the normal size.

Documentation of the age at which boys stop growing is tedious because it involves frequent, careful measurements. In contrast, the age of **menarche** in girls (onset of menstruation) is relatively easy to pin-point exactly, and has long been recognized as an indicator of sexual maturation (although girls do not become fully fertile or capable of mature adult sexual behaviour until several years later). Reliable records have been kept in various countries since the 1850s. Figure 1.4 shows some data for samples of girls living in various Western countries, where there have been major improvements in nutrition and public health during the 20th century. In the final years of the 19th century, there were large differences between countries in the average age of menarche, with Finnish girls maturing more than 2.5 years later than those living in the USA. The age of menarche in all the populations studied decreased at an almost steady rate of 3–4 months per decade. The data from different countries gradually converge, so that girls in these countries now reach menarche up to 3.5 y earlier than they did in 1860.

■   Can this change in the age of menarche be explained as a simple consequence of the effect of nutrition on the growth rate and the age at which growth stops?

No. If you compare Figures 1.3 and 1.4 you can see that the very rapid growth has almost stopped by the time menarche occurred at age 15.75 y in the 1883 Swedish sample. In contrast, menarche at 13.0 y in 1968 takes place while the girls' rate of growth is just beginning to slow down after the period of fastest growth.

Simple measurements like these highlight the importance of endogenous (internal) control of growth in mammals, particularly the relationship between chronological age and capacity for growth.

1.2.2 The effect of undernutrition on the relative growth of tissues

The quantity of food an animal eats can easily be controlled from birth until weaning. The usual procedure in laboratory experiments is to cross-foster newborn rats so that some are fed in groups of 18 to a mother and others in groups of nine or fewer to a mother. Assuming that each pup gets an equal share, those in large groups are undernourished but not malnourished: they receive smaller quantities of a diet of the same composition. After weaning, rats can be given normal or reduced quantities of rat chow, a synthetic food known to contain all nutrients necessary to sustain healthy rats. Such experiments show that underfeeding during the 21-day suckling period produces undersized rats, but the treatment affects all organs studied more or less equally. When the tissues were analysed for DNA, RNA and protein content, it was found that the ratios of DNA : protein were similar to those of the larger well-fed controls.

■   What important aspect of growth can be deduced from measuring the DNA : protein ratio in tissues?

Total DNA content in a tissue is a measure of the total number of cells in it (assuming that each cell has the same amount of DNA, which is roughly true for most animal tissues). Except in a few kinds of specialized cells such as adipocytes, most of the non-genetic material (other than water) in cells is protein, so the ratio of DNA : protein is a rough measure of the mean size of the cells. A constant DNA : protein ratio indicates that average cell size is also unchanged. So the miniature rats have fewer cells, but each cell is of normal size.

Smaller rats were also produced when undernutrition was imposed for the 21 days immediately following weaning, but in this case, different tissues were affected in different ways. Most of the organs studied were affected in the same way as in the previous experiment, but two organs, the brain and the lungs, were smaller in size, and had less protein and RNA than expected although the same quantity of DNA was found in these tissues as in the well-fed rats of the same age.

■   What conclusions can you draw from these data?

In the brain and lungs only, cell division, which gives rise to an increase in the DNA content of the tissue, was either complete before the diet was restricted, or continued unabated in spite of the poor nutrition. The point is that the brain and lungs were affected in a different way by the treatment, compared to the heart, liver, kidneys, glands and muscles.

Rats that had been undernourished during the suckling period were allowed to grow to adulthood on a plentiful diet; although such animals grew substantially after weaning, they never caught up with rats that had been well-fed since birth and all their tissues remained smaller than those of controls of the same age. Rats which were underfed only when aged 21–42 days, and then raised to adulthood on an adequate diet, had brains and lungs which were as large as those of the continuously well-fed rats. The other organs failed to grow as fast as those of the controls, and as a result these rats became out of proportion as adults, with normal-sized brains and lungs, but small bodies and limbs.

These experiments show that undernourishment early in life impedes cell division, and the consequences of the deficiency cannot later be rectified in full. The outcomes of treatments that reduce cell enlargement, without affecting cell proliferation, are more quickly repaired because the tissues can complete their growth later, when normal nutrition is restored. How badly tissues are affected by undernutrition depends in part upon the stage in the life history at which the cells are dividing most rapidly. The growth of a tissue is likely to be permanently stunted if the animal is undernourished during its period of cell proliferation.

Conversely, continuous good nourishment during the juvenile period favours the growth of limbs, muscles and fat, which grow fastest after the brain and other essential organs are almost full-size. This effect is well known among farm animals raised for meat. It is also occurring in the human population of modern Japan. Under the influence of America from 1945 onwards, many new foods, such as milk, cheese and red meat that are rich in fats and protein, were introduced to Japan and quickly became popular. The average standing height of the present generation of teenagers and young adults is several centimetres greater than that of their parents and grandparents, whose childhood diet consisted largely of rice, fish and vegetables. However, the average sitting height of adult Japanese has hardly changed: tall young Japanese have proportionately longer legs but the dimensions of their trunk and head are largely unaffected by the change of diet.

It remains to be seen whether these changes in stature and body proportions are beneficial for general health in the long term. The longevity of Japan's present generation of old people is one of the highest in the world, a record that will be hard for their much taller grandchildren and great-grandchildren to exceed. Experimental data relevant to this topic are discussed in Section 4.4.2.

1.2.3 The effect of specific nutritional deficiencies on growth

It was explained in the previous section that reducing the quantity of food available to a growing animal retards the growth of all tissues; the extent to which each tissue recovers from the treatment depends mainly upon factors endogenous to itself, i.e. upon the stage of the tissue's development at which the deprivation occurred. There are many specific components of the diet, e.g. minerals and essential amino acids and lipids, that cannot be synthesized in the body from other constituents of the diet. When such specific 'essential' nutrients are reduced or eliminated from an otherwise adequate diet, orderly growth is disrupted.

Elimination of essential amino acids such as leucine, or of minerals such as zinc or copper, in the diets of growing piglets produces a complex syndrome of growth deficiencies, with almost every tissue affected in one way or another. Pigs raised in this way are clearly failing to thrive, but it is often difficult to be specific about exactly what basic mechanism has been disturbed. In contrast, the effect of calcium deficiency on growth is relatively easy to study, because nearly all of this nutrient is incorporated into a single tissue: bone. If calcium is in short supply, or the biochemical machinery for absorbing it is defective, the growth of the skeleton is likely to be affected soonest and to the greatest extent.

Bone consists of a connective tissue matrix impregnated with inorganic salts. Its structure and mechanical properties will be explained more fully in Chapter 7; to understand this section it is sufficient to know that substantial quantities of inorganic ions, mainly calcium and phosphate, plus smaller amounts of magnesium and zinc, are needed for its formation. The skeleton contains 99% of the body's calcium (and 80% of its phosphorus), so any formation of 'new' bone depends upon incorporation of calcium recycled from elsewhere in the skeleton or obtained directly from the diet. In most birds and mammals, vitamins A and D are necessary for the normal assimilation and metabolism of calcium, and for its incorporation into bone. Diets that are deficient in calcium or lack either of the two vitamins give rise first to slower growth of more or less normal bone, and eventually to the formation of abnormal bone.

Such bone is biochemically abnormal because the flexible connective tissue component continues to grow at almost the normal rate in spite of insufficient calcium to stiffen and harden it. The bones are of abnormal shape because forces generated by the muscles and the body's weight continue to apply stresses to the skeleton as usual, but the poorly calcified bones are so weak that they become permanently bent. The result is an animal with somewhat short stature and, most strikingly, with bowed legs. (In humans, this condition is called 'rickets'.) If low levels of calcium or vitamins are maintained for a large proportion of the growing period, the limbs may become permanently deformed. Even if the shortage of available calcium is not sufficient to cause the development of abnormal bone, a chronic scarcity of this nutrient, combined with the body's own ability to give 'priority' to the growth of certain components can give rise to characteristic changes in body size and shape. One of the best studied cases is that of the skull, jaws and teeth.

Although the brain, eyes and ears are relatively large at birth, the teeth of most mammals do not erupt until after birth. The skull as a whole, and particularly the jaws, grow very rapidly immediately after birth. For unknown reasons, the timing of the formation and eruption of the teeth in humans and many domestic mammals is fixed by genetic factors; only drastic nutritional deficiencies or endocrinological imbalance can delay or accelerate the development of this tissue. Growth of the jaws, on the other hand, is very susceptible to the availability of nutrients and since they grow fastest during suckling, their growth is particularly affected by an inadequate supply of mother's milk. The teeth erupt anyway, whether or not the jaw has grown large enough to accommodate them. If the jaw is too small because its growth has been delayed, the teeth become unduly crowded and those of the upper jaw are not exactly opposite those in the lower jaw, giving a less efficient bite, and a higher risk of dental problems later in life.

The limbs, girdles and other components of the skeleton that are relatively small at birth in humans undergo extensive post-natal growth, during which time they are vulnerable to the effects of inadequate nutrition.

■ Figure 1.5 shows a severely undernourished child from an advertisement for a famine relief organization. Figure 1.6 shows a well-nourished Western child of about the same age. List some features of the skeletons of these two children which indicate that the differential nutrition of the two children has affected them for much of their lives.

The child in Figure 1.6 is obviously much fatter, but she also has broader shoulders, in spite of the fact that girls normally have narrower shoulders than boys. The malnourished child's face appears to have relatively large eyes and the lower part of the face appears to be foreshortened. The girl's face has a relatively larger jaw and more adult proportions generally; the hands are about the same relative size in both children, with the result that the boy's hands appear to be too big for his body.

Figure 1.5 An African boy who has suffered prolonged nutritional deprivation.

Figure 1.6 A European girl who has never suffered from nutritional deprivation or from illness sufficiently severe or prolonged to interfere with growth.

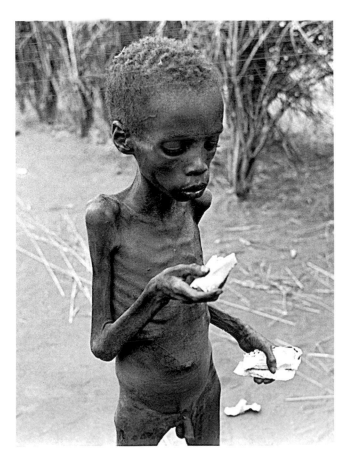

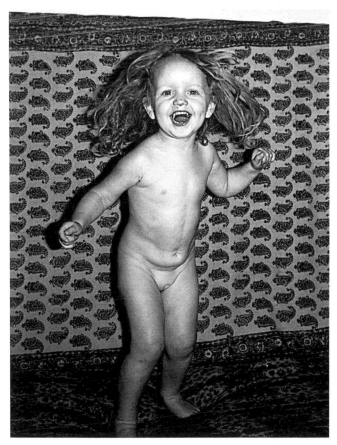

Undernourished children often appear to be younger than their chronological age, not only because they are short, but also because the skull retains the foreshortened shape that is also a feature of infants. Even if people and animals which have endured periods of prolonged nutritional deficiencies as juveniles are fed well later in their lives, the effects of growth retardation on the shape (as distinct from size) of the skeleton are never totally eradicated. Notice, however, that the muscles and tendons of both children 'fit' their skeletons; the growth of these tissues follows that of the skeleton closely, with the result that the musculo-skeletal system is functional over a range of different body sizes and shapes. Some experiments that demonstrate in more detail how the soft tissues 'know' what size they should be to match the growing skeleton are described in Section 2.4.1.

In concluding this section it should be pointed out that many texts emphasize the role of poor nutrition and other adverse environmental influences in bringing about delays or defects in growth. Perhaps more impressive, however, is the ability of mammalian growth to continue on schedule and with only slight detriment even under severely abnormal conditions. In young mammals, growth is remarkably resilient: juvenile mammals achieve something approaching the 'correct' size and shape of the body, in spite of hazards such as frequent illness, undernutrition and diets that contain an excess of certain nutrients and a deficiency of others. Mammalian growth cannot be stopped completely except by measures so extreme that they would be likely to kill the animal. Children with severe mental or physical handicaps grow to almost normal size and shape, even if they are completely bedridden. Mammals, more than other classes of vertebrates, are able to regulate the relative growth of different tissues with the result that a more or less functional organism develops even when fed on abnormal diets.

Summary of Section 1.2

Greater quantities of nutritionally balanced food makes humans grow slightly faster, particularly during their early teens, but they also reach sexual maturity and stop growing at an earlier age. Thus, the mean height of adults is only a little greater in very well-nourished populations than in adequately nourished populations. The relative growth of different tissues can be studied in rats that are given reduced quantities of their normal diet at different periods of their development. Such experiments show that undernutrition retards both cell proliferation and cell enlargement, but failure of cell division cannot be completely compensated for later in life if adequate nutrition is restored. The growth of tissues that would normally have undergone extensive cell proliferation during the period of nutritional deprivation is therefore permanently stunted. Experiments in which particular nutrients are reduced or eliminated from an otherwise adequate diet show that the growth of certain tissues can be selectively retarded. Insufficient calcium first slows the growth of bone, and then causes the formation of abnormal bone. If the deficient diet is prolonged, the abnormal growth cannot be made good later in life. Certain tissues are given 'priority' in claiming nutrients for growth even in times of shortage, and their development is largely unaffected. Other components of the body are severely affected by malnutrition; as a result, the body proportions are permanently altered and there may be a mismatch between parts.

1.3 Growth before and immediately after birth

One of the most important differences between mammals and birds, and 'lower' vertebrates such as reptiles and amphibians, is that the parents tend and, in the case of all mammals and most birds, feed their young. In mammals, the mother supplies all the food her offspring consume from conception to weaning. This dependent period is divided into two distinct phases: gestation and suckling, which differ sharply both in the rate and the physiological control of growth, as well as in many other physiological mechanisms.

1.3.1 Growth before birth

In Section 1.2 some ways in which the growth of the whole animal and relative growth of different organs are affected by the availability of nutrients were described. In contrast to the uncertainties of foraging in the outside world, the uterus would seem like the ideal environment for rapid, orderly growth. The mother provides the fetus with the nutrients it needs, if necessary mobilizing her own metabolic reserves to support the fetus during temporary food shortages. Nonetheless, the growth velocity of the fetus during the first three-quarters of gestation is quite slow in all mammals studied. Figure 1.7 shows some data obtained from normal and premature births of human infants. The increments in body mass per year have been calculated and expressed as a function of gestational age (weeks since conception). Thus, Figure 1.7 expresses the growth velocity of body mass; the data have been calculated in a similar way to those in Figure 1.2 which shows velocity of growth in length.

The velocity of growth is slower during most of the gestation period than it is during most of the suckling period. However, as pointed out in Section 1.1.1, younger fetuses are also smaller, and the growth velocities *in utero* may actually indicate that a higher proportion of the body's resources is directed towards growth before birth than is the case after birth. The high growth velocity after birth does, however, have important implications for the physiological energetics of the mother, because it is from her that the fetus derives all its nourishment both before and after birth.

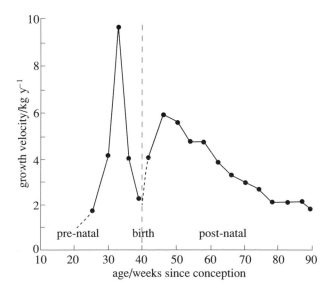

Figure 1.7   Growth velocity before and after birth in singleton children (i.e. not twin and other multiple births).

■   If the mother mammal devotes a constant proportion of her own body resources towards sustaining her offspring, what relationship between linear growth velocity and fetal or neonatal age would you predict?

The linear growth velocity would be expected to decline steeply as the fetus gets older and larger because of the cubic relationship between growth in length and growth in body mass (Section 1.1.1). Growth in mass is directly proportional to the demands that the fetus makes on its mother for nutrients.

The fact that growth velocity does not decline sharply as the growing offspring becomes larger indicates that the mother is making available increasing amounts of nutrients for her offspring as it gets older. The high growth velocities of many neonatal mammals are in fact sustained only at very considerable energetic cost to the mother. For example, the blue whale gives birth to a single offspring weighing about 2 500 kg after a pregnancy lasting 8 months, but she adds a further 18 000 kg to its body mass in the course of a lactation period lasting 7 months.

The period in the protective environment of the uterus is useful mainly for the development of particularly elaborate, delicate organs such as the nervous system and sense organs. However, the rate of growth achieved before birth can influence the animal's final dimensions because the growth rate *in utero* sets the pace for post-natal growth. Differences in size between breeds, races and subspecies seem to be due mainly to changes in the rate of growth both before and after birth, rather than to shortening or lengthening of the growing period: thus the gestation time and age at maturity of all breeds of domestic dog from chihuahuas to Great Danes are almost identical, but the latter are much larger at birth, and grow much faster post-natally than the former.

The concept of the **runt** of the litter has long been familiar to pig farmers: in a litter of perhaps a dozen piglets of normal size, one can be unusually small, although it was born at the same time as the others. This runt fails to catch up and remains permanently undersized, even if it manages to get its fair share of the sow's milk. The formation of runts in pigs seems to be due to implantation of the blastocyst in the upper region of the uterine horn where the blood supply is low. A placenta in that region is poorly perfused and hence the fetus gets fewer nutrients and grows more slowly. The important point is that slower growth *in utero* sets the pace for post-natal growth, and the runt remains undersized, even if its diet during suckling is normal.

Exceptionally small, full-term infants are also often born to women who smoke heavily during pregnancy. The mechanism seems to be very similar to runting in pigs: some of the toxins in tobacco are vasoconstrictors,* and while under their influence, the placenta is less efficiently perfused with blood than normal. The greater the proportion of the total period of pregnancy for which this situation prevails, the less nutrients can pass from the mother's blood to the fetus and hence the slower it grows.

Evidence from old records of the weights of human neonates and their placentas suggest that chronically undernourished or underoxygenated human fetuses have proportionately larger placentas at birth.

How could a larger placenta be an adaptive response by the fetus to its circumstances?

* Vasoconstrictors are agents that cause collapse of small blood vessels, thus reducing the flow of blood in them.

Much of the placenta is fetal tissue, so the fetus's own growth rate partly determines its size (Book 1).* Growing a larger placenta would facilitate the extraction of scarce nutrients from the mother's blood. In spite of such countermeasures, runt piglets and 'small-for-dates' babies, that are born after a gestation of normal duration but are undersized at birth, almost always grow more slowly than those of normal size at birth.

In contrast, premature infants who are physiologically normal and were growing at the normal rate, but for one reason or another are expelled from the uterus sooner than normal, very often maintain the normal pace of growth after birth, as long as they receive adequate, suitable food. The technology of artificial feeding has improved so much that babies born as early as 28 weeks and weighing only 1 kg can now maintain the normal high rate of post-natal growth (see Figure 1.7) on an artificial diet, and be almost the same size as infants of the same gestational age which remained *in utero* for the full term. Their growth rate follows its normal course and most become normal-sized adults in spite of having been born prematurely. Thus the average birth weight of babies born as twins (and other multiple births) is always lower than that of infants born as singletons but, on an adequate diet, they catch up within a few months to become indistinguishable in size from other children.

However, the prognosis is not nearly so good for full-term, undersized infants who are small because insufficient nutrients crossed the placenta or from some genetic defect. The pace of growth established during gestation determines the ability to grow throughout life, possibly by some lasting change in neural or endocrinological mechanisms which control growth rates. Some physiological mechanisms behind this association are described in Section 1.4.

1.3.2 Post-natal growth in mammals

It was pointed out earlier in Section 1.3 that sustained fast growth is typical of the phase immediately after birth, when mammals still obtain all their nutrients from the mother in the form of milk. The biochemistry of milk secretion and the endocrinological control of its production was discussed more fully in Book 1; it is important to stress here that in many mammals growth of tissues such as bone, muscle and adipose tissue is faster during the brief suckling period than at any

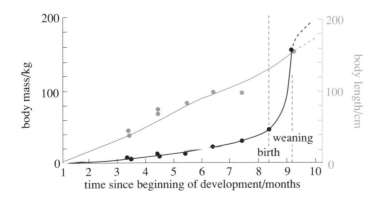

Figure 1.8   Growth in length and in body mass of elephant seals, *Mirounga leonina*, before and after birth.

* Pond, Caroline (ed.) (1992), S324 *Animal Physiology*, Book 1: *Reproductive Physiology*, The Open University.

other period of the life history. Figure 1.8 shows some data on the length and mass of fetal and suckling elephant seals, *Mirounga leonina*. These impressive animals are belong to the largest living genus of seal, with adult males reaching 3 700 kg. *Mirounga leonina* lives in the southern oceans around Antarctica; the females come ashore for about a month each year to give birth and suckle their young. You can see that, although growth in body length continues at an almost constant rate through gestation and suckling, growth in mass is very slow *in utero,* but increases sharply after birth, even more sharply than would be predicted from the usual cubic relationship between body length and body mass (Section 1.2).

■   From the point of view of energy expenditure of the newborn, why might you be surprised that growth in body mass increases so sharply after birth?

As stressed in Book 2,* a substantial fraction of the energy budget of newborn mammals is devoted to thermogenesis and thermoregulatory behaviour. The relatively large size and thick white fur of the neonate minimizes heat loss but even so, the growth rate of baby *Mirounga* is impressive in view of the fact that it is achieved on a draughty sub-Antarctic beach, not in a cosy nest.

Seal milk (and indeed the milk of nearly all marine mammals) is up to 50% by weight lipid, about the consistency of thick cream, and supplies all the nutrients necessary for growth. However, it should not be concluded that the seal's impressive rate of growth is due simply to the rich milk supplied by the mother. Human growth rates can only be speeded up to a very modest extent by feeding infants on a richer diet. Infants given undiluted cow's or goat's milk, which contain a higher proportion of fat than women's milk, tend to develop digestive and metabolic disturbances, and so they grow even more slowly than normal. Like most aspects of neonatal physiology, the properties of the infant are closely geared to those of the mother; although dietary deficiencies can impair growth (Section 1.2.2), it is difficult to improve upon Nature!

■   Using the data in Figures 1.7 and 1.8, calculate the maximum rate of growth in body mass for humans and elephant seals.

The maximum growth velocity (gain in mass) of humans is 6 kg y^{-1}; the seals gain body mass at a mean rate of $1\,440 \text{ kg y}^{-1}$ during the first month of life (120 kg in 1 month = $120 \times 12 = 1\,440 \text{ kg y}^{-1}$). Even if allowance is made for the fact that at birth seals are ten times larger than human neonates, the rate of gain in mass per kg is still much faster in seals than in humans. Even more impressive is the rate of post-natal growth of domestic pigs. Piglets are smaller than human infants at birth but, if well fed, modern breeds of pigs grow to be heavier than a man (and suitable for use as pork) by the age of 7 months. Growth at this rate is unnatural and has evolved under artificial selection: wild boars (the ancestor of the domestic pig) do not reach this body mass until the age of about 18 months.

Humans and other large primates are among the slowest growing of all mammals, particularly during the post-natal period. It has been suggested that this situation arose during the evolution of the primates because their natural diet

* Robinson, David (ed.) (1994), S324 *Animal Physiology*, Book 2: *Temperature and Exercise*, The Open University.

of fruit and leaves is low in proteins, fats and calcium, all of which are essential to support rapid growth, and because the nervous system is large and complex. As explained in Section 1.2.3, permanent abnormalities can develop if the endogenous controls of growth programme tissues to grow faster than the availability of nutrients in the diet allows. The evolution of slow growth rates may be viewed as a safeguard against stunting if the young are fed a relatively poor diet. Many monkeys and apes supplement their usual diet with eggs, insects and small vertebrates during late pregnancy and suckling, perhaps as a means of increasing intake of proteins, lipids and calcium.

Summary of Section 1.3

Growth velocity during most of gestation is slower than growth during suckling in all mammals studied. The growth rate achieved during gestation sets the pace for post-natal growth; full-term but undersized neonates do not 'catch up' and often continue to grow more slowly than normal and hence become undersized adults. Premature neonates, which were growing normally before birth, can maintain growth rates typical of their gestational age as long as they have adequate nutrition. Different species of mammals differ greatly in the rate of growth of the neonates; although the mothers of fast-growing neonates produce richer milk, artificially increasing the nutrient content of the milk does not significantly increase growth rate over the normal maximum. Thus, endogenous mechanisms are the chief regulators of growth during suckling. Like other primates, humans grow relatively slowly both before and after birth.

1.4 Endocrinological control of growth

The data presented in previous sections all strongly indicate that the rate of growth in mammals is controlled mainly by internal factors that are not readily disturbed or modified by external factors such as diet. In this section some of those internal factors are identified and their properties described. Because of their importance for selective breeding and management of meat and milk-producing animals, the genetics and physiology of growth are now rapidly advancing areas of research. We can expect new techniques and concepts to emerge during the lifetime of this course.

1.4.1 Growth hormone and insulin-like growth factors

One of the first hormones to be identified positively with growth rate in mammals was given the name **growth hormone (GH)**; it is a polypeptide of relative molecular mass, M_r,* about 21 000 whose exact primary sequence differs slightly between species. It is synthesized in the pituitary gland where it is present in large quantities. Although GH may be 1 000 times more concentrated than any other hormone in the pituitary, its secretion is regulated by growth-hormone-releasing factors and its concentration in the blood is often very low.

* Relative molecular mass is defined as the ratio of the mass of one molecule of a compound to one-twelfth of the mass of one atom of ^{12}C.

Normal quantities of GH in the blood are essential for growth to full stature in both rats and humans, but children (and other young mammals) who lack it are still capable of a fair amount of growth. Unless treated, they become 'miniature' adults: healthy and of sound mind and normal body proportions but only about two-thirds the expected height. Although GH is present in the pituitary and in the blood from quite early in fetal life (see Book 1, Section 6.2.3) and its concentration does not decline until late in adult life, it seems to be essential for growth only during the juvenile period. Fetuses and neonates that lack GH are healthy and of normal size, and adults with low levels of GH appear to be none the worse for it. GH is known to influence various adult metabolic processes, among them milk production in dairy cattle, and doubtless more remains to be discovered about just what so much GH is doing in the pituitary during the fetal, neonatal and adult stages in the life cycle (Section 4.3.2).

For a long time it was thought that GH exerted its effect by promoting division and maturation of cells. However, attempts to demonstrate such a role *in vitro* were never successful and it is now established that GH does not act directly on growing tissues, but via small, single-chain polypeptides called **insulin-like growth factors** (IGFs, formerly called somatomedins; see also Book 1, Section 6.2.3), which interact directly with growing cells. IGFs are polypeptides about 67–70 amino acids long that resemble insulin in molecular structure and, as well as having their own receptors, can bind to insulin receptors, producing many of the same effects as insulin when applied to muscle or adipose tissue *in vitro*. IGFs stimulate division of various kinds of stem cells, thus promoting growth by enlarging the pool of cells that form particular tissues. They also play an essential role in the differentiation and maturation of cells in structurally complex tissues such as the kidney and the nervous system.

Two IGFs, IGF I and IGF II, are important for many aspects of growth and metabolic regulation from early in fetal life to adulthood and can be synthesized by many different tissues. For reasons that are far from completely understood, the relative abundance of IGF I and IGF II and their apparent contribution to growth regulation differs between species and with the age of the growing organism. In general, IGF I is most abundant post-natally and its synthesis is partly controlled by growth hormone (and other hormones, see Section 1.4.3), whereas IGF II predominates in controlling growth before birth and is independent of GH. However, while adult mice and rats lack IGF II everywhere except in the brain, both polypeptides are fairly abundant in all tissues of guinea-pigs and humans (and possibly many other animals) at all ages. The contributions of different IGFs to determining growth rate at different stages of development help to explain some of the contrasts in pre-natal and post-natal growth described in Section 1.3.

Like other hormones, IGFs are effective only on cells that produce receptors for them. The plasma concentrations of IGFs are several times higher than that needed to stimulate maximally all the IGF receptors on cell surfaces. This paradox can be explained by the fact that most, perhaps more than 90%, of the IGF in the serum is bound to **binding proteins** (BPs) and is thus unavailable to receptors. At least six distinct binding proteins for IGFs (IGFBPs) have been isolated, all of them much larger than the IGFs themselves. They attach specifically to IGFs in the serum and play an important role in regulating their action, by delivering the hormone to the cell surface receptors, or by preventing such activation. The BPs have a half-life of only about 90 min in humans; their production, and that of IGFs, changes with time of day, the frequency and nutritional quality of meals and many other factors, thus they act as sensitive regulators of hormone action.

IGFs are general growth factors: they modulate the growth and, in many cases, aspects of metabolism, of many different tissues, but their action is often very difficult to quantify. One of the simplest assays for IGF is its ability to promote the enlargement and maturation of cartilage cells *in vitro*. This reaction, which works particularly well with cartilage from the ribs of a young pig, forms the basis for a sensitive assay for measuring the levels of the hormone in blood samples. Such measurements have shown that, although some children who are growing abnormally slowly on a nutritious diet have exceptionally low levels of GH and IGFs, individual differences in the growth rates of humans cannot be correlated with the levels of these substances in the blood. Experimental studies of growth rates of mice also fail to reveal any association between growth rate and the blood concentration of GH and IGF. This apparent paradox is partly resolved by the realization that only some IGF, especially that synthesized in the liver, is secreted into the blood and hence acts as an endocrine hormone. Many tissues, including the skin, gut, many parts of the nervous system and the growing regions of bones also synthesize IGFs but, instead of entering the circulation, the hormones act mainly on the same cells that produce them (autocrine activity) or on adjacent cells within the same tissue (paracrine activity).

■   Would it be as easy to detect and study autocrine and paracrine activity of a hormone as it is to document endocrine activity?

No. By definition, endocrine hormones circulate in the blood so they can usually be identified in blood samples taken from anywhere in the body, but to detect autocrine or paracrine hormones, samples of extracellular fluid must be taken from inside the tissue, which may be technically difficult and destructive. In practice, much of the information about the autocrine action of IGFs comes from tissue culture experiments. These different modes of action and 'spheres of influence', and the fact that many, perhaps most, kinds of cells can synthesize IGFs and some, notably certain bone cells, can store them in an inactive form for long periods, make the study of IGFs extremely complicated. There is much current research on the topic, which may eventually clarify and simplify what is now a very complicated and confusing story.

As well as determining the rate of growth of the whole body, IGF I can also alter body composition by stimulating muscle growth and promoting the release of fatty acids from adipose tissue. Higher levels of circulating GH or more locally produced IGF I alter the mass of adipose tissue and muscle in growing animals and to some extent in adults. Not surprisingly, farmers are taking a great interest in the possibility of producing leaner, more muscular meat animals by administering GH or IGF I or by manipulating the genes that produce these hormones.

1.4.2 Genetic manipulation of growth hormone and IGFs

Molecular biology, particularly the capacity to modify, insert or delete particular genes, is providing many new insights into the natural control and organization of growth. In this section, there is space only to offer a taste of the kinds of mechanisms that these rapidly advancing techniques are revealing.

Although the M_r of GH is about the same in all mammals studied, the exact sequence of amino acids differs between species; GH from rats (rGH), for example, differs from GH from humans (hGH) at 67 of the 191 amino acid residues. Growth hormones from different species can thus readily be distinguished using specific antibodies, even at very low concentrations. The DNA sequence that codes for production of hGH and its releasing factor in human cells can be introduced into fertilized mouse eggs along with other genes known to promote the incorporation of foreign genes into the genome.

Such techniques have been used to develop a strain of mice that has hGH in its blood because its cells contain the gene for hGH and its releasing factor (as well as the usual gene for mGH). Many such mice grow faster than normal littermates between the age of 3 and 12 weeks and a few end up as giant mice, three times as large as the controls. In such mice, hGH and IGFs are present at somewhat higher concentrations than the normal level of mGH and other hormones in unaltered mice. However, although hGH can readily be distinguished from mGH by using antibodies, it appears that hGH is just as effective as mGH at binding to the receptor sites on the cells that produce IGFs. Further clues about how the introduced hGH gene produces giant mice can be obtained from measuring the mRNA corresponding to the hGH gene in various tissues. mRNA produced by the hGH gene has been found in detectable levels in a variety of tissues, including lung, brain, kidney and intestine, but levels on a per cell basis are particularly high in the liver, testis and heart.

■   Would you expect these results from what is known about the production of GH in normal mammals?

No. In normal mammals GH is produced only by the pituitary gland, where it seems to be stored in quite large quantities relative to the amount which is released.

Thus it appears that, in the transgenic mice, GH may be produced in tissues that normally have nothing to do with either the synthesis or metabolism of the hormone. At the same time, the cells in the pituitary gland that normally produce the GH are atrophied and greatly reduced in number. The mouse's ability to produce its own mGH by the normal physiological mechanism thus appears to have been inhibited by the arrival of the alien GH gene. These experiments show that hormones such as GH can be produced by a variety of cells, apart from the pituitary, without upsetting the metabolism of those cells, and that the action of GH on IGF production does not depend upon its having a species-specific amino acid sequence.

A similar conclusion is reached from the study of IGF genes artificially introduced into embryonic mice. Insertion of the gene for IGF II (which in rats and mice is inactive in adult tissues) into the cells that form the skin produces normal size, apparently healthy mice with disproportionately large pelts (Figure

1.9a). The excess skin forms wrinkles, making the mouse resemble a bloodhound.* If the IGF II gene is inserted into the uterus-forming region of female embryos, their uterus has 143% more DNA than normal, and is up to seven times heavier than that of normal mice by the age of 9 months (Figure 1.9b). The uterus produces extra IGF II and so it grows to be disproportionately larger. But IGF II produced in the skin, gut and uterus does not circulate, and the additional gene is not present in the kidneys, so these organs grow to normal size (Figure 1.9b). The total body mass of the genetically altered mice is only slightly larger than that of the normal mice. Compare Figures 1.9a and 1.9b: the uterus of the mouse with the exogenous IGF II gene is so disproportionately large that it would have compressed and distorted adjacent organs in the normal-sized abdomen.

One aspect of the physiology of GH, its role in the organism at different ages, appears to be unaffected by experimental manipulation of the genes. It was mentioned earlier in Section 1.4.1 that GH was present throughout fetal, juvenile and adult life, although it could be shown to play a role in promoting growth only during the juvenile period. hGH produced by the introduced gene is subject to the same limitations: the mice cease to respond to the higher levels of hGH at the age of 3 months, about the age at which growth ends in unaltered mice.

■ What mechanism can you suggest for this observation?

GH ceases to be effective because the mouse's cells stop producing receptors for it. Control of receptor production is distinct from, and unaffected by, the production of the hormone. Similarly, the gene for hGH seems to be actively producing its messenger RNA well before birth in the mice, but differences in the growth rate are not detectable until about the time of weaning, at 3 weeks old.

It is believed that changes in the abundance, or efficiency of the hormone receptor sites are behind these differences in the 'sensitivity' of the mouse cells to hormone levels. One would not expect the properties of the receptor sites to be affected by the introduction of an exogenous gene for hormone production. Regulation of the action of hormones by means of changes in the hormone receptor sites at the target cells is undoubtedly an extremely important and widespread phenomenon. Less is known about receptor sites because it is more difficult to study them tucked away in inaccessible cells, than it is to measure hormone levels in blood samples. As better techniques are developed, especially the use of specific antibodies that selectively block and/or locate hormone receptors, their significance is becoming apparent.

Gene manipulation and careful monitoring of the form and timing of growth of transgenic and normal embryos have also revealed a phenomenon called genetic imprinting: the expression of certain alleles at certain loci depends not upon their structure or their product, but upon whether the alleles were inherited from the mother or the father. Thus, in normal mouse fetuses, only the paternally derived allele for IGF II supports protein synthesis (except in the brain, where both alleles are 'switched on'). If the paternal allele for IGF II is selectively inactivated, the pups at birth are 30% smaller (but otherwise normal) than

---

* You should not conclude that bloodhounds owe their appearance to anomalies in IGF production: there are other ways of producing hypertrophied skin.

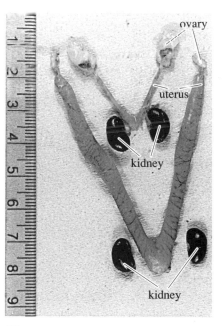

(a)

(b)

Figure 1.9 (a) Ventral view of a mouse (*left*) genetically engineered to produce extra IGF II in the skin, gut and uterus with a genetically normal littermate (*right*). (b) The uterus and kidneys of the same mice: *below*, genetically engineered mouse; *above*, normal littermate. The scale is in centimetres.

unmanipulated mice or those in which the maternal allele is eliminated. However, IGF II is ineffective except on cells that produce the IGF II receptor protein to which it binds. Modification of the paternal gene for this receptor has no effect on growth, but if the maternal allele for the IGF II receptor protein is destroyed, 5–10 times more IGF II can be measured in the neonate's serum.

■ What do these observations suggest about the roles of (a) the paternal allele for IGF II receptor protein, and (b) the maternal allele for IGF II receptor protein?

(a) Either the paternal allele is not transcribed or its product is inaccessible to IGF II. (b) Most of the fetus's IGF II receptor protein comes from the maternal allele. If it is inactivated, there are not enough receptors to bind to, so the 'spare' IGF II from the father's allele enters the circulation and remains there. However, a small amount of IGF II receptor protein must come from somewhere (possibly by activation of the paternal allele), otherwise the fetuses thus manipulated would not survive long enough to be born.

■ How does the differential activity of the alleles for IGF II and the IGF II receptor protein determine the partitioning of energy and nutrients between the mother and her growing young?

By setting the pace of growth of the fetus, the abundance of IGF II determines how much energy and nutrients the young take from their mother. By being fully 'switched on' throughout gestation, the father's IGF II-producing allele maximizes the growth rate of his offspring, at the expense of the mother's resources. Larger neonates usually (though not invariably) survive better and as adults, produce more offspring themselves. By limiting the binding of IGF II to the growing cells, the maternal allele that normally produces most of the IGF II receptor protein acts as a brake, containing the fetus's growth rate to within the limits of the mother's physiological resources. Such mechanisms may be behind the matching between maternal nutrient supply and fetal and post-natal growth described in Section 1.3.

Genetic imprinting has been described for only about half a dozen gene loci, IGF and insulin being among the best known, so how widespread the phenomenon is remains to be seen.

1.4.3 Other hormones and growth factors involved in growth

Several hormones have been implicated in determining the rate of growth of the whole body or its parts. There is only enough space to describe one of these hormones in any detail. **Thyroxin** is an iodine-containing peptide hormone produced by the thyroid gland, that promotes growth during childhood by facilitating the action of IGFs (which are secreted in response to GH in the blood) on the growing cells. However, unlike GH, thyroxin also plays an essential role in the fetus by promoting protein synthesis in several tissues, particularly the brain.

■ Suggest what developmental abnormalities you would expect to see in children who: (a) are born with thyroxin deficiency; (b) develop thyroxin deficiency at the age of about 8 y.

Since the brain and nervous system are growing very rapidly around the time of birth, they are particularly affected by thyroxin deficiencies at this period of development. Children born with low levels of thyroxin become mentally deficient unless they receive treatment promptly. Since brain growth is almost complete by age 8 y, those whose thyroxin deficiencies do not appear until later in childhood are undersized and grow more slowly, but their mental development is not necessarily impaired. Growth of the skeleton and body in general, however, is disrupted by deficiencies at both stages of development.

Like GH, thyroxin continues to be produced long after growth stops; however, in contrast to GH, the role it plays in maintaining physiological wellbeing in adults is quite well understood. Thyroxin is important in determining the metabolic rate of many, perhaps all, kinds of vertebrate cells; too little thyroxin thus causes sluggish movement and low body heat production as well as slow growth. In severe cases of thyroxin deficiency, affected animals and people become passive and inert, lacking all physical and mental energy.

The commonest cause of insufficient thyroxin in infants is prolonged lack of iodine in the maternal diet, and hence insufficient transfer of iodine across the placenta or via the milk. Such children may be born cretins, with defective growth capacity that eventually produces small stature, deformed limbs and face, and severe, irreversible mental retardation. Iodine deficiency causes the thyroid gland to hypertrophy, producing the disease called goitre, characterized by a massive swelling in the neck and general lethargy. One of the main reasons why goitre was (until the installation of railways permitted cheap importation of marine fish and, later, the use of iodized salt) much more common among women than men in places (such as Derbyshire) where the drinking water lacks iodine was the greater requirement for the nutrient during pregnancy and lactation. Cretinism is still common in parts of Bangladesh and other places where people are completely dependent upon iodine-deficient soil and water.

■   How is growth of the thyroid gland an adaptive response to iodine deficiency?

More gland cells would presumably be better able to scavenge for the traces of iodine in the blood and hence to maintain the body's supply of thyroxin. So, moderate or transient hypertrophy could be beneficial in maintaining thyroxin supplies, and hence normal growth, during temporary shortages of iodine, but massive or prolonged enlargement generates its own problems.

Thyroxin, and hence iodine, apparently have essential and fundamental roles in the growth and metabolism of all vertebrates. Symptoms similar to cretinism can appear in animals such as terrapins (Figure 1.10, *overleaf*) if they are deprived of iodine for long periods. From the time it was a few centimetres long (less than 1 y old), the specimen shown in Figures 1.10a and 1.10b was mistakenly kept in iodine-deficient waters and fed an iodine-deficient diet, almost exclusively trout caught in such waters. After more than 10 years under such conditions, its body was much smaller than well-nourished conspecifics (Figure 1.10c), its shell had grown deformed and its neck grotesquely swollen. Eventually the thyroid gland in its neck became so swollen that the terrapin was unable to retract its head or its limbs (which had grown more or less normally) into its shell and had great difficulty in swallowing (Figure 1.10a). It died after several years of almost total lethargy and failure to eat. The bony skeleton of its shell (Figure 1.10b) is

(a)

`|—————| 1 cm`

(b)

`|—————| 1 cm`

Figure 1.10 The effects of prolonged iodine deprivation on body form in a captive red-eared terrapin (*Trachemys scripta elegans*). (a) Side view of an adult terrapin that had been kept for many years on an iodine-deficient diet. (b) The dried shell of the specimen in (a). (c) A healthy adult terrapin of the same species. Note the relative sizes of the head, limbs and shell compared to (a).

(c)

`|—————| 1 cm`

grossly abnormal in shape, and contains splits and cavities never found in normal specimens. Its major components have grown out of proportion to each other: compare the relative sizes of the scutes around the edge of the upper half of the shell with the central plates in the normal and defective specimens.

Other terrapins that had been kept on a similar regime for a shorter period of time had similar but milder symptoms, but they recovered completely within a few weeks when fed marine fish and vegetables. In the wild, such terrapins are most common in lowland swamps and tidal rivers of eastern America, where they eat plants and invertebrates as well as fish, a diet that provides sufficient iodine.

When the growth rate of members of a normal population of people or rats is compared with their natural levels of thyroxin or GH (or most of the other hormones that promote growth) no clear correlation can be demonstrated: it cannot be said that taller people are growing faster because they secrete more GH or thyroxin. Although these hormones must be present in quantities appropriate to the individual's needs to permit normal growth to proceed, they do not appear to determine it in a quantitative manner. The key factor that makes tall people tall and shorter ones short has defied detection; a likely candidate is difference in abundance or properties of the hormone receptor sites, either at the IGF-producing cells or the growing cells themselves.

Recent advances in techniques and equipment for keeping isolated tissues alive for days or weeks have greatly facilitated the study of growth *in vitro*, and the number and variety of chemical agents found to influence the process have enormously increased. The agents may be named after the tissue from which were first isolated, such as platelet-derived growth factor (PDGF), which stimulates proliferation of connective tissue cells and certain cells in the nervous system, or after the tissue in which they are most active, such as nerve growth factor (NGF). Some are active on just one type of tissue, while others, e.g. transforming growth factor (TGF-β), seem to stimulate or curb growth wherever they are applied, often by modulating the response to other growth factors. In many cases, the roles, if any, of these substances *in vivo* are as yet unknown, and their interactions *in vitro* extremely complicated, so it is not appropriate to describe them in any detail here.

Summary of Section 1.4

Growth hormone (GH) is the most thoroughly studied of several hormones that promote growth by stimulating the production of IGFs, which act directly to promote proliferation and maturation of cells, including the secretory cells themselves and adjacent cells of the same tissue. Although its best known functions are during the post-natal growing period, GH is present in large quantities in the pituitary for most of a mammal's life. The gene which codes for GH in humans can be artificially incorporated into the mouse genome. Embryos so treated grow larger than normal and GH is produced in several tissues other than the pituitary, the normal GH-producing cells of which are damaged and depleted. The stages of development at which GH exerts its maximum influence on the mouse's growth rate are the same in normal and transgenic specimens. Genetic manipulation of mouse embryos shows that maternally derived and paternally derived genes for IGF II and its receptor have different roles in the growth of the fetus. Changes in the hormone receptor molecules on the target cells are believed to be responsible for individual differences in growth rate. It is much more difficult to study changes in hormone receptor sites in the intact, growing animal. Thyroxin is another hormone which promotes growth in mammals by stimulating IGF production. It is also important for normal growth *in utero* and for normal metabolism in fully grown adults.

1.5 Growth in non-mammalian vertebrates

The maximum growth rate, and the organization of growing periods in relation to age and food availability, are as important to the ecology of a species as its diet or habitat. In mammals, the hormones that promote the maturation of the reproductive organs and the development of secondary sexual characters greatly slow, and in many species terminate, skeletal growth (Section 1.2.1), so the body is full size, or nearly so, by the time reproduction begins. It is important to understand that this close association between growth rate and sexual maturation is a special feature of mammals.

Most fish, amphibians and reptiles do not show the tight relationship between chronological age and capacity for growth. Most such species start to reproduce when they are less than half maximum size. As they get older, more energy is put into reproduction and less into the individual's own tissues, but growth can continue for most, in some species all, of the lifespan. Although they usually grow faster early in life than when older, the capacity for growth is retained for a long time, and individuals, especially of large, long-lived species whose growth was delayed for one reason or another can 'catch up' almost completely if conditions favourable to growth appear later in their lives.

In fishes, reptiles and amphibians, overall rate of growth is usually much slower than in mammals and birds and is strongly dependent upon the availability of nutrients; in captivity, on a plentiful, well-balanced diet, alligators reach sexual maturity at about half maximum length. But they can take three times as long to reach sexual maturity at this length in the wild, where food is less plentiful or less nutritious. In animals such as large fish, and certain terrapins and tortoises, the body mass of healthy individuals of the same age can differ by a factor of ten. Such variable growth does not cause stunting and misproportioning of body parts because the growth of all tissues and organ systems is slowed down or accelerated proportionately.

■　What happens in mammals when growth is restricted by nutritional deficiencies?

Some tissues continue to grow, while the growth of others is stunted. If the diet is poor for a long period, the body proportions may be permanently altered (Section 1.2.2). Some of the habits and physiological capacities that may have promoted the evolution of the close link between age and growth rate in mammals, and hence their susceptibility to stunting, are described in Chapter 4.

Many birds resemble mammals in that the parents provide most or all of the food which sustains the young after hatching. Birds that adopt this breeding strategy are called **altricial**; those, such as most ducks and the domestic fowl, in which the hatchlings have to forage for themselves and are merely escorted by the parents, are called **precocial.** In many altricial birds, growth in body mass is very rapid while the hatchlings are being fed by the parents, and slows abruptly as soon as the nest is abandoned. The young of many altricial birds, such as penguins and kestrels, are significantly heavier than their parents at fledging, by which time growth of the skeleton, and hence growth in length, is also almost complete. Although they are as large as their parents, they do not become sexually mature at this age; small species may breed the following season, but many large altricial species such as albatrosses, vultures and the larger parrots do not breed until they are as much as ten years old. They are sexually inactive during this period of their lives (though some may help their parents raise subsequent broods) and may have a special juvenile plumage that indicates their immature status. It has been suggested that the young birds require several years experience of foraging and avoiding predators before they are able to cope with the demands of breeding themselves. Whatever the ecological explanation, it is clear that physiological control of the termination of skeletal growth in birds is not closely tied to sexual maturation.

The very rapid post-natal and post-hatching growth of mammals and altricial birds is made possible because most or all of the food needed to sustain growth is supplied by the parents. Both the quantity and quality of such food is likely to be more reliable than if the young animal were foraging for itself, in the way that young reptiles, most young fishes and precocial birds do. It could be suggested that one of the factors promoting the evolution of the lactation habit in mammals is that by providing adequate quantities of a readily digestible, nutritionally balanced diet it promoted the fastest possible post-natal growth rate. However, when the growth rate of mammals of a range of body sizes is compared to growth in birds, it is found that altricial birds grow faster than all mammals of similar body size. Young mammals grow at about the same rate as precocial birds of the same body mass. So, although the evolution of the lactation habit in mammals may have made possible the spectacular growth rates of some species, it is unlikely that the need for maximum post-natal growth was the main factor promoting the development of the trait, because altricial birds achieve a higher growth rate when their parents bring them solid foods. Many altricial birds, particularly small passerines, bring protein-rich animal foods such as insect larvae to their nestlings, although they are mainly herbivorous as adults. Although the abundance and chemical composition of the nestlings' diet inevitably vary from day to day, the nestlings of altricial birds achieve one of the fastest growth rates known in the Animal Kingdom.

1.6 Conclusion

Perhaps the most striking aspect of mammalian and avian growth is the predominance of internal control mechanisms: the termination of growth and, in humans, its acceleration at puberty are endogenously controlled. Considering that growth depends upon protein synthesis and the deposition of minerals, growth processes are surprisingly little affected by diet and habits. In contrast to the constancy within species of the relationship between age and size, growth rate differs greatly between species: in size, structure and metabolism, pigs and humans have a great deal in common, so much so that transplantation of porcine organs such as hearts into humans is now a real prospect, but piglets grow twenty times faster than children. In many mammals, including humans, the onset of puberty curtails growth, but in other species, such as most birds, sexual maturation takes place a long (and often variable) time after skeletal growth has ended. Other vertebrates achieve something approaching the 'correct' size and shape of the body in spite of undernutrition and other hazards, although the duration of the growing period is flexible.

Such tight control is mediated by many local and systemic factors that act synergistically, probably including some that are not yet identified. The study of growth has recently become more urgent with the realization that diseases such as cancer and muscular dystrophy arise from defects in growth, rather than defects in function. Indeed, as explained in the next chapter, growth and repair are integral parts of the function of many tissues.

Objectives for Chapter 1

When you have completed this chapter, you should be able to:

1.1   Define and use, or recognize definitions and applications of each of the **bold** terms.

1.2   Describe some methods used to quantify growth and explain the mathematical basis for the expected relationship between growth in height and growth in body mass.

1.3   Describe the effect of periods of undernourishment at various post-natal ages on the growth of different tissues, and explain why recovery from undernutrition is more complete in some tissues than in others.

1.4   Describe some effects of calcium deficiency on post-weaning growth of the skeleton and its associated tissues.

1.5   Describe the relationship between growth during gestation and growth during the suckling phase in mammals with respect to (a) the rates of growth of different tissues, and (b) the control of growth rates.

1.6   Describe the roles of growth hormone, IGFs and thyroxin in the control of mammalian growth.

1.7   Outline how gene transplantation experiments have clarified the action of growth hormone and demonstrated genetic imprinting.

1.8   Explain some differences in the relationship between skeletal growth and the onset of sexual maturity in the major classes of vertebrates, and relate these differences to the post-natal or post-hatching diets of the species.

Questions for Chapter 1

(Answers to questions are at the end of the book.)

Question 1.1 (Objective 1.2)

How are (a) growth velocity, and (b) growth in body mass, calculated from simple linear measurements of growth? Discuss the validity of any assumptions which must be made in these calculations, and explain the relevance of growth velocity and growth in mass to the understanding of the physiological mechanisms of growth.

Question 1.2 (Objective 1.3)

List the circumstances under which deficiencies caused by undernutrition can be (a) completely rectified by restoration of a normal diet, (b) the cause of permanent anatomical imperfections.

Question 1.3 (Objective 1.4)

Describe the effects of a calcium-deficient diet on the growth of (a) calcified tissues such as bones and teeth, (b) soft, non-calcified tissues.

Question 1.4 (Objective 1.5)

Which of the following factors have been definitely shown to promote the maximum possible growth velocity in mammals?

(a) A physiologically constant environment such as that experienced *in utero*

(b) An easily digested, liquid food such as milk.

(c) Being maintained at a high, constant body temperature.

(d) Endogenous control mechanisms not directly determined by any of the factors (a)–(c).

Question 1.5 (Objective 1.5)

In which of the following ways do 'small-for-dates' infants differ from premature infants?

(a) 'Small-for-dates' infants are always smaller at birth than premature infants.

(b) The maximum rate of growth of which 'small-for-dates' babies are capable is lower than that of premature infants of similar gestational age.

(c) 'Small-for-dates' babies can catch up with normal infants if they are given a richer diet; premature infants cannot be thus treated because they cannot digest richer milk.

(d) Because infants grow faster after birth than before birth, premature infants eventually become larger as adults because they have been growing at a higher rate for a greater proportion of their lives.

(e) The birth of 'small-for-dates' babies is delayed until they reach the same size as normal infants. The longer than average gestation is beneficial to their subsequent growth; shorter than average gestation of premature babies impairs growth.

Explain in one or two sentences:

(a)   Why thyroxin deficiency is often caused by diet but GH deficiency is very rarely thus caused.

(b)   Why thyroxin is associated with hypertrophy of the thyroid gland but GH deficiency is not associated with hypertrophy of the pituitary.

(c)3Why thyroxin deficiency causes lethargy as well as growth defects.

Classify the following statements about growth hormone as true or false:

(a)   GH plays a role in regulating growth whenever and wherever it is present.

(b)   GH is of identical structure and plays identical roles in all mammals studied.

(c)   GH from one mammalian species can interact successfully with GH receptor sites on target cells of another species.

(d)   Taller humans and larger rats grow faster in their juvenile growth period because they have higher concentrations of GH in the blood.

(e)   GH interacts with cells to promote their division and maturation.

(a)   List three different ways in which the action of IGF I is regulated.

(b)   List three differences between IGF I and IGF II.

(c)   List two similarities between IGFs and insulin.

(d)   List two contrasts between IGFs and insulin.

(a)   List some behavioural and physiological characteristics of birds and mammals that are compatible with very rapid growth immediately after birth, followed by a period of much slower growth.

(b)   Why does the growth of fishes, reptiles and amphibians at different ages not follow the same pattern?

CHAPTER 2 CELLULAR MECHANISMS OF GROWTH AND REPAIR

2.1 Introduction

Chapter 1 was concerned with growth during the early part of life when the animal as a whole is increasing in size. The emphasis was on the role of exogenous factors, such as nutrition, and of endogenous hormones in modulating the growth of the whole animal and the relative growth of its parts. In mammals, enlargement of the skeleton and of many other tissues stops before or shortly after sexual maturity, so the animal remains the same height (or length) for the rest of its life, but the mechanisms that produce growth are not eliminated. Equally significant for a long and arduous adult life is the ability of tissues to repair and replace themselves following injury, atrophy (becoming smaller than normal) or disease. **Regeneration**, the replacement of defective or excised tissue continues, albeit with declining efficiency, throughout life.

At the cellular level, growth early in life and regeneration throughout the life cycle have much in common and can usefully be discussed together in this chapter. The basic mechanisms, and how they change with age, differ fundamentally from one tissue to another. To understand the general principles behind the 'big picture', these phenomena must be studied in several tissues.

2.1.1 Basic cellular mechanisms of growth

In a multicellular organism, enlargement of any one tissue or organ could be accomplished in several different ways, as shown diagrammatically in Figure 2.1. In Figure 2.1a (*overleaf*) the mass of the hypothetical organ doubles because each cell

enlarges, and in doing so increases its complement of organelles. In Figure 2.1b the number of organelles per cell remains unchanged but additional cells have formed, either by division of the original cells or by recruitment of more cells from elsewhere. Growth of the organ in Figure 2.1c is due to a combination of both the processes in (a) and (b). The control of growth could rest with the smaller unit, the larger unit or with some master control system which controls the growth of the whole organism.

■ What biochemical measurements could distinguish cell proliferation (Figure 2.1b) from cell enlargement (Figure 2.1a)?

In most tissues, the approximate number of cells can be estimated by measuring the ratio of protein (i.e. cytoplasm and protein components of the nucleus) to DNA (i.e. genetic material). If the number of cells is constant, growth must be due to cell enlargement (Section 1.2.2). The rate of uptake of isotopically labelled DNA precursors, usually thymidine, is used as a measure of the formation of new cells. However, the method is only accurate for fairly rapid cell division and may be confounded by chromosome duplication and other forms of DNA synthesis not accompanied by cell division.

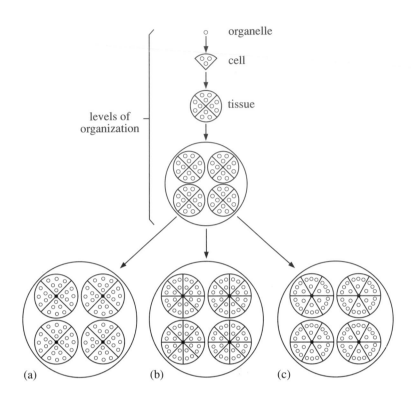

levels of organization

organelle

cell

tissue

(a)   (b)   (c)

Figure 2.1 Schematic representation of three different ways in which an organ could double its mass. (a) Growth takes place by increase in cell size and hence there is proliferation of intracellular components. (b) Growth due to increase in cell number. (c) Growth by a combination of cell enlargement and cell division.

There are three possible schemes by which growth could be regulated. The first is that growth at one level directly causes the growth at the next highest level; thus, the number of organelles in a cell continues to increase until cell division and the production of more cells is triggered, thereby preventing each cell from becoming too large. An alternative scheme is to start at the highest level and work down to the smallest unit: thus, each unit of the organism is of a predetermined size, with a fixed number of organs each containing a fixed number of cells. Each unit then grows until it reaches its quota and then stops. A third scheme incorporates features of the first two schemes: there is some sort of centrally programmed 'grand plan' for the whole organism, but also a feedback sensing mechanism allowing for proliferation of units at any lower level if unusual demand, damage, wear, injury or other circumstances peculiar to the individual required it.

All three 'growth schemes' are used by living organisms. Some colonial protistans and some kinds of sponges and algae grow in a way similar to scheme 1, at least during the vegetative phases of the life cycle. These organisms have an ill-defined adult shape and the rate of growth of different parts of a single individual is strongly dependent upon the availability of nutrients to that part. Except for the inconvenience caused to taxonomists trying to classify organisms on morphological criteria, there are few obvious disadvantages to this type of growth. The organism can adapt its size and shape to a wide range of circumstances and thus exploit the resources of its environment quickly and efficiently. This pattern of growth is called indeterminate because the various parts of the organism are not able to regulate each other's rate or direction of growth.

Some other kinds of invertebrates, notably nematode worms such as *Ascaris,* grow according to scheme 2. One particular species of nematode, ***Caenorhabditis*** **elegans*** (adult length about 1 mm), has been studied intensively by Professor Sydney Brenner and his colleagues in Cambridge over the last 30 years. The remarkable feature of *Caenorhabditis* (first noticed by 19th-century anatomists) is that all normal adults consist of exactly 945 somatic cells, of which 302 form the nervous system and the rest form the muscles, intestine, reproductive organs and cuticle. Furthermore, the size of each cell varies little from specimen to specimen. When each worm is fully grown there is a place for every cell and every cell has its own place, and presumably its own unique role to play.

Particular cell lineages or the genes controlling them can be selectively destroyed in the growing worm and many of the numerous mutant worms which have been studied differ from the wild forms only in that one group of cells, or even a single cell, is deficient or absent. In many cases it appears that no other cells can take over the roles of the one whose growth fails through genetic or somatic damage. Surprisingly, in a large number of cases, the rest of the cells carry on with their growth and development nonetheless, and produce adult worms deficient in just one or a few cells and so, presumably, in just one or a few functions. Growth and development of this type is called determinate.

■   How could this property be exploited for studies of physiological mechanisms?

By comparing normal worms with those lacking a single cell (or a single cell type, or a single gene), it is possible to demonstrate the role of that single component for the physiology of the body as a whole. Convenient though it might be for biologists interested in exploring the physiological mechanism, this form of growth means that the worms are unable to vary their body form or the relative sizes of their organs in response to different environmental conditions, or to compensate for injuries. Wild *Caenorhabditis* live on the forest floor, where they feed on rotting vegetation. Many other species of nematodes are found in similarly constant environments; many are internal parasites and others live on the floor of deep oceans. Such habitats are environments where lack of flexibility in growth and the inability to repair damage may not be a serious disadvantage. However, other kinds of nematodes can also be abundant in unstable and variable habitats, such as soils and freshwater pools, so their 'determinate' pattern of growth should not be seen as restricting them to a limited range of habitats.

Most larger animals, including insects and mammals, grow according to scheme 3; the maximum and minimum dimensions of each kind of cell, tissue, organ and organism, and the age at which the potential for growth is greatest, are genetically determined. However, the exact timing of growth, its rate, and so the final size of each unit, can be adjusted to meet the special circumstances experienced by each individual. Among the best understood of these 'special circumstances' are the availability of suitable nutrients and body temperature. When growth is controlled partly by genetic factors and partly by environmental factors, the result is a population of organisms which are broadly similar in structure and behaviour but which are not necessarily composed of anything like the same number or size of cells, so healthy individuals of the same age are not necessarily the same size. Nonetheless, to function effectively the sizes and shapes of all the body parts must be integrated together: the mechanisms by which the relative sizes of organs and tissues are coordinated is an important aspect of the study of growth.

* *Caenorhabditis* is pronounced 'seen-oh-rab-dy-tis'.

The advantage of adaptability in growth is that each individual can grow rapidly when food is plentiful, but can also avoid stunting or restriction of its normal energy expenditure when there is insufficient food to support both normal activity and rapid growth. Adaptability also enables an animal to respond to excessive wear, injury and disease by prompt and thorough repair or replacement of the affected part, regardless of its age at the time.

Constant wear and replacement of cells is an integral part of the function of some tissues, notably the outer layers of the skin, the blood and the lining of the gut. The delicate lining of the small intestine, containing secretory and absorptive cells, erodes rapidly from exposure to digestive enzymes and contact with food. In adult humans, the entire lining of the intestine is renewed about every 5 days, with the loss into the faeces of about 250 g of dead cells. This turnover rate is very high compared to the rate of growth of the body as a whole (see Chapter 1): all that is needed for the gut to grow in childhood, or to hypertrophy (i.e. enlarge beyond normal size) in adulthood, is for the rate of formation of cells to be slightly higher than their rate of loss. The new tissue is formed by division and rapid maturation of **stem cells**. The chief, probably sole, function of stem cells is to divide to form daughter cells, which may differentiate and grow into functionally mature cells or may continue as undifferentiated stem cells. Sometimes one daughter cell differentiates, while the other continues to divide as a stem cell. Stem cells are small and often lack distinctive anatomical or biochemical features, but detailed study of them in culture shows that any one kind can give rise to only one or a limited range of cell types.

The nervous system is among the few tissues from which stem cells have disappeared entirely before or shortly after birth: all regeneration and growth other than by cell enlargement are thus impossible. In many other tissues, among them liver (Section 2.2.1), bone (Section 2.3) and muscle (Section 2.4), the rate of loss and replacement of cells is normally very low (often too low to be measured accurately) but major injury can restart division. In a third group of tissues, cell replacement is an integral part of their function: there is a continuous turnover as the mature cells die and are replaced by newly formed ones that differentiate from proliferating stem cells.

Tissues in which cell turnover is high obviously contain numerous stem cells which are relatively easy to locate and study *in vivo*. Those that replace the inner surface of the gut, for example, are embedded deep in crypts between the villi (finger-like protrusions of the gut lining), and their physiology is quite well understood. They can differentiate into any one of four different types of secretory and absorptive cells, which then move to a position where they are in close contact with gut contents.

Another high-wear surface is the epidermis of the skin, the outer layer of which consists of dead cells filled with the tough, insoluble protein, keratin. New cells are formed continuously by mitosis of stem cells in the base of the epidermis; they fill themselves with keratin, die, and after a few days as functional, protective epidermis, are sloughed off as white 'scurf'.

2.1.2 Basic subcellular mechanisms of growth

The intracellular fabric of almost all living material undergoes constant replacement, even in tissues not subjected to mechanical wear or chemical erosion. Cells and tissues age or become inappropriate when their habitual use changes, and individual proteins become fragmented through encounters with proteolytic enzymes, or oxidized or in other ways become denatured. The breakdown and replacement of redundant or defective proteinaceous material are called **protein turnover**. The process is fundamental to both growth of tissues and maintenance of body function: 'turnover' means that the rate of tissue formation equals its rate of breakdown. Growth occurs when synthesis exceeds degradation, and atrophy when the latter exceeds the former. Protein turnover may entail proliferation and destruction of cells but equally the cell fabric may turn over without any replacement of the cells themselves. The amino acids released by the degradation of proteins are incorporated into new proteins being synthesized in the same cell or elsewhere in the body. By releasing amino acids that can be 'recycled' into new tissues, protein turnover provides much of the raw materials for growth and repair.

Compared to the vast amounts of information now available about protein synthesis, the mechanisms of protein degradation and turnover are neglected topics. Larger particles such as bacteria, erythrocytes and fragments of dead tissue are engulfed and digested by phagocytes. Some organelles, including mitochondria, are broken down in lysosomes, but neither of these processes is fast enough or widespread enough to account for the bulk of protein recycling in the mammalian body.

Most protein recycling probably depends upon the local action of proteolytic enzymes, the best known of which is **calpain.** This calcium-dependent enzyme is found in almost all kinds of vertebrate cells, and in most invertebrate cells where it has been looked for. It exists in two forms: m-calpain, thus called because it is active at calcium concentrations of around 1 mmol l^{-1}, and μ-calpain, which is active at micromolar calcium concentrations (3–50 μmol l^{-1} Ca^{2+}). Both forms of calpain are inhibited by another protein, calpastatin, and in most tissues, most of the time, these proteins together regulate the rate of degradation of proteins.

How do the proteolytic enzymes 'know' which proteins to degrade? In the cases of many enzymes, it appears that they don't: the proteins 'live' for between a few minutes to a few days (depending on the particular enzyme) and a newly formed molecule is as likely to be degraded as an 'old' one. Short-lived proteins (i.e. those that turn over rapidly) often have certain characteristic amino acid sequences that are not present (or at least not exposed) in long-lived forms, but it is not clear how these sequences promote degradation.

Proteins may also be 'labelled' for destruction by attachment to one or more small (76 amino acid) peptides called collectively **ubiquitin**, which, as their name implies, are found in most kinds of plant and animal cells (but not prokaryotes). The mechanism is surprisingly complicated, involving several enzymatic steps and adenosine triphosphate (ATP). Protein turnover thus involves substantial amounts of energy. In skeletal muscle, for example, degradation and replacement of proteins at a rate of 4–5% per day uses up to 25% of the tissue's ATP production. Once attached to ubiquitin, a protein is degraded within minutes, but the ubiquitin molecules themselves escape destruction and are released for further rounds of protein degradation. Certain chemical modifications of amino acids within a protein may promote attachment to ubiquitin, thus marking out proteins for breakdown.

The rate of protein turnover differs greatly between tissues and according to physiological conditions. In general, extracellular proteins such as collagen turn over much more slowly than intracellular materials, but in some tissues, notably the pregnant uterus, collagen turnover is quite fast. The process is infinitely slow in the lens of the eye and parts of the teeth, but many enzymes, especially digestive enzymes, and hormones are degraded within seconds or minutes (at most an hour or two) of becoming physiologically active. For example, insulin may be stored for some hours in the pancreatic cells that synthesize it but once secreted, it normally binds within a few minutes to an insulin receptor on the membrane of cells elsewhere in the body and is broken down by that cell.

■   Can you name some proteins involved in growth that turn over rapidly?

IGFs (Section 1.4.1) circulate for only about an hour before they are degraded (probably in the liver). Their binding proteins also turn over rapidly.

Protein turnover has been most thoroughly studied in the liver, where in well-fed adults about 40–50% of the protein is replaced each day. In starvation, the rate of protein degradation can be as high as 70% per day while the rate of protein synthesis remains relatively constant. Consequently, the protein content of the liver can fall at a rate of up to 2% per hour.

■   What would happen to the amino acids thus released?

In starvation, many amino acids would be converted into glucose in the metabolic pathway called gluconeogenesis and oxidized. In a well-fed animal, there would be sufficient glycogen to meet the demand for glucose, so most of the amino acids would be reincorporated into proteins. On refeeding, the rate of degradation falls to only 11% per day and the rate of protein synthesis increases a little, so the protein content of the liver increases rapidly.

There do not appear to be special 'storage' proteins that have no role other than to act as a source of amino acids, but some kinds of protein seem to be more dispensable than others. The amino acid glutamine is present in muscle in much larger quantities than seem to be necessary for its incorporation into proteins. It may have a role in the storage and transport between tissues of the amino groups necessary for the synthesis and interconversion of amino acids.

Summary of Section 2.1

A few organisms grow by determinate growth and thus contain a constant number of cells. In most others, the contributions of cell proliferation and cell enlargement to growth are variable and the sizes of organs and tissues are adaptable to different conditions. The mechanisms of growth and regeneration are basically similar in most tissues. Proteins turn over in almost all tissues, but at widely different rates. The major mechanism involves locally acting proteolytic enzymes, and proteins often combine with ubiquitin before they are degraded. The amino acids thus released are incorporated into new proteins. Growth depends upon the relative rates of protein synthesis and degradation. Both processes are modulated by physiological conditions such as starvation.

2.2 Growth and regeneration in viscera

Both protein synthesis and turnover proceed faster when tissues are growing, regenerating or combating disease. The net rate of accretion of a tissue depends upon the relative rates of protein synthesis and degradation. Cells cannot grow beyond a certain size so any substantial net increase in organ size involves cell proliferation. The way in which these processes are controlled is quite different in the liver and the kidneys.

2.2.1 The liver

As explained in Section 2.1.2, the adult liver is in a constant state of protein turnover and its mass fluctuates greatly with nutritional state. Nonetheless, there is no clearly identifiable population of stem cells and very little cell division in the undisturbed liver: fewer than one in 10 000 cells is seen to be in mitosis at any one time. If any part of a rat's liver is surgically removed, the first response, as might be expected from Section 2.1.2, is protein accumulation in the cells of the remaining portions. Within 15 h after the operation (Figure 2.2), cell division, as measured by an increase in incorporation of DNA precursors, also increases abruptly.

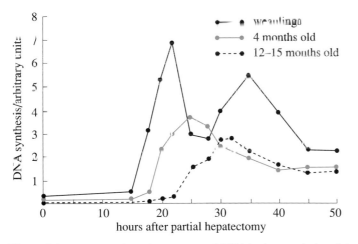

Figure 2.2 Incorporation of precursors of DNA in the remainder of the liver following surgical removal of a large part of the liver in rats. Weanlings are about three weeks old.

■   How does the course of regeneration change with age?

The rate of rise of cell division, and the maximum observed rate of cell division are lower in older rats, although the time to the onset of DNA synthesis is unchanged.

Even if as much as two-thirds of the total mass of a rat's liver is removed, the animals not only survive the operation in good health, but also regenerate the liver remarkably quickly: the mass of the part remaining is doubled in 3 days and the original size is restored within 3 weeks. Since there are no 'stand-by' stem cells in the liver, it must be the fully formed, functionally mature cells which are dividing. Microscopic examination of the tissue shows that newly formed cells quickly become indistinguishable from longer established ones.

The rate of protein synthesis in the liver is remarkably constant throughout regeneration and during fetal growth: increase in liver mass is due mainly to a decrease in the rate of protein degradation, and in the rate of lysosomal destruction of organelles such as mitochondria. In the experiment shown in Figure 2.2, the livers of older rats were the same size (in proportion to body mass) as those of weanlings.

■   What do this observation and the data in Figure 2.2 suggest about age changes in the cellular mechanism of growth?

They suggest that cell enlargement, rather than cell proliferation, contributes more to liver growth in older rats but, in weanlings that were at an age when most of the other tissues were also growing rapidly, more new cells are formed.

■   Would you expect IGFs to be involved in growth and regeneration of the liver?

Yes, because the liver is the chief source of circulating IGFs (Section 1.4.1). But in spite of this fact, there is very little evidence for a stimulatory or regulatory role for IGFs in liver growth or regeneration. In transgenic mice that overexpress the IGF I gene, there is more IGF I and more IGF I mRNA, but the animals' livers are not proportionately larger and they do not differ in histological structure. The only detectable change in regenerating livers is slightly more IGF I receptors: there is no more mRNA for either IGF I or IGF II.

The mammalian liver is thus one of the few tissues in which cell division and mature function are not mutually exclusive. Many other kinds of mature cells, red blood cells, nerve and muscle, to name just a few, have elaborate cytoplasmic structures when fully functional and never normally divide. However, the reorganization necessary to permit division cannot be impossible because many tumours arise from cells that resume mitosis in circumstances in which cell division does not normally occur. The question of tumour formation is discussed again in Chapter 4.

Although the liver's response to surgical removal is remarkable both for its promptness and for the precision with which absent tissue is replaced, liver damage through poisoning is less satisfactorily corrected. In humans, frequent consumption of excessive amounts of alcohol is one of the commonest forms of chronic liver poisoning. The liver responds by growing larger, but perfect function is rarely restored completely. The 'beer belly' appearance of many chronic alcoholics is due mainly to massive enlargement of the liver, but in spite of this compensatory growth, organ function is still deficient and liver failure is a common cause of death among such people.

2.2.2 The mammalian kidney

Changes in the relative size of organs are an integral part of adaptation to different environments. Such adjustment is particularly important for organs that have high energy requirements: the kidneys account for only about 0.5% of the body mass of a typical mammal, but they use 8–10% of its oxygen consumption. Too little kidney tissue may produce deficient excretion, but too much is wasteful of energy.

The kidneys are relatively large in marine mammals and desert species which have access to little or no fresh water or to foods with low salt concentration, and the urine they produce is very concentrated. In some species, the relative size of the kidneys changes seasonally: those of Svalbard reindeer are relatively larger in winter, when all the fresh water is frozen, than in summer when the animals have access to plenty of water. An organ's capacity to adjust its mass to functional demands may result in its atrophy (i.e. shrinkage and/or loss of function) as well as its growth. Age as well as functional demand interact to determine the size of vital organs such as the kidney and the heart.

The control of kidney size has been the subject of much recent research because of its importance in predicting the long-term outcome of operations to replace incurably defective kidneys with transplants. In many texts, the immunological aspects of the new technology of tissue transplantation and 'spare part' surgery receive most attention. However, since the whole point of transplanting kidneys (and hearts, livers, etc.) is that the replacement tissue functions satisfactorily in its new host for many years, it is equally important to understand how introduced organs adjust their size and shape to the new environment over a long period of time. As well as helping physicians to predict and manipulate the outcome of accidental or surgical loss or damage to organs, the study of regeneration can also tell us a great deal about the mechanisms by which each organ or tissue 'knows' when it is the right size.

In mammals, the number of glomeruli in each kidney reaches a maximum early in life. Rats have their full complement of 35 000 glomeruli at about the time of birth. Under normal circumstances, growth after birth takes place by thickening and elongation of the nephrons and their components, but the number of nephrons remains constant or declines. However, if one of the kidneys is surgically removed, the number of nephrons in the other increases to a degree which depends mainly upon the age of the animal at the time of surgery. If the operation is performed on rats at 20 days old or younger, the remaining kidney compensates almost completely for the absence of its partner and has double the usual number of nephrons at maturity. If the operation is delayed until the rat is 45 days old (at which time it is not yet fully grown or sexually mature), only about 50% more nephrons form in the remaining kidney.

Kidney growth by hypertrophy of the nephrons and by increase in size and number of the constituent cells also plays an important role in older animals from which a kidney has been removed. Figure 2.3 shows the time course of the response of the remaining kidney to surgical removal of its partner in an adult rat.

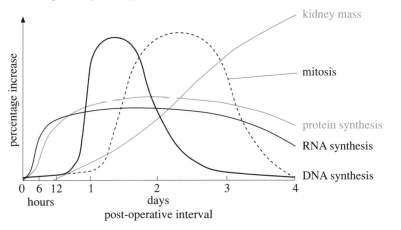

Figure 2.3 Various structural and biochemical changes in the remaining kidney following surgical removal (at time 0) of the other kidney in an adult rat.

■   From Figure 2.3, what are the cellular mechanisms behind (a) the initial response, and (b) the delayed response of the tissue to excision of the other kidney ?

The first response is expansion of function of the surviving kidney, with cell enlargement without cell division, because there is a concurrent increase in RNA and protein synthesis beginning 2 h after the operation. The kidneys, like the liver, are richly perfused with blood that brings plenty of nutrients to support rapid protein synthesis. The process is so prompt and effective that excretion and the regulation of body fluid composition are hardly impaired, even in the first few hours after the operation. Some of the extra proteins produced early in the kidney's regeneration response are additional enzymes that enhance kidney function; the rest are structural proteins associated with the formation of additional cells. DNA synthesis increases detectably after 16 h and cell division after 1 day but mitosis does not reach a maximum until more than 48 h after the operation. Thus, the kidney shows remarkable capacity to combine mature function with both cell enlargement and cell division.

There are two main ways by which the remaining kidney could 'know' that growth is necessary: the first is some central control mechanism, probably in the central nervous system (CNS), which responds to the loss or malfunctioning of the kidney and issues neural or endocrine 'commands' for the surviving kidney to grow rapidly. The second possibility is that the response is coordinated in the remaining kidney itself. The kidney is an organ that is in continuous use: an adult mammal cannot survive more than a few hours at normal body temperatures with total renal failure. So, from the moment one kidney is removed, its remaining partner becomes functionally overloaded.

A technique called parabiosis has been used to distinguish between endocrine and neural factors on the one hand, and the role of functional overload on the other, in determining the extent of compensatory growth in kidneys. Experiments using parabiosis are summarized in Figure 2.4.

■   If the investigator had performed only the experiment shown in Figure 2.4b, what would have been concluded?

The conclusion would have been that the pressure and/or composition of the blood received by a kidney was the most important factor regulating its growth and that centrally secreted hormones which would have entered the circulation of both parabionts, play an insignificant role.

If further experiments of the kinds shown in Figures 2.4c and 2.4d are performed, the contribution of central control mechanisms comes to light. A rat can survive the loss of both kidneys if it is joined in parabiosis to another with both kidneys, as indicated in Figure 2.4c. In this experiment, the blood pressure on the kidneys comes from the heart of only one rat, but both the remaining kidneys respond equally and enlarge to meet the functional demands of the whole tissue mass of two rats. Clearly some factor other than blood pressure is stimulating growth. This conclusion is confirmed by the experiment shown in Figure 2.4d, in which a single greatly enlarged kidney is maintaining both rats in parabiosis.

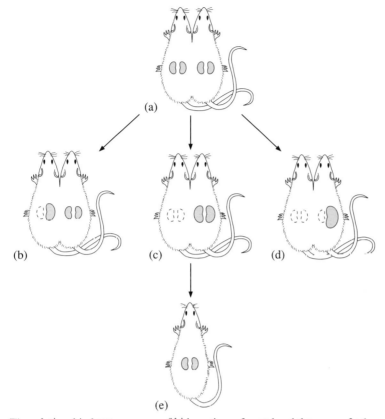

Figure 2.4   The relationship between mass of kidney tissue formed and the mass of other body tissues, as demonstrated using parabiosis of adult rats. (a) The circulatory systems of rats from an inbred strain are joined. (b) If the kidney of one rat is removed ((kidney shown in dotted outline only), the other kidney of the same rat enlarges. (c) If both kidneys of one rat are removed, both rats remain viable, but the kidneys of the other rat enlarge equally. (d) If three of the four kidneys are removed, a single, greatly enlarged organ is sufficient to sustain both rats. (e) If the parabionts in (c) are later separated, the one lacking kidneys dies and the kidneys of the other regress to normal size.

Such enlargement seems to be a direct response to functional demands, and is reversible; if the two rats in the experiment shown Figure 2.4c are later separated surgically, the one without any kidneys dies within a few hours, as would be expected, but the kidneys of the other rat regress to their original size (Figure 2.4e). This experiment suggests that the size of the kidneys and the total tissue mass of the whole body is continuously 'under review' and tissue is promptly removed as soon as it becomes superfluous to requirements.

This conclusion is further substantiated by experiments in which additional kidneys are grafted into both normal and kidney-deficient rats. Some such experiments are summarized in Figure 2.5 (*overleaf*). In Figure 2.5a, a third kidney is grafted into an intact adult rat and quickly atrophies. If one of the host's own kidneys is removed at the same time (Figure 2.5b), the new kidney grows more than in Figure 2.5a, but still fails to reach normal size. Instead, the host's own remaining kidney grows larger, so that it and the grafted kidney together make up about the normal complement of kidney mass. Only if both the host's kidneys are removed (Figure 2.5c) does a single grafted kidney grow large, showing that failure of growth in the earlier experiments was due to the kidney's environment, not to any intrinsic lack of growth capacity.

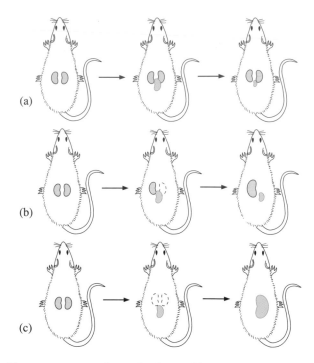

Figure 2.5   The consequences of transplanting additional kidneys into adult rats. Endogenous kidneys are shown in grey; all introduced kidneys are shown in blue; excised kidneys shown in dotted outline only. (a) A third kidney transplanted into an otherwise intact rat atrophies. (b) If an additional kidney is transplanted into a rat from which one of its own kidneys is removed, the host's remaining kidney enlarges and the introduced organ does not atrophy as much as in (a). (c) If both the host's kidneys are removed when the additional organ is transplanted, the introduced kidney grows much larger.

These experiments indicate that in adults, the career of any particular kidney depends largely on its host environment, with the incumbent organs having the power to control the growth of newcomers. Different conclusions emerge from experimental transplantation of tissues from young animals: although the histological structure and physiological function of kidneys in weanling and adult rats are indistinguishable (except on the basis of size), the regulation of their growth is different. If a kidney is transplanted from a weanling rat to an adult rat (Figure 2.6a), it fails to enlarge. It grows more if one or both of the recipient's kidneys are removed at the same time (Figures 2.6b and c), indicating that the juvenile kidney is not simply inhibited from growing because it is in a mature organism. However, if a kidney from a weanling rat is transplanted into a littermate (Figure 2.6d), all three kidneys grow at about the same rate, and the resulting adult has three kidneys, all of normal size.

■   How does this experiment seem to contradict the conclusions reached from the experiments shown in Figure 2.5?

The experiments suggest that each kidney has an intrinsic potential for growth, which it carries out notwithstanding the fact that each kidney is doing only one-third, instead of half, of the total work-load. Previous experiments indicated that atrophy and hypertrophy were closely linked to the amount of functioning kidney tissue in the body.

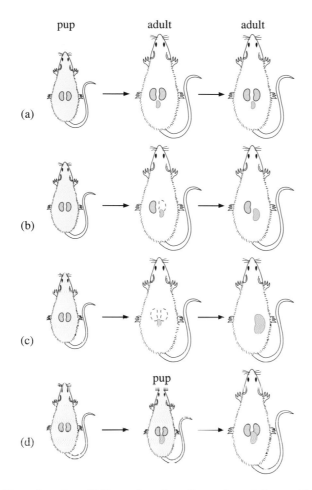

Figure 2.6   Transplantation of kidneys from juvenile rats into adult rats. (a) A pup's kidney transplanted into an otherwise intact adult fails to grow. (b) and (c) A pup's kidney grows better if one (b) or both (c) of the host's kidney(s) are removed. (d) If an additional pup's kidney is transplanted into a littermate, all three kidneys grow to about the same size.

However, the experiments in Figure 2.6 suggest that juvenile kidneys are similar to those of adults in that their rate of growth can be increased very substantially by functional demands. So the current thinking on the matter is that juvenile kidneys possess intrinsic potential for growth which can be suppressed by adult tissues but not by tissues from other juveniles. However, like the adult organ, the rate of growth of the juvenile kidney can be greatly modified by its environment.

Some of these differences can be correlated with the action of IGFs. IGF I is present in kidney cells from birth onwards and its abundance correlates with kidney size: overexpression of the IGF I gene in transgenic mice produces five times as much IGF I and larger kidneys. Removal of one kidney stimulates an increase in IGF I production in the other.

■   How could you show that the IGF I was produced by the kidney itself?

If measurements of IGF I in the blood and liver reveal no increase following excision of a kidney, the extra peptide must have been produced endogenously.

The chief difference between juvenile and adult animals seems to be that kidney cell proliferation makes a major contribution to growth in the former, while hypertrophy is mainly due to cell enlargement in the latter. In spite of these impressive powers of prompt and complete increase in kidney tissue mass, and the restoration of normal function, you may have noticed that *de novo* formation of a whole new kidney separate from established ones never happens. Kidney-forming cells cannot migrate within the body, and cell lineages that are not committed to careers as kidney cells early in fetal life cannot later acquire this function.

The promptness and thoroughness of regeneration of these large, vital organs may have surprised you. Excision of the liver or kidneys in the ways described above could never happen in the wild: an accidental wound that destroyed these internal organs would quickly cause death through excess bleeding.

■   What natural processes would have promoted the evolution of such impressive powers of regeneration?

Parasites, especially liver flukes and other metazoan worms, infest richly perfused viscera such as the gut, lungs, liver and mechanically destroy tissue. The capacity of the viscera to maintain almost normal function in spite of such damage, and to regenerate quickly and thoroughly, probably evolved as an adaptation to deal with parasites, which are common among all wild mammals.

Summary of Section 2.2

Starvation and refeeding produce large and rapid changes in the mass and protein content of the liver without significant cell division. Surgical removal of part of the liver leads within a few hours to extensive cell division of functionally mature cells. IGFs are present in and secreted from the liver but there is little evidence that they regulate its growth or regeneration. Transplanted or endogenous kidneys can become larger or smaller if the ratio of kidney mass to mass of other body tissues is disturbed. In adult rats, the incumbent organ tends to suppress the growth of introduced organs, but in weanling rats transplanted organs grow to about the same size as the endogenous organs. In general, cell proliferation is the major mechanism of growth in young mammals, but cell enlargement predominates in older animals.

2.3 Growth in mammalian long bones

As mentioned in Section 2.1.1, most tissues grow mainly by an increase in cell number as a result of cell division. In some tissues, such as the lining of the gut and the epidermis of the skin, cell division takes place in numerous sites scattered throughout the organ. In other tissues, notably adipose tissue, and several kinds of white blood cells, the site(s) of cell proliferation are still hotly disputed. However, in one tissue, bone, most of the cell division and growth during the fetal and juvenile periods takes place at well-defined growth zones. The biochemical composition and fine structure of bone are very distinctive and calcified tissues show up very clearly on histological sections, X-ray pictures and ultrasound scans, and so are readily quantifiable. All these properties simplify investigations of cellular mechanisms of bone growth both *in vivo* and *in vitro*.

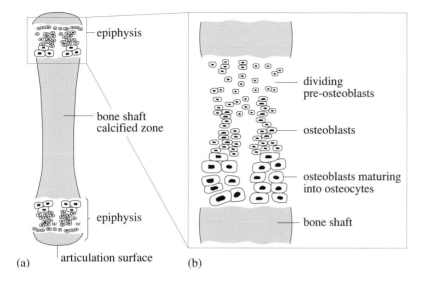

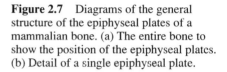

Figure 2.7 Diagrams of the general structure of the epiphyseal plates of a mammalian bone. (a) The entire bone to show the position of the epiphyseal plates. (b) Detail of a single epiphyseal plate.

In mammalian fetuses, the long bones first appear as cartilage rudiments (see Section 7.4.1 for more about cartilage), but the cartilage is infiltrated and eventually replaced by bone-forming cells beginning quite early in gestation. From birth onwards, most of the growth in length is concentrated at the **epiphysis**. Most long bones have two epiphyseal plates, one at each end, a short distance from the joints (Figure 2.7a). Figure 2.7b is a single epiphysis, enlarged to show the stages in the development of mature bone.

Skeleton formation has been studied in detail in fetal sheep and fetal and neonatal rats. The distal ends of the epiphyses contain rapidly dividing cells, called pre-osteoblasts, that are small and uncalcified. Pre-osteoblasts mature into the basic bone-forming cells, called **osteoblasts** (Figure 2.7b). Osteoblasts do not divide, but enlarge and develop large quantities of the apparatus involved in protein synthesis and secretion: rough endoplasmic reticulum (ER) and Golgi bodies. Epiphyseal osteoblasts are concentrated towards the middle of the growth zone, where they secrete collagen, glycoproteins* and proteoglycans† to form around themselves an extracellular matrix that accumulates crystals of calcium salts. The glycoproteins and proteoglycans are particularly important for this process because they are large, highly ionized molecules that attract inorganic salts. The chemical structure and abundance of the proteins determines how the inorganic crystals form: insufficient or abnormal collagen or glycoproteins leads to abnormal calcification and weak bones.

Bones grow in thickness as well as, or instead of, in length. Thickening arises from the proliferation and maturation of lineages of pre-osteoblasts in the two well-vascularized cellular layers that cover the whole bony skeleton: the **periosteum** on the outer surface and the **endosteum** on the inner (marrow) surface. The stem cells in these layers mature into osteoblasts that secrete the extracellular matrix and maintain a chemical environment suitable for

* Glycoproteins consist of a peptide core with carbohydrate side chains.

† The structure of proteoglycans is similar to that of glycoproteins but the number and length of carbohydrate side chains are greater, so the proportion of carbohydrate is greater (see also Section 7.4.1).

calcification in much the same way as in the epiphyses. The bone thus formed widens and strengthens the skeleton. Unlike growth at the epiphyses, bone formation at the periosteum and endosteum continues until old age, so bony skeletons can become thicker and stronger at any time of life (e.g. in response to local friction or pressure, or because the whole body becomes heavier due to pregnancy or obesity).

The calcified matrix hardens, surrounding and enclosing the osteoblasts as they form mature cells called **osteocytes**, in which the rough ER and Golgi bodies are greatly reduced. These tiny cells remain singly or in small groups in osteocytic lacunae, which permeate the entire bone at a density of 25 000 per mm^3. The osteocytes maintain contact with each other and with the cells of the periosteum and endosteum by means of long fine processes that penetrate the calcified bone through a system of very fine interwoven channels.

Many hormones and growth factors are known to modulate bone formation, and several more are currently being characterized. Their roles change as the cells mature: thus fibroblast growth factor (FGF) is a major stimulator of proliferation of pre-osteoblasts that acts in an autocrine and paracrine way. As the cell division stops, the osteoblasts bind less FGF but more IGF II (Section 1.4.1), and they hypertrophy. Under the influence of another paracrine agent, transforming growth factor (TGF-β), the cells secrete collagen, glycoproteins and proteoglycans in proportions that seem to be regulated by this growth factor. Various circulating hormones promote or inhibit bone formation: insulin stimulates the formation of the extracellular matrix without affecting cell proliferation, but glucocorticoids and parathyroid hormone curtail proliferation of pre-osteoblasts, and/or matrix production, and/or calcification. The sequential action of these and other factors determine the eventual size, shape and composition of the bone.

■   Would you expect the bone fabric to have a high rate of turnover?

No. Much of the protein is extracellular and structural which would be expected to turn over very slowly. However, the skeleton is the body's main store of calcium and phosphate ions (Section 1.2.3) and there is extensive exchange of these ions between bone and other tissues, especially during lactation, when large quantities of calcium are secreted in the milk.

Epiphyses are often represented in diagrams as flat plates (e.g. Figure 2.7), and a few of them are of this shape. A moment's thought, however, tells you that a flat plate of soft, uncalcified tissue would be a place where sprains and breaks would happen repeatedly, particularly in a big animal that moves fast over rough terrain. Figure 2.8 is a photograph of the parts of the dried bones that formed the knee joint of a young camel. The soft epiphyseal tissue has rotted away, leaving the hard bone behind. You can clearly see that the epiphyseal 'plate', far from being flat, was deeply crenulated in three dimensions, and indeed when the two parts of the lower end of the femur are put together, it is impossible to twist them on each other.

■   What function can you suggest for this crenulated shape?

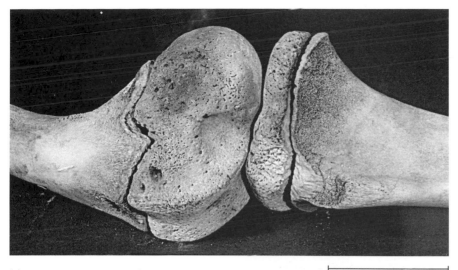

(a)   5 cm

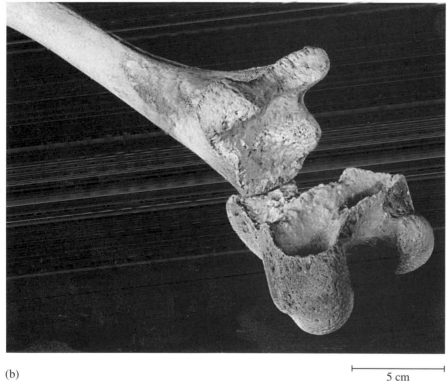

(b)   5 cm

Figure 2.8   Bones of the knee (stifle) joint of an 11-month-old Bactrian camel. (a) The left bone is the femur and the right is the tibia. (b) Close-up of lower epiphysis of the femur.

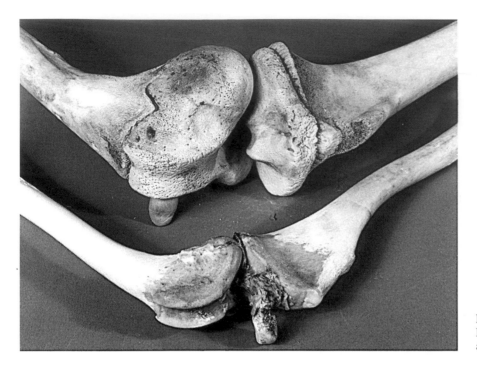

Figure 2.9   Knee bones of the camel in Figure 2.8 (*above*) and of a fully grown adult wolf (*below*).

It minimizes the risk of damage to the epiphyseal plates every time the young animal stumbles or twists its knees a little. Camels, of course, have very long legs, and growth of the femur and tibia continues for several years after birth, during which time the animal travels long distances between grazing grounds, and may often have to run fast to escape predators. The soft, delicate tissues of the growth zones of other slow-growing but athletic species such as humans are protected from sprains in similar ways.

As the animal gets older, the formation of new, unossified cells slows down, and the epiphyses become thinner, and are finally occluded altogether. Figure 2.9 is a photograph of the knee bones of the young camel and the corresponding bones of an adult wolf. The epiphyses have disappeared completely from the wolf bones: you cannot even see where they once were. Clearly, such bones can no longer grow in length.

In some mammals, such as rats and probably most marine mammals, the epiphyses of the limb bones never close completely and some growth in length of the long bones is possible throughout life. In humans and many other mammals, the hormones secreted at sexual maturity promote complete closure of the epiphyses of the limb bones and hence terminate growth in height.

■   How could you decide whether the hormones that control maturation of the sex organs also act directly on the skeleton, or if this effect depends upon a mediator produced elsewhere in the body?

Oestrogens and androgens should promote bone maturation *in vitro*, and cells in the epiphyses should have receptors for these hormones. In fact, it is difficult to demonstrate oestrogen receptors on any bone cells and the hormones have little effect on cultured osteoblasts, so their actions are believed to be indirect.

As noted in Section 1.2.1, Figures 1.3 and 1.4, menarche occurs towards the end of a period of very rapid growth in girls in the 1968 sample, or at a time when growth had already started to slow down in the 1883 sample. These data serve to emphasize that, in mammals, sex hormones can intervene to end growth in height whether or not other mechanisms of growth have already caused the process to slow down. The process is irreversible and, although the concentration of sex hormones may decline with age, the epiphyses cannot reform so growth in length cannot restart. If a bone is an inappropriate length at the time of sexual maturity, it normally remains so for the rest of the animal's life.

■   Would you expect to find a tight link, similar to that described in mammals, between sexual maturity and the closure of epiphyses in birds, reptiles, amphibians and fish?

No. Most birds are full size (and their skeletons cannot grow longer) at or shortly after fledging, long before they become sexually mature (Section 1.5). The skeletons of most reptiles, fish and amphibians continue to lengthen as well as thicken for years after they are capable of breeding.

Although the onset of sexual maturity plays a major role in determining the length of the long bones and hence final stature in mammals, there is some evidence that regulation of bone growth is coordinated within the bone itself. Figure 2.10 shows an experiment which demonstrates such a mechanism. The tibia (the longest bone in the hindleg) of one leg of a young rabbit was prevented from growing at one end only by inserting a surgical clip into the proximal epiphyseal plate. You can see that the bone grew more at the other epiphyseal plate, than in the homologous epiphysis of the unaltered control leg. The extra growth was, however, still not sufficient to compensate completely for the lack of growth at the pinned end. Variants of this procedure are used in both human and veterinary medicine to unbend deformed limbs and match pairs of limbs whose growth has 'got out of step' following some misadventure.

It is not clear how the bone 'knows' how long or how thick it should be, but mechanical forces in the periosteum are a strong possibility.

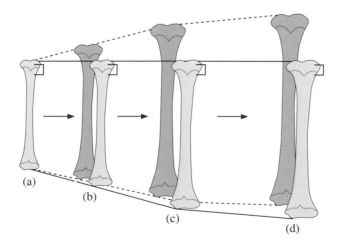

(a)   (b)   (c)   (d)

Figure 2.10   Compensatory growth at one epiphyseal plate (shown in blue), when growth at the epiphyseal plate at the other end of the bone is artificially reduced by inserting a surgical clip (shown in black). The bone studied is the tibia in the hindleg of a young rabbit. The altered bone (light grey) on one side is compared with the unaltered bone (dark grey) in the other leg at (b) 20, (c) 40, and (d) 140 days after the surgical clip was inserted into the proximal epiphysis (a).

2.3.1 Bone healing and remodelling

It is common knowledge that bones retain the capacity to heal breaks throughout life and can change in density and, in extreme cases, shape according to the regime of the forces applied to them. Healing and remodelling take place by the complementary activity of osteoblasts in the periosteum and the endosteum, and other cells, called **osteoclasts**, that break down mature bone. Osteoclasts (Figure 2.11a) are large, multinucleate cells with up to 20 nuclei, a folded and ruffled outer membrane and cytoplasm that contains so many small vacuoles, Golgi bodies and lysosomes, that they appear foamy under the microscope.

■ Can you suggest a function for cells with such structure?

Numerous vacuoles and a ruffled surface suggest secretion of large quantities of protein. Many of these features resemble those of macrophages (a kind of phagocyte that scavenges within tissues but does not circulate in the blood), and indeed developmental studies indicate that osteoclasts derive from the haemopoietic cell lineage (i.e. from stem cells similar to those that give rise to cells of the immune system such as lymphocytes and phagocytes). The ruffled border attaches firmly to the surface of the bone, and with the help of a ring of contractile proteins, seals off a small area into which proteolytic enzymes, including collagenases, and hydrogen ions are secreted.

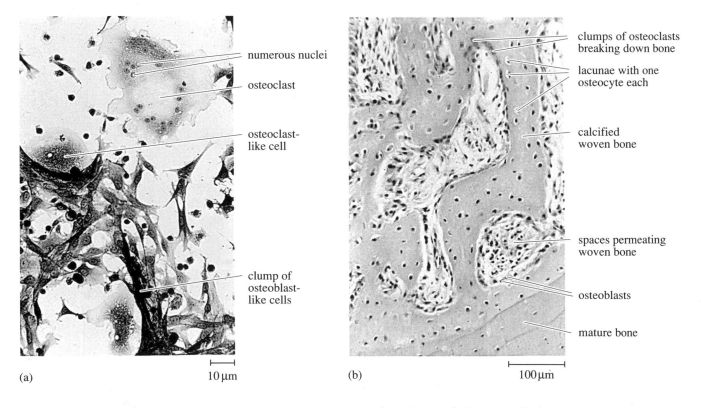

(a) 10 μm

(b) 100 μm

Figure 2.11 Cells involved in bone growth and remodelling. (a) A fixed, stained image of cells derived from the bone marrow and endosteum of a rat femur in tissue culture that are differentiating into osteoblasts and osteoclasts. The smaller mononucleate elongated cells are osteoblasts, many of which are clumping together. The stain picks out the enzyme alkaline phosphatase, which is a marker for osteoblasts. The larger, rounded, multinucleate cells are osteoclasts. (b) A stained section (haematoxylin and eosin stain) of a wing bone (ulna) of an adult turkey that is undergoing remodelling.

■   What would be the action of hydrogen ions on bone?

The acidity would dissolve the extracellular calcium salts, thereby decalcifying the bone. By means of these secretions, osteoclasts destroy mature bone.

In normal bone, osteoclasts are more abundant in the endosteum than the periosteum, but they become very much more numerous at both bone surfaces at sites of healing, remodelling or tumour formation. Their action is an essential part of bone maintenance and remodelling: in normal adults, the formation of new bone only occurs where there has previously been bone reabsorption. In Figure 2.11b, numerous osteoclasts and osteoblasts have assembled on the surfaces of spaces called remodelling units in woven bone (see Section 7.3.1). As established bone is dissolved away and new bone deposited, the shape of these spaces is continually changing. Also visible scattered throughout the calcified bone are osteocytic lacunae, each containing one or a few osteocytes.

Osteoclast and osteoblast activity is modulated by various circulating and locally produced chemicals, including IGFs. As bone grows, some IGFs are incorporated into the bone matrix in an inactive form, but are released in the very acid environment generated by the osteoclasts as they erode the calcified bone. The balance between these and other growth factors becomes precarious in old age, leading to depletion of skeletal mass (Section 7.3.4).

One of the most powerful stimulants to bone formation is the application of mechanical stresses and strains (e.g. Figure 2.11b). As well as promoting thickening and strengthening of the 'proper' skeleton, repeated stresses such as those experienced by soldiers marching and horse riders can sometimes lead to the formation of ectopic bones and ossifications of connective tissue within and between muscles. Such growth involves protein synthesis: the mechanisms by which such forces are detected and translated into gene action are not yet clear.

Local and systemic factors that promote bone formation in adults are being intensively investigated because of their importance for the long-term outcome of orthopaedic repairs using metal or plastic implants. Replacement hip joints, knees and other skeletal parts are initially cemented into position, but they do not become strong enough to withstand strenuous activities until a web of new bone has grown around and through them, which may take several months.

If a bone is broken, the numerous small blood vessels permeating the hard bone from the periosteum are ruptured and a clot forms. As the clot disintegrates, a mass of cells of uncertain origin accumulates at the site of the break forming a callus and, providing the broken ends are not too far apart, serves as a temporary bridge across the gap. These cells form cartilage (Section 7.4.1), which then calcifies and forms normal bone in much the same way as at the epiphyses of elongating bones. Small fragments of bone are reabsorbed by osteoclasts, but larger ones may become sites for further bone formation. The fragments of shattered or splintered bones must be removed or put back in the right place, otherwise they form an enormous callus that compresses adjacent muscles and restricts the blood supply to the rest of the limb. Until modern surgical techniques made such intricate reconstruction possible, the only treatment for limbs shattered by bullets or swords was amputation.

For the repair to be perfect, the position and alignment of the broken ends must be correct throughout callus and cartilage formation. Figure 2.12a (*overleaf*) shows the complete, but imperfect, healing of a break in the clavicle (wishbone)

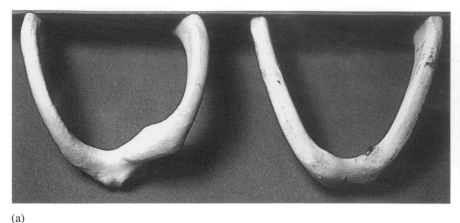

(a)

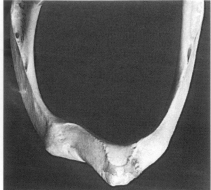

(b)

of an Australian black swan. An undamaged corresponding bone of the closely related mute swan is shown for comparison. The close-up (Figure 2.12b) shows that, although the healed area is as thick and robust as the original bone, the upper portion has been displaced laterally, with the result that the whole of the left half of the clavicle is elongated and bent. If the bone had been artificially 'set' and immobilized within a few hours of the injury, such malformation could probably have been prevented.

Figure 2.12   (a) Clavicle (wishbone) of a normal adult mute swan (*right*), and (*left*) an elderly Australian black swan with an imperfectly healed fracture, viewed from in front and below. (b) Close-up of the healed break in the left of the clavicle of the black swan, viewed from behind and below.

■   Does immobilization hasten healing?

No. New bone actually forms faster where the skeleton is subjected to mechanical stresses, than where it is rested. The amount of movement recommended for treating broken bones is always a balance between the desire to promote healing as rapidly as possible, and the risk that the broken ends become misaligned.

The swan whose clavicle is shown in Figure 2.12 lived for many years after the injury, but completely normal function was never restored. It developed severe arthritis at the end of its life, probably exacerbated by prolonged application of abnormal stresses on its joints as a result of the anatomical defect. Breakage and healing of bones are common occurrences in many wild animals; over a third of all gibbon skeletons collected from the wild are found to have at least one healed fracture.

Summary of Section 2.3

Bone is among the few tissues in which the formation of new cells takes place in discrete zones, which makes study of the course of bone formation and growth very much easier. The long bones grow in length at two epiphyses near the two ends and in thickness at the soft, cellular periosteum and endosteum. Osteoblasts proliferate and secrete a matrix that calcifies. They mature into osteocytes and become 'trapped' in lacunae surrounded by calcified bone. In mammals, but not most other vertebrates, hormones secreted at sexual maturity promote the formation of hard bone across the epiphyses and hence terminate growth in height. Mammalian bones are capable of regulating their own growth rate to a limited degree; if growth is prevented at the epiphysis at one end of a long bone, the epiphysis at the other end grows faster than it does in the unaltered bone.

Osteoclasts are cells of haemopoietic origin that break down bone. The sequential action of osteoclasts and osteoblasts repairs breaks and induces remodelling of bone in response to changes in loading and/or prolonged, frequent stresses. Such new bone formation can take place at any time throughout life.

2.4 Growth of muscle

The impression given from Chapter 1 and Section 2.2 is that, except for the brain and lungs, growth of the skeleton sets the pace and 'calls the tune', and the other tissues somehow get the message and adjust their own size accordingly. The brain and lungs respond differently to experimental treatments because proliferation of their cells takes place during a relatively brief period, early in the animal's life.

Muscle is one of the most specialized tissues in the body: its elaborate structure and intricate properties are described in detail in Chapters 5 and 6. To understand the principles behind its growth, it is sufficient to know that muscle consists of large fibres with up to several hundred relatively small nuclei and large quantities of highly organized cytoplasmic proteins. The number of nuclei reflects how many cells have fused to form the muscle fibre. The most abundant, and from the point of view of contraction speed and fatiguability the most important, cytoplasmic protein is myosin.

Skeletal muscle resembles the nervous system in that proliferation of the cells destined to form it, called **myoblasts**, is most rapid during early fetal life. Myoblasts fuse with each other to form myotubes, which grow into muscle fibres. At least in tissue culture *in vitro*, fibroblast growth factor (FGF) is a major stimulator of myoblast proliferation, and a protein called myoD can turn fibroblasts into myoblasts. MyoD is a DNA-binding protein that attaches directly to the chromosomes where it 'turns on' muscle genes. Regardless of their origin, all myoblasts stop dividing and fuse together to form myotubes as soon as FGF is withdrawn.

Once a developing muscle fibre establishes contact with a motor neuron and becomes capable of contraction, cell division ends, local IGF II production declines sharply and hypertrophy takes over as the mechanism of growth. Neonatal mammals have small muscle fibres with a proportionately small number of nuclei. In small mammals such as rats, the formation of new muscle fibres ends just before birth, but in humans, the number of muscle fibres approximately doubles during childhood, by bifurcation of large fibres and/or by *de novo* formation from myoblasts. This increase is still surprisingly modest in view of the fact that babies' muscles clearly grow enormously, particularly if they grow up to be weightlifters or football players.

Post-natal growth seems to be coordinated by the paracrine action of IGF I and involves increases in both fibre size and the number of nuclei per fibre, but the nuclei already in the muscle fibres do not divide. The 'new' nuclei are derived from **satellite cells** (Figure 2.13, *overleaf*), small (1–6 μm across), flattened cells of fusiform outline that have a single, relatively large nucleus. They are found between the **plasmalemma** membrane of the muscle fibre, and the basal lamina, a thin layer of collagen that encases the entire fibre. (These structures are described more fully in Section 5.2.) Satellite cells are scattered over the whole muscle fibre, but are concentrated around the neuromuscular junctions.

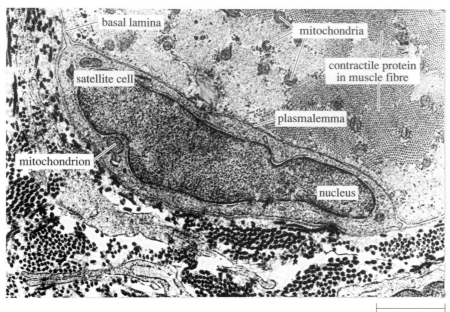

Figure 2.13   Electron micrograph of a satellite cell on the plasmalemma of a muscle fibre of a child suffering from muscular dystrophy. The upper right shows part of the inside of the muscle fibre, with the contractile structures and mitochondria seen in cross-section. The lower left shows collagen fibres and other extra-fibre material.

Seen with an electron microscope (Figure 2.13), satellite cells appear to have little in common with mature muscle (see Chapter 5) but they are the foundation of its growth and repair. At least in young mammals, satellite cells divide and about half of the new cells so formed differentiate as muscle tissue and become incorporated into existing fibres, forming new contractile material.

■   Do satellite cells fall within the definition of stem cells (see Section 2.1.1)?

Yes. They are small, undifferentiated cells that on division produce either more stem cells or mature into non-dividing, highly specialized cells.

The numbers of satellite cells, and thus their contribution to fibre growth, decline with age: in human neonates, about 30% of all nuclei in and around muscle are in satellite cells, compared to only 1–2% in adults. The potential of satellite cells for proliferation seems to be limited and their abundance at birth sets the maximum size to which muscles can grow. Rat pups and children born to undernourished mothers have smaller muscle fibres and fewer satellite cells at birth and, although growth 'catches up' to some extent, the muscles, especially those of males, remain smaller than those of the offspring of well-fed mothers.

Both protein synthesis and protein degradation are much higher during growth (and regeneration) of muscle: turnover rates are about 30% per day in fetal skeletal muscle, compared to 4–5% in adult muscles, even though the latter normally perform much more exercise. The rate at which the muscle accumulates protein is modulated by several hormones, including growth hormone (Section 1.4.1). As in the liver, the rate of protein degradation changes to a much greater extent than that of synthesis. The increase in muscle mass promoted by regular doses of synthetic anabolic steroid hormones (sometimes used, often controversially, by beef-cattle farmers and by athletes, weight-lifters and boxers to promote muscle growth) is due mainly to suppression of protein degradation rather than to stimulation of protein synthesis.

In starvation, when insulin levels are low and glucocorticoids are secreted, protein synthesis in muscle decreases abruptly, followed by a slower fall in the rate of degradation. These effects release into the circulation large quantities of free amino acids that support gluconeogenesis in the liver. Surprisingly large quantities of protein can be thus lost without significant impairment of muscle function, and the protein content is replenished within hours of refeeding. If starvation is prolonged, the muscles become wasted and greatly weakened, but the tissue has remarkable capacity for regeneration even in elderly individuals: during illness or malnutrition, the muscle fibres may, over a period of weeks, shrink to the size of fetal fibres, but their basic organization is unimpaired and they can regrow to normal size when good nutrition is restored.

Insulin stimulates protein synthesis in muscle and thus its rate of uptake of circulating amino acids. Under favourable conditions, a large proportion of the amino acids derived from a protein-rich meal are incorporated into muscle.

■   What are the implications of these effects for planning children's diets?

Mixed meals containing proteins as well as carbohydrates promote muscle growth much more efficiently than foods such as sweets and soft drinks that cause insulin secretion without increasing the supply of amino acids to support protein synthesis in muscles. Thus children who eat many snacks and sweets tend to become obese but not muscular. Similar considerations apply to formulating diets for rapidly growing meat animals such as calves and pigs.

2.4.1 The regulation of muscle mass

Everyone is familiar with the fact that muscles hypertrophy if they are used regularly for strenuous activity, or atrophy following prolonged inactivity. This capacity for adaptive growth that matches size to habitual usage continues throughout life, although it is fastest and most extensive in young adults.

■   In what other tissue is growth regulated by usage?

In the kidney (Section 2.2.2), but the effect is much greater in muscle. Most genes in most tissues are switched on (i.e. they produce mRNA, which directs protein synthesis) by the action, via intracellular signalling systems, of hormones and growth factors. In contrast, the genes for many of the major muscle proteins are regulated by the mechanical stretching and contraction of the muscle fibres in which they are contained.

The activity of the muscle determines the type of contractile protein as well as its quantity. Leg muscles of rabbits can be immobilized at particular lengths by putting the whole limb in a little plaster cast (similar to those used to set broken bones). Although the muscle cannot shorten under such conditions, when stimulated through fine wires, it exerts tension that stretches itself. Experiments showed that either electrical stimulation sufficient to produce such contraction, or fixing the limb so that the muscle was continuously stretched for a few days, had little effect on the kind of myosin being synthesized. But when both these stimuli were applied together, the muscle stopped producing the 'fast' type of myosin and began to produce a 'slow' type of myosin that would equip the muscle to perform many sustained contractions without becoming fatigued. As well as inducing adaptive growth, such stimuli also cause the familiar stiffness and soreness of muscle that follow an abrupt change in habitual activity (e.g. swimming or horse-riding for the first time for many months).

■ In which other tissues are mechanical stimuli known to influence growth?

Regular stress promotes bone formation (Section 2.3.1). In fact, the intermittent application of mechanical forces affects the growth of a wide range of tissues including the cardiac muscle and parts of the gut and the skin. The link between such forces and gene action remains to be elucidated.

Exercise also stimulates and maintains the production of the tricarboxylic acid (TCA) cycle enzymes, especially citrate synthetase, that enable the muscle to utilize glucose aerobically. They soon disappear if not used frequently: people become 'unfit' (i.e. incapable of sustained aerobic exercise) after only a few days of idleness. Captive birds (e.g. poultry, caged parrots) grow nearly as much breast muscle as free-living birds but, unless given the opportunity to fly very frequently, their muscles lose, or never develop, the metabolic pathways to produce ATP fast enough to sustain flight.

■ Could muscle activity be a sufficient stimulus to muscle growth in very young mammals and birds?

No. Fetal mammals and bird embryos hardly move at all. However, although neonates and hatchlings are much weaker than adult animals of similar size, they have enough muscle to breathe and swallow, and some species, such as ungulates (hoofed mammals) and precocial birds such as poultry, can run within hours of birth. The answer to this paradox seems to be that birds and mammals confined in an egg or uterus have a special fetal myosin, the gene for which is not activated by exercise. Fetal myosin is replaced by adult forms of the protein over the first few weeks of life. At the same time, the jerky movements characteristic of infants gradually give way to slower, more controlled movements, partly as a result of maturation of the nervous system, and partly from changes in the composition of the muscles themselves. Exercise is still essential for the production of the TCA cycle enzymes: birds and mammals are born 'unfit' and need frequent exercise to achieve adult capacity for sustained activity.

For reasons which are not yet well understood, the ratio of cytoplasm to nuclei has a fixed maximum, so the size to which muscle fibres can grow is set by the number of muscle-forming cells that are available for incorporation into that fibre. As their skeletal attachments grow, muscle fibres and tendons elongate so that the whole musculo-skeletal system is continuously functional. Muscle fibres grow in length by adding more sarcomeres and membranes (Section 5.2) to the ends of the fibres, rather than by insertion of contractile material into the middle.

It was pointed out in Section 1.2.3 that the muscles and tendons somehow grow to 'fit' the skeleton even when growth of the latter is distorted by malnutrition. Recent experiments have shed some light upon how growth in length, as well as in thickness, of muscles and associated tendons can depend upon the mechanical arrangement of the tissues themselves. One such experiment is shown in Figure 2.14.

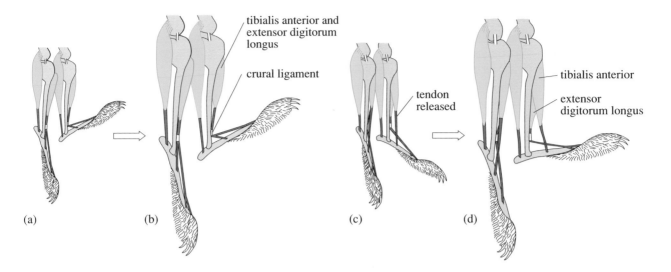

tibialis anterior and
extensor digitorum
longus

crural ligament

tendon
released

tibialis anterior

extensor
digitorum longus

(a)   (b)   (c)   (d)

In the hindleg of normal rabbits, the tibialis anterior muscle is attached to the tarsal bones by means of a tendon, which is held against the distal end of the tibia by a band of connective tissue called the crural ligament, under which it can slide as the joint flexes and extends (Figure 2.14a and b). It is a simple operation to cut the crural ligament and arrange the tendon of the tibialis muscle so that the two tissues are no longer in contact (Figure 2.14c). Such an arrangement means that the rabbit is unable to flex its ankle joint to more than about 150° because the tendon is now too long.

If such an operation is performed on young, growing rabbits, the tibialis muscle grows exceptionally long, and its tendon becomes correspondingly shorter, so that by the time the rabbit is fully grown, it is able to hop almost normally (Figure 2.14d). Somehow, the abnormal anatomy, and/or the inability of the animal to hop normally has been a factor in controlling the relative growth of these two tissues. If the rabbit is encouraged to hop more while the altered leg is growing, the change in proportions of the muscle and tendon are more exactly matched to the modified anatomy. However, very little is known about how the mismatch between the neural command to hop and failure of the muscle joint system to carry out the movement satisfactorily plays its part in determining the relative growth of the two adjacent tissues.

2.4.2 Muscle regeneration

Most injuries severe enough to fracture the skeleton also involve damage to muscle, but the latter heals so well that it is usually given little attention. If its profuse blood supply and normal innervation are maintained, skeletal muscle can regenerate well following injury or disease. The critical factors seem to be the integrity of the basal lamina, the numbers of satellite cells (Figure 2.13) present around regenerating muscle and their capacity to proliferate sufficiently to contribute to the regeneration of the fibres. At least in young mammals, new fibres sometimes form alongside existing ones. Regeneration of muscle recapitulates its development and early growth quite closely, with the reappearance of IGF I and fetal contractile proteins, due to reactivation of fetal genes.

Figure 2.14 Compensatory growth following experimental alteration of the anatomical relations of the tendon from the tibialis anterior muscle to the tarsi: (a) and (c) young rabbits; (b) and (d) resulting adult rabbits. (a) and (b) In the normal situation the muscles and their tendons are of about equal length and the full range of flexion and extension is possible. If the crural ligament is cut in a young rabbit, releasing the tibialis anterior muscle from the attachment of its tendon to the tibia, (c) the muscle tendon system is too long to permit full flexion of the foot. The muscle grows relatively longer and stouter, thus increasing its pulling distance and restoring nearly normal function (d) in the resulting adult. The extensor digitorum longus muscle, which is also held by the crural ligament, extends the toes, not the bones of the feet.

If large proportions of the satellite cells are destroyed, as may happen after severe burns or mechanical wounds, or prolonged exposure to the venom of certain snakes, or if the blood or nerve supply is damaged (e.g. by an extensive wound to a limb), regeneration of the muscle may be too slow and scar tissue forms in its place. Scar tissue, which is mainly fibroblasts and the extracellular collagen they produce, tends to form wherever healing is delayed by local infection, systemic malnutrition or illness, or poor alignment of regenerating tissues. It usually prevents further growth of the 'proper' tissue, and, if extensive, alters the blood supply to the rest of the organ.

■   Would permanent loss of a few fibres impair the muscle's function?

Not necessarily. Muscle fibres can both thicken and elongate in response to increased use, so undamaged neighbouring fibres can often expand sufficiently to compensate functionally for the loss of a few fibres in a muscle.

Cardiac muscle develops in much the same way as skeletal muscle but it loses all its satellite cells early in post-natal life and none can be detected in adult mammals.

■   What are the implications of this property for recovery from damage to cardiac muscle, such as heart attacks?

Regeneration following atrophy or disease would be minimal compared to that of skeletal muscle, so damaged or diseased cardiac muscle fibres would be replaced by scar tissue. Surgeons may try to strengthen weak hearts by transplanting a piece of skeletal muscle (usually taken from the patient's back) onto the defective cardiac muscle. By mechanisms not yet understood, such transplantation soon activates previously latent genes for slightly different muscle proteins, so the contractile properties of the transplanted muscle quite quickly become adapted to its new situation, in much the same way as muscles adapt to changes in use when *in situ* (Section 5.3).

Summary of Section 2.4

Muscle fibres are formed from myoblasts in the early fetus but once innervation is established they grow mainly by incorporation of satellite cells into existing fibres. Post-natal increase in numbers of fibres is modest in large mammals such as humans and negligible in rats. Substantial fibre elongation and thickening can take place throughout life, but the maximum dimensions are set by the number of satellite cells present at around the time of birth. Protein turnover is extensive in muscle and changes with age and nutritional and endocrine status. Fibres become functionally weak only when grossly depleted of protein during starvation and recover completely on refeeding.

The relative lengths of a muscle and its tendon become adjusted to the mechanical arrangement of the bones and other tendons; increasing the frequency of use of an altered limb hastens and improves the growth of correctly 'matching' anatomy. Muscle fibres can atrophy or hypertrophy in response to changes in exercise regime or injury. Satellite cells retain some capacity for division throughout life and contribute to healing and regeneration of damaged fibres.

2.5 Growth of white adipose tissue

In making a firm distinction between 'fat' and 'lean' tissue, many texts create the impression that white adipose tissue is fundamentally different from other tissues in its formation and the regulation of its mass. This section puts the record straight by examining the growth of adipose tissue from the same point of view as that used for other tissues.

Growth, in the sense of becoming larger or smaller, is an essential part of the normal functioning of adipose tissue throughout life: white adipocytes (fat cells) can reversibly undergo at least a 100-fold change in volume. Human or guinea-pig adipocytes can change from about 0.03 nl to about 3.0 nl ($1 \text{ nl} = 10^{-9}$ l) in volume, or from less than 40 µm to more than 0.25 mm in diameter. Adipocytes live a long time, possibly the entire lifespan of the animal: there are no known natural mechanisms (apart from excision) by which fully functional adipocytes can disappear.

The expansion and shrinkage of the whole tissue is normally due only to changes in the size of the adipocytes so the numbers of such cells is the main determinant of the maximum and minimum mass that it can become. Fortunately, it is quite easy to measure accurately the numbers of adipocytes in adipose tissue because they are among the few kinds of fully differentiated cells that are spherical, so their diameter can be measured whatever their orientation and their volume calculated from a simple measurement of diameter. Many tissues, including muscle, liver and kidney degenerate rapidly after death, but adipocytes retain their basic shape for many hours *post mortem*. Consequently, their mean diameter can be measured even from tissue that has been dead for some time. If the mean volume and the total mass of the tissue are known, the numbers of cells present can be estimated quite accurately.

Adipose tissue is among the last of the major tissues to appear in the fetus. Most mammals (humans and pigs being familiar exceptions) are born with very little white adipose tissue, and nearly all that present develops right at the end of gestation. In neonates, white adipocytes are both very small and few in number, and some of the sites where white adipose tissue is found in the adult contain brown adipose tissue at birth. In most mammals, the **pre-adipocytes** (stem cells that form white adipose tissue) proliferate rapidly during the suckling period and for a short time afterwards.

Many, but not necessarily all, cells thus formed acquire the enzymic capacity to synthesize triacylglycerols from fatty acids taken up from the blood and thus become mature adipocytes. The proportion that mature and the size to which they grow are influenced by several factors, among them GH, which promotes differentiation of pre-adipocytes, while at the same time stimulating lipolysis in mature adipocytes. Young mammals injected with GH (Section 1.4.1) thus grow leaner but more muscular than the controls. Evidence is now accumulating that the kind of dietary fats to which pre-adipocytes are exposed influences how quickly they become adipocytes. Saturated fats of the kind found in the milk and meat of ruminants such as cattle and sheep promote differentiation more than fish or vegetable oils.

At least in rats, it has been established that in normal individuals, the full complement of adipocytes (about 10^8 mature cells) is present well before sexual maturity. In rats, guinea-pigs and humans, undernutrition during the suckling period slows down, and perhaps halts, the proliferation of pre-adipocytes. As in the case of skeletal growth, cell proliferation increases again if the animal is better fed later in life and the number of cells 'catches up', either partially or totally depending upon the age at which the different nutritional conditions prevailed.

In experimental rats and guinea-pigs, continuous overfeeding early in life can sometimes cause the number of functional adipocytes to double or treble. However, it is still a matter of hot debate whether these additional adipocytes arise from the filling of a pre-existing but latent population of pre-adipocytes, that have been awaiting their chance to become mature adipocytes as the animal's initial population of adipocytes becomes replete, or whether cell division has restarted in the stem cells to produce more pre-adipocytes. The main reason why such a simple but fundamental question cannot be resolved is because it is at present impossible to recognize a pre-adipocyte histologically or biochemically, or to distinguish the cell lines which would become adipocytes from those which give rise to other kinds of connective tissue cells.

From the point of view of how much fat can be stored, or the likelihood of becoming excessively obese, does the number of adipocytes matter? This question is difficult to answer experimentally, since becoming obese is the only way of inducing more mature adipocytes.

Naturally obese mammals, for whom massive adipose tissue is an adaptation rather than a pathology, can suggest an answer. Figure 2.15 shows the relationship between adipocyte complement and body composition in a random sample of specimens of four naturally obese species of arctic mammals. Figure 2.15a is a histogram showing the frequency of individuals that have more or fewer adipocytes than the number expected from a comparison with naturally lean mammals of similar body mass. Most of the Svalbard reindeer had only <1.5–3.0 times more adipocytes than expected from the data from lean temperate zone and tropical mammals, although all specimens were about 17% by weight dissectible adipose tissue (Figure 2.15b), about as obese as young humans. The data for the three species of Carnivora (bears, wolverines and arctic foxes) were much more variable. Some arctic foxes and wolverines had fewer than the expected number of adipocytes while a minority of others had almost five times as many.

■   What endocrine conditions could promote the formation of a large number of very small adipocytes?

Growth hormone promotes the maturation of pre-adipocytes into small adipocytes and stimulates lipolysis.

In these samples of specimens, there were no relationships between age and fatness or adipocyte complement, even though most were mature adults and a few were elderly.

■   What does this information indicate about the contribution of chronic, long-term obesity to proliferation of adipocytes?

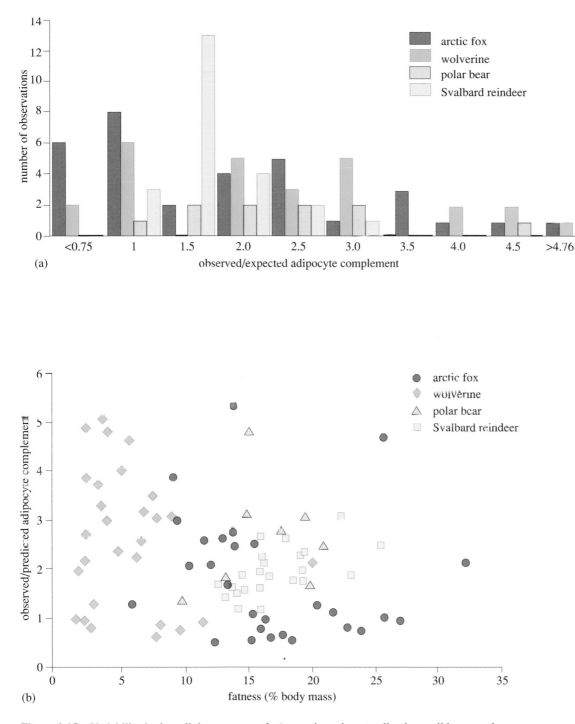

Figure 2.15   Variability in the cellular structure of adipose tissue in naturally obese wild mammals.
(a) Histogram of the frequency of different ratios of observed adipocyte complement for 90 arctic
mammals of four species to that calculated from equations derived from temperate-zone and tropical
mammals. Values that fall between 0.76 and 1.24 are displayed as 1.0, those between 1.25 and 1.74 as
1.5, and so on. (b) The relationship between fatness (mass of all dissectible adipose tissue as a
percentage of total body mass) and the ratio of observed adipocyte complement to that calculated for
the same specimens from equations derived from temperate-zone and tropical mammals.

It suggests that, at least in these naturally obese mammals, being obese for much of the year does not necessarily lead to adipocyte proliferation in middle age. At the time these specimens were collected, some, especially the arctic foxes, were obese by any standards (up to 35% by weight dissectible adipose tissue), but there was no consistent relationship between adipocyte complement and fatness (Figure 2.15b). This comparison shows that the total number of adipocytes in the adipose tissue is apparently not a major determinant of fatness in these naturally obese animals: it doesn't matter whether their adipose tissue consists of numerous small adipocytes or fewer, larger adipocytes.

■   Is the relationship between cell size and cell number variable in any other tissues?

Yes. The number of nuclei in muscle fibres depends upon the numbers of myoblasts and satellite cells that form during fetal life, which in turn depends upon maternal nutrition (Section 2.4.1). Although the number of satellite cells determines the maximum possible size of muscle fibres, those with fewer nuclei are not functionally impaired. Regenerated kidneys and liver also have a smaller number of larger cells or more, smaller cells depending upon the age at which regeneration takes place. Such differences have no obvious effects on function. In having an indeterminate number of cells, adipose tissue is probably not different from any other mammalian tissue that consists of long-lived cells that turn over very slowly.

■   Would there be much protein turnover in adipose tissue?

No. Only about 2–5% of the dry weight of adipose tissue is protein, much of it extracellular collagen. But the storage triacylglycerols are constantly broken down and reformed, and in so doing, the products become available to other tissues to be oxidized for energy production or incorporated into other cellular structures or metabolites as required.

Adipose tissue has significant capacity for regeneration after injury. Depots at different anatomical sites respond in different ways to experimental removal of part of the tissue: for example, the depots medial and anterior to the thigh of the rat regenerate extensively following excision, but those in the abdominal cavity regenerate to a much lesser extent, possibly because they receive a poorer blood supply.

It is most unlikely that a cell as large as a mature adipocyte would be capable of division. The new tissue must form by the maturation of newly formed or newly recruited pre-adipocytes scattered throughout the tissue. Natural or artificial restriction of growth at one depot does not necessarily promote growth at other depots. As people become older, some depots shrink (e.g. those of the lower leg) while others, especially intra-abdominal ones, expand.

■   How do these properties compare with regulation of growth of viscera?

The mass of kidney tissue (Section 2.2.2), and to a lesser extent liver, changes so that the organs represent a constant proportion of the total body mass. However, adipose tissue mass is not adjusted in relation to that of lean tissues of the body in the same way: it is possible to be lean or puny, obese or well-muscled in any combination.

2.5.1 Obesity

It is probably fair to say that obesity is by far the commonest disorder which arises directly from 'abnormalities' of the growth process. The word 'abnormalities' is in quotation marks because in much of Europe and the Americas, and parts of Africa, obesity is so prevalent in middle-aged adults that until recently it was regarded as hardly worth worrying about. However, it is now clear that being 'too fat', particularly early in life, promotes several more serious disorders including diabetes, cardiovascular disease and infertility.

Like muscle, adipose tissue grows in response to functional demand, which in its case is the excess of food ingested over short-term energy use. Factors such as appetite and satiety are brain mechanisms and as such are adjustable. The commonest basic cause of artificial obesity (i.e. in domestic animals) and pathological obesity in humans is now thought to be inappropriate appetite in relation to energy utilization, rather than any abnormality of the adipose tissue itself.

Moderate obesity is due mainly or entirely to enlargement of adipocytes and can, in theory at least, be corrected by adopting a diet and exercise regime which promote lipolysis and thus make adipocytes become smaller. In severe obesity in humans, in which up to half the body mass is adipose tissue, there are up to ten times more mature adipocytes than expected. The mechanism of such increase is still not clear: a greater proportion of pre-adipocytes may mature, or their stem cells may resume proliferation later in life. Obesity involving an increase in cell number is much more difficult to treat because each adipocyte must become even smaller to reduce the total tissue mass.

Opinion on how to prevent obesity was strongly influenced in the 1960s and 1970s by experiments on rats that showed that adipocyte proliferation takes place mainly during suckling and can be retarded by underfeeding and stimulated by overfeeding. The idea was that if babies were allowed to get too fat during the first year of life, they would develop too many adipocytes and hence their adipose tissue would be too massive later in life, even if the individual cells were not unduly enlarged. Limiting the quantity of food to babies and young children was therefore recommended.

■   Do the data in Figure 2.15 suggest that it is valid to extrapolate the conclusions based upon rats to human growth?

No. In contrast to rats, in the naturally obese species for which data are shown in Figure 2.15, the adipocyte complement differs greatly between individuals but its size makes no difference to fatness. Growth of most tissues is much more indeterminate in humans and other large, long-lived mammals than in short-lived, fast-maturing rats. The cellular basis of human obesity seems to be much more like that of the wild animals: by no means all obese children become obese adults, and many obese adults were lean, even thin, as children.

As with most disorders that depend upon abnormal growth (as distinct from abnormal metabolism) there is no simple cure because it is remarkably difficult to prevent or modify the growth processes except by measures so drastic that they prevent the normal functioning of other tissues and physiological systems. It is a source of constant frustration to pig farmers, cattle stockmen and physical training teachers that it is easy for adipose tissue to expand at any time of life, but almost impossible to increase the size of muscles beyond the limits set by cell division early in life.

2.6 Conclusion

It was emphasized in Chapter 1 that the growth of young mammals shows a remarkable resilience in the face of adverse conditions: juvenile mammals achieve something approaching the 'correct' size and shape of the body in spite of undernutrition and other hazards. This capacity is reflected in the plasticity of cellular mechanisms of growth. Continual replacement and turnover of both cells and intracellular components enable tissues to respond to changes in use and to recover from injury or disease. A thorough understanding of growth, the maintenance of tissue mass and regeneration are made more urgent with the increasing importance of tissue and organ transplants within and between individuals.

Tissues differ in the way in which they grow and in the stages of development at which cell proliferation and differentiation are most rapid, and in the location and properties of any persistent population of stem cells. Whereas the relative mass of tissues such as the liver and kidneys seems to be closely tied to the mass of the rest of the body, bone, muscle and adipose tissue can expand (within limits) in response to functional demand.

Objectives for Chapter 2

When you have completed this chapter, you should be able to:

2.1   Define and use, or recognize definitions and applications of each of the **bold** terms.

2.2   Distinguish between 'determinate' and 'indeterminate' modes of growth and explain why the growth of most large organisms shows components of both kinds of organization.

2.3   Outline some general features of protein turnover and its contribution to the growth and the maintenance of tissues.

2.4   Describe the response of remaining tissues to the removal of part of the liver or one kidney in young and elderly rats.

2.5   Explain how the techniques of parabiosis and organ transplantation have demonstrated suppression of growth, intrinsic potential for growth and compensatory hypertrophy in mammalian kidney tissue.

2.6   Give an account of cellular processes in the elongation, thickening and repair of mammalian long bones.

2.7   Outline the roles of myoblasts and satellite cells in the growth and regeneration of muscle.

2.8   Describe some mechanisms by which the structure and composition of muscle and bone alter to adapt to a change in function.

2.9   Describe the roles of cell division, cell differentiation and cell enlargement in the post-natal growth and regeneration of muscle and adipose tissue in mammals.

Questions for Chapter 2

(Answers to questions are at the end of the book.)

Question 2.1 (Objective 2.2)

Classify the following properties according to whether each is likely to be a feature of an organism which shows (i) indeterminate growth, or (ii) determinate growth.

(a)   The absence of tissues destroyed by a predator does not affect the functioning of the organism as a whole.

(b)   Individuals of similar genetic make-up can become larger and hence produce more offspring under favourable conditions than those living under worse conditions.

(c)   The organism can have elaborate mechanisms for posture or movement because all components are exactly matched in size and shape.

(d)   Tissues can be highly interdependent, with some specialized for food gathering, some for oxygen carrying, etc.

(e)   Each group of cells must be more or less self-sufficient and able to obtain its own food, oxygen, etc.

Question 2.2 (Objective 2.3)

Explain in a few sentences:

(a)   the role of ubiquitin in protein turnover;

(b)   the role of protein turnover in growth;

(c)   the role of hormones in regulating protein turnover.

Question 2.3 (Objective 2.4)

Describe the roles of cell enlargement and cell division in compensatory growth and regeneration of the liver and kidneys.

Question 2.4 (Objective 2.5)

What is the experimental evidence for the following statements about growth of kidneys?

(a)   A kidney can enlarge at the same time as performing its normal function in the body.

(b)   The body maintains a constant ratio of kidney tissue to total tissue mass.

(c)   The kidneys of young rats show greater intrinsic potential for growth than do adult kidneys.

Question 2.5 (Objective 2.6)

List three reasons why growth of the skeleton has been studied in greater detail than growth of most other tissues.

Question 2.6 (Objective 2.6)

Describe three different control mechanisms which are involved in determining the rate of growth of bone at any particular epiphysis.

For which of the following processes are satellite cells essential?

(a)   The formation of new muscle fibres during fetal growth.

(b)   Fibre expansion.

(c)   Maintaining the integrity of the plasmalemma.

(d)   Depletion of muscle proteins in starvation.

(e)   Adaptation of muscle mass to more or less exercise.

(f)   Adaptation of tendons to changes in muscle size or activity.

(g)   Repair of wounded muscle.

How do (a) immobility, (b) the frequent application of moderate forces in regular exercise, and (c) the sudden application of large forces, affect the structure and composition of bone and muscle?

List the similarities and differences between the growth of muscle and the growth of adipose tissue in terms of (a) cell proliferation, (b) cell enlargement, and (c) the role of 'usage' of the tissue in modifying growth processes.

CHAPTER 3
THE CONSEQUENCES OF SIZE

3.1 Introduction

Many biochemical, cellular and physiological mechanisms described in this and other texts have been elucidated by observations and experiments on rats (adult body mass 300–500 g), mice (adult body mass about 30 g) or other convenient laboratory animals. The incentive for such studies is usually not to find out more about these species *per se*, but because the conclusions reached from the study of the anatomy and physiology of small rodents are believed to apply to the comparable physiological processes in humans and other large species such as horses and cattle (body mass up to 10^6 g). Indeed, a belief in the essential similarity between physiological processes in small rodents and in humans underpins a great deal of basic and applied research in biology.

One reason for believing in the validity of extrapolation from rats to humans is their morphological similarity: you are already familiar with the theoretical and practical basis for establishing taxonomic and phylogenetic relationships between organisms. However, using morphological similarity as the only criterion for transferring conclusions from small rodents to humans depends upon the assumption that the larger species are simply scaled-up versions of the smaller species. In this chapter, this assumption is scrutinized by comparing the anatomy and physiology of organisms of similar body plan but widely different size. Some general patterns emerge that describe the way that physiological processes are adapted to the organism becoming larger or smaller, and a theoretical framework develops that guides the extrapolation of physiological data from small, easy-to-study laboratory animals to species such as whales, dinosaurs and humans, which, for practical and ethical reasons, cannot be studied experimentally.

Organisms are different sizes as adults, and juveniles pass through different sizes as they grow to maturity. For example, the mammalian family Felidae includes species from cat-size (2–4 kg) to lion-size (150–300 kg). A lion cub is smaller than an adult domestic cat when it is born, and passes through stages when it is similar in size to a cheetah, lynx, leopard, jaguar and tiger before reaching adult size. Are the effects of size on these transient growth stages similar to interspecific differences between adults of different body size? Some contrasts might be expected because, as mentioned in Chapters 1 and 2, body proportions and body composition change with age in large as well as small animals. This chapter is devoted mainly to three aspects of the consequences of size: the role of structural tissues, the relationship between metabolic rate and body mass, and the implications of body size for an animal's locomotory habits, energy supply, diet and life history.

3.1.1 Concepts in the study of size in organisms

The first serious approaches to the question of how body tissues change as organisms become larger or smaller were theoretical. Several engineers and mathematicians, starting with Galileo in the early 17th century, pointed out that as a structure (living or inanimate) increases in size, its mass increases much faster than its linear dimensions: if an organism's linear dimensions are L, its surface area is L^2, and its volume is L^3 (see also Section 1.1.1). If the density is constant, the body mass, M, is proportional to its volume, so:

$$M \propto L^3$$

An increase in body mass may not matter very much in fishes, many of which are almost weightless in water, but most of the forces acting on the structural tissues of terrestrial organisms increase in proportion to L^3. An increase in body size of a terrestrial organism thus *automatically* requires modification of the mechanical properties of its structural tissues, and hence in its body proportions. These concepts, based upon elementary geometry and engineering, alerted biologists to expect size-specific differences in the mechanical properties of the supporting and protective tissues. Such adaptations of the body's structural components to its body size are discussed in Section 3.2.

The surface area is also related to body mass. As organisms of similar shape become larger, their surface area becomes *proportionately* smaller; this relationship of body mass to surface area can be written as surface area $\propto$ body mass, $M^{2/3}$ or surface area $\propto M^{0.67}$. Any exchanges of heat, nutrients or oxygen between organisms and the environment that take place at a body surface, such as the skin or lungs, are limited by this relationship. For most vertebrates, the decline in the ratio of surface area to volume that occurs with increasing body size plays a significant part in determining the structure and properties of several physiological systems. But the surface areas of some very large organisms, notably trees, jellyfish and reef corals, are greatly extended by the formation of thin, flat leaves and tentacles, that minimize many of the limitations that their large size may impose upon exchange of materials with the environment.

It is important to realize that precise measurement of the areas of such surfaces, or the length of highly convoluted linear structures such as blood capillaries, poses conceptual as well as practical problems. For example, estimates of the surface area of human lungs (i.e. the area available for exchange of gases) based upon data obtained with the light microscope are about $80\,m^2$, but calculations based on data from electron micrographs produce a figure of $140\,m^2$. The discrepancy arises because many biological surfaces, including that of the lungs, are folded and invaginated at all levels from gross morphology to ruffles on the cell membranes. Geographers face similar difficulties in arriving at values for the lengths of coasts and meandering rivers, or the surface areas of countries: for example, in the latter case, should corrections be made for mountains and valleys? river banks and railway cuttings? hedges and ditches? molehills and cart-ruts? pebbles? sand grains? During the last thirty years, a special branch of mathematics, called **fractal geometry**, has been developed to deal with such problems. Briefly, such analysis suggests that fractal 'area' is proportional to $L^{2.17}$, not L^2 as in conventional geometry.

While theoreticians were grappling with these concepts, practical studies of biological tissues were advancing rapidly, with, at first, minimal attention to the implications of organism size. In the mid-19th century, microscopists examined fixed and stained sections of dead tissues and established the cell theory of biological material. Their observations suggested that larger animals and plants were larger because they contained more cells, but that each cell was essentially identical, regardless of the size of the organism from which it was derived, much as larger houses consist of more bricks, each identical to those of which smaller ones are constructed. It was believed that, with obvious exceptions such as motor neurons, there were few, if any, differences in the structure or metabolism of cells derived from morphologically similar organisms of different sizes.

However, at about the same time, physiologists studying living organisms were making some important observations which showed that this assumption, which was based on anatomical study of dead tissues, must be false. They noticed that the resting metabolic rate per kg body mass of morphologically similar organisms of different sizes changed in ways that were not anticipated from the geometrical analyses just described. For many years these observations received little attention because they could not be explained, but new techniques and ideas have revived interest in the topic and have greatly extended our knowledge of how metabolism and body composition change with the size of the organism, as discussed in Section 3.3.

It was only after Darwin's theory of evolution by natural selection became well established in the middle of the 20th century, that the ecological and behavioural implications of differences in body size and growth rate were studied in detail. All metazoans begin life as a single cell, so species with small adult body size have less growing to do than very large species. The hatchlings of large fishes and reptiles are only a tiny fraction of the size of their parents, and are usually not able to find or digest the same foods as the adults. The juveniles pass through stages during growth at which they have different dietary requirements, and all growth stages must be able to find sufficient suitable food. The relationship between body size, habits and habitat is the subject of Section 3.4. The topic helps us to understand some fundamental differences between the growth and nutrition of mammals and birds and those of poikilothermic vertebrates.

3.1.2 The principles of allometry

Allometry is the study of the relationship between the dimensions of the anatomical and physiological features of organisms, and is a major tool in making meaningful comparisons between structures and processes in organisms of different body sizes. One of the simplest and most widely used allometric characters is the organism's gross body mass (M). The basic equation of allometry, relating an anatomical or physiological feature Y to body mass is:

$$Y = b(M^a)$$

The two constants a and b are respectively the *exponent of allometry* and the *coefficient of allometry*.

When converted into logarithms, this equation becomes:

$$\log Y = a(\log M) + \log b$$

A graph drawn on logarithmic axes not only enables data from organisms of widely different sizes to be shown on a single scale, but, since the equation is in a linear form,* the constants a and b can easily be calculated from a graph of log Y against log M.

If $a = 1$, then Y is directly proportional to M and the character is said to change **isometrically** with body mass. If $a < 1$, Y is said to show *negative allometry* in relation to body mass: its increase in size is less than that of the body as a whole. If $a > 1$, then character Y shows *positive allometry* in relation to body mass.

Allometry can thus be used to summarize measurements of anatomical, physiological or behavioural features of organisms of the same species but different sizes or ages, or to make comparisons between species with different adult body sizes.

3.1.3 Organ size in the cat family

The family Felidae includes lions, tigers, leopards, jaguars, pumas, lynx and the domestic cat; it is unusual among mammalian families in that the adult body mass of the largest species is more than 200 times greater than that of the smallest. The similarities in form, diet and habits of these animals are due to common ancestry. However, lions are not simply scaled-up versions of cats: the evolution of larger or smaller species involves a change in body proportions.

The data in Figures 3.1 and 3.2 were obtained from both wild and captive specimens; they correspond to the following equations:

$$Y_{heart} \propto M^{1.03}$$

$$Y_{brain} \propto M^{0.611}$$

These equations mean that the mass of the heart (Figure 3.1) increases almost exactly in proportion to the increase in mass of the whole body for all the species, i.e. it scales isometrically. However, larger felids have smaller brains in proportion to their body size than smaller species (Figure 3.2).

■ What aspects of brain function would you expect to show (a) isometric scaling to body mass, and (b) negative allometry to body mass?

Assuming that large and small species have a similar repertoire of movement, the areas of the brain involved in controlling the muscles might be expected to scale isometrically with body size, because the mass of the muscles increases in proportion to body mass. However, much of the mammalian brain is involved with processing sensory information from the eyes, ears and other sense organs, and with memory and reasoning; none of these functions would necessarily change very much with body size. There is no compelling evidence that lions have greater capacity for learning or reasoning in spite of the fact that the lion brain is about ten times bigger than the brain of the domestic cat.

* An equation of form $y = ax + b$ always produces a straight line.

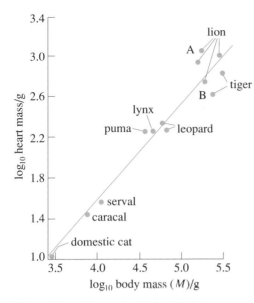

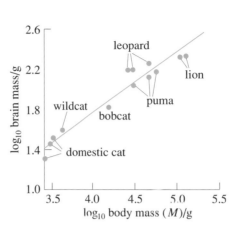

Figure 3.1   Allometric relationship between the mass of the heart and the mass of the whole body for various felids. Both axes are logarithmic. The straight line represents heart mass $\propto M^{1.03}$.

Figure 3.2   Allometric relationship between the mass of the brain and the mass of the whole body for various felids. Both axes are logarithmic. The straight line represents brain mass $\propto M^{0.611}$.

Larger felids have a greater volume of tissue to be perfused with blood; however, as well as supplying *more* tissues, the heart of larger animals also has to pump blood through a greater distance to reach distal structures such as the tips of the limbs. One might therefore expect that the heart would show positive allometry with body mass. This point is discussed again in Section 3.3.

■   What is the difference in the relative mass of the heart of lion A and tiger B in Figure 3.1? Can you suggest an explanation for this difference?

The heart of lion A is more than three times the size of that of tiger B, relative to their body masses. The lion's heart represents about 0.7% of its body mass $[(10^{3.05}/10^{5.2}) \times 100 = 0.71]$; that of the smaller tiger accounts for only 0.2% of its body mass $[(10^{2.6}/10^{5.3}) \times 100 = 0.20]$.* One possible explanation for the discrepancy is errors in measuring body mass; if the tiger was obese, and the lion thin, the positions of the points on the horizontal axis could be inaccurate. Another possibility is that, like other muscular tissues (Section 2.4.1), the heart is capable of hypertrophy and atrophy in response to exercise and other forms of physiological stress. The lion may have been living in the wild, where the heart would be subjected to regular exertion; the tiger may have been living a sedentary life in captivity, where its heart musculature may have atrophied. However, there is no reason to expect that the brain would atrophy in captive specimens (Sections 1.2 and 2.1.2).

* Note that logarithms are powers of ten, so log 2.0 = 10^2 = 100.

Summary of Section 3.1

Some of the ways in which larger organisms differ from those of morphologically similar but smaller organisms can be explained in terms of simple geometrical and engineering considerations: when organisms of similar shape are compared, their body mass increases as L^3 and the surface area to volume (and hence mass) ratio decreases as $L^{0.67}$. These changes affect body proportions and the structure of physiological systems that involve exchange of materials between the organism and its environment, such as respiratory and heat regulatory organs. However, there are other size-related differences in structure and metabolism that are not predicted from elementary geometrical considerations. Allometry is a useful technique for deriving equations that summarize size-related anatomical and physiological changes in morphologically similar organisms. Where such data incorporate organisms of a wide range of sizes, they are most effectively displayed on logarithmic axes.

3.2 Structural allometry

This section is about how the mechanical properties, dimensions and shape of the structural components of the body are adapted to body size. Most of the discussion concerns terrestrial or intertidal organisms, because their weight in air increases in proportion to the cube of their linear dimensions (Section 3.1.1).

3.2.1 The skeleton

The chief skeletal tissue in vertebrates is bone, which is a complex material consisting of crystals of inorganic calcium salts embedded in a matrix of the fibrous protein, collagen (Sections 2.3 and 7.3.1). The ability of bone to resist deformation and breakage depends upon how the external forces are applied in relation to the internal structure of the material. Figure 3.3 shows three common modes of applying forces to test pieces of materials. The force required to break a piece of bone (or other material) in one or other of these modes can be measured using standard engineering apparatus.

There are two ways in which the mechanical strength of a skeleton can be increased: the properties of the bone tissue itself can change, so that the strength per unit mass is increased, or the skeleton can become more massive. Figure 3.4 shows how the mechanical properties of the human femur change with age. Test pieces of the same size and shape were made from femurs taken from human cadavers of various ages and bent in standard test apparatus so that the energy required to break them could be measured. You can see that the ability of bone to absorb energy before breaking is high in infants and decreases to about half its maximum value during childhood and adolescence. There is no significant change between the ages of 25 and 50, in spite of the fact that most people become heavier during middle age.

Such size-specific adaptations in the properties of the skeletal materials make only a small contribution to the adjustments of the skeleton to change in body mass. Much more important are changes in the shape and relative mass of the skeleton, and in the way the animal uses its limbs during movement.

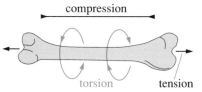

Figure 3.3   Three modes of application of forces to bones.

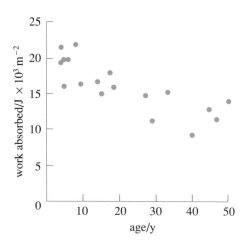

Figure 3.4   Energy absorbed before breakage by the femurs of humans of various ages.

■   From Section 3.1.1, how would you expect the relative mass of an animal's skeleton to increase in relation to its body mass?

The length L of the long bones is proportional to body mass $M^{0.33}$ ($M^{1/3}$). If the compressive strength and cross-sectional area of the limb bones scale isometrically with body mass, then the mass of the entire skeleton should increase in proportion to $M^{0.33} \times M^1 = M^{1.33}$.

Figure 3.5 shows some measurements on the relative mass of the skeleton in some terrestrial mammals. As expected, the skeletal mass scales positively to the mass of the whole body, but the exponent of allometry is smaller than that predicted, only 1.13 (similar data from slightly different species produce exponents as low as 1.09). The body masses of a 30 g mouse and a 10 000 kg elephant differ by a factor of 3×10^5, but the elephant's skeleton is only 10^6 times heavier than that of a mouse, instead of 22×10^6 heavier (= [$(10\,000)^{1.33}/(0.03)^{1.33}$]), as predicted by the theory just outlined: mice apparently have relatively stronger legs than elephants.

The main reason for this anomaly is an erroneous assumption in formulating the theory: the skeleton is not adapted primarily to withstand static gravitational forces such as those experienced in standing or sitting, but to cope with the rapidly changing, transiently very high accelerations and decelerations generated by vigorous movement. (This topic is discussed in Chapter 8.)

Small mammals both stand and run with the legs bent in a crouching position, a posture which imposes large bending forces on the skeleton (i.e. one side of a bone is subject to compression, the other to tension, Figure 3.3). If you have kept pet mice or hamsters, you will be aware that they do not hesitate to jump from a height of several feet onto a hard surface, and frequently support, or suspend, themselves using only one toe. Such actions impose very large forces on the skeleton in torsion and tension as well as compression, although such forces may be transient and local.

The natural postures and gaits of elephants are such that their leg bones are arranged more or less in a straight line. The weight of the body is always supported by at least two legs and all four legs take approximately equal shares in supporting and propelling the body, so they cannot gallop, jump or climb. Like all very large animals (e.g. rhinos, camels and buffalo), elephants move very slowly and carefully when going up or down very steep slopes. In fact, they normally avoid situations in which such locomotion would be necessary: these species do not occur in mountainous terrain and reach caves and water holes via well-worn, often lengthy paths. Zoo-keepers exploit this limitation: elephants can be confined in pens surrounded by a shallow, steep-sided moat, across which a smaller animal would have no difficulty jumping or scrambling. Circus elephants trained to stand on one hindleg move very slowly: an abrupt or incautious movement would bring the animal dangerously near to breaking its leg.

The strengths of the skeletons match these size-related differences in habits and habitats. Indirect estimates and *in vivo* measurements show that the maximum stresses imposed upon limb bones are always between 50 and 150 MN m^{-2}, regardless of the body mass. Small animals have relatively massive, strong skeletons and impose large forces on them; elephants and other large species use their limbs in a way that avoids imposing very large forces on their relatively flimsier skeletons.

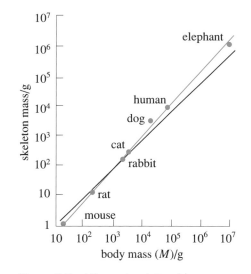

Figure 3.5   Allometric relationship between the mass of the skeleton and total body mass for various mammals. Both axes are logarithmic. The black line represents the isometric relationship. The blue line is fitted to the data and represents skeleton mass $\propto M^{1.13}$.

3.2.2 Safety factors

Breaking a large bone or tearing a tendon is a serious matter for a wild animal, because its ability to forage for food or run away from its predators may be impaired by the injury. Nonetheless, antelopes gallop at full speed over rough ground at the first whiff of danger, squirrels leap from branch to branch in tall trees, and frightened houseflies fly at full speed in confined spaces, producing an audible thump as they crash into plate-glass windows. How close do these animals come to doing themselves serious injury? The concept of safety factor, long familiar to architects and engineers, helps to answer this question.

The safety factor is defined as the ratio of the force required to cause breakage to the maximum force normally sustained. The forces that, when applied in various ways, can tear or break skeletal materials can be measured from samples taken from dead specimens. However, it is much more difficult to establish the maximum force to which a biological material is ever *normally* subjected, particularly in the case of wild animals whose habits may be poorly known. It is almost impossible to persuade wild animals to perform strenuous activities in the appropriate apparatus, and newly captured specimens are often so frightened that they can (and frequently do) injure themselves in ways that are probably very rare in the wild.

Professor McNeill Alexander in Leeds and his colleagues tackled the problem using a dog, which, like a human athlete, can be trained to exert itself to order, but usually stops short of incurring serious injury. Figure 3.6 shows the forces measured using photographic and force platform apparatus when a 36 kg Alsatian dog takes off for a long jump of about 3 m. The forward momentum of the body and forces exerted by many different muscles at the moment of take-off all contributed to accelerating the body into the air. The investigators were interested in the ability of the muscles, tendons and bones to withstand the forces exerted on them at take-off.

The maximum recorded force occurred at frame 17 and was 1 120 N, or 3.3 times the body weight of 36 kg force (= 350 N). Only the hindpaws were on the force platform at this time, so it is reasonable to assume that the force exerted by each foot was 1 120/2 = 560 N. Figure 3.7 shows the principal skeletal and muscular elements in the lower part of the hindleg which power the jump. The mechanical properties of bone will be described more fully in Chapter 7; to understand this section, it is sufficient to note that forces of about 190 MPa* applied in tension, or 284 MPa when applied in compression, would break the limb bones of adult mammals.

At the moment of take-off, the long, slender tibia and the ankle extensor muscles beside it must balance the forces acting on the paw. Forces act both longitudinally along the bone and at right angles to it, the latter tending to bend it; together, they produce a maximum of 60 MPa tensile forces on its front surface and 100 MPa compressive forces on the rear side (Figure 3.3).

■   How do these forces compare with those required to break bones in tension or in compression?

---

* The units of stress or force per unit area are $N\,m^{-2}$ or pascals (Pa), named after the French mathematician and philosopher, Blaise Pascal (1623–1662) who invented the mercury barometer for measuring atmospheric pressure.

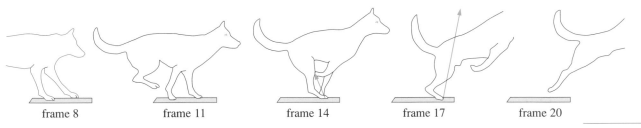

| frame 8 | frame 11 | frame 14 | frame 17 | frame 20 |

scale for forces
1 000 N

Figure 3.6   Tracings from a high-speed film of an Alsatian dog jumping to order across a long jump. The lines of action of forces acting through the hindlimb are shown. The lengths of the arrows indicate the magnitude of the forces.

They are about a third of those required to break mammalian bones; so, assuming that the largest forces ever imposed on the legs occur during jumping, the safety factor for dog leg bones is about 3.

However, the calculations show that muscles and tendons operate with a much smaller safety factor. Figure 3.7 shows the balance of forces at the moment of take-off; the distance from the paw to the ankle joint is about 4.3 times greater than the length of the calcaneus bone, so the forces exerted by the paw on the ground must be balanced by forces in the leg of about $4.3 \times 560 \approx 2\,400$ N. The internal structure of the muscles that extend the ankle joint is complex (Section 7.2.2) but their effective cross-sectional area is 6.4×10^{-3} m^2. So, at the moment of take-off, the stress in the extensor muscles is $2\,400/6.4 \times 10^{-3} = 0.38$ MPa ($= 3.8 \times 10^5$ N m^{-2}). Tendons are, of course, thinner than muscles, so they must sustain an even greater force per unit area; in this example the dog's tendons were subjected to a force of about 84 MPa, which is close to the stress required to break pieces of tendon in an engineering testing machine. Therefore this specially trained dog was using its limbs with a safety factor of about 1.

■   What would happen if the dog was jumping from an uneven surface, or if the support under one of the hindlegs suddenly collapsed? Could all dogs of similar body size perform such jumps without injury?

If an uneven surface or the sudden collapse of a support resulted in all the force being thrust onto just one leg, there is a serious risk of injury. No two animals or humans are absolutely identical; there are small differences in the mechanical properties of the tissues, due to inherited defects, malformations during growth, or imperfectly healed injuries. Strenuous activities such as jumping are likely to give rise to injuries if undertaken by individuals with minor anatomical defects that would not cause problems during movements for which the safety factor is greater.

The tendon is at risk from being torn by forces acting in tension, because the forces imposed on it are close to the breaking stress. Tendons are compliant in torsion (see Figure 3.3) and simply crumple under compressive forces. Bones, on the other hand, are much weaker in torsion than in either tension or compression; broken bones in the lower leg or foot are particularly common injuries among skiers and ballet dancers because the limbs are often subjected to large torsion forces. But rupture of the tendons sometimes occurs in working dogs, horses raced in steeplechases and human basketball players because powerful jumps and sudden changes in direction may momentarily impose unusually large strains on them.

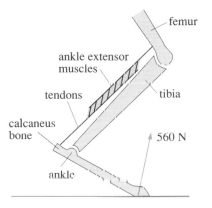

Figure 3.7   Stylized diagram of the principal bones and muscles in the lower part of the hindleg of the dog shown in frame 17 of Figure 3.6. The ankle extensor muscles include the gastrocnemius and the plantaris muscles. The measured force exerted by the paw on the force platform is shown.

Similar measurements and calculations of activities such as the fast running of ostriches and buffalo, and the flying of pigeons and geese, show that safety factors are nearly always greater than 2 and are usually around 3–5 in healthy individuals. Nonetheless, skeletal injuries are common and a significant proportion of wild-caught mammals show evidence of having healed a broken bone (Section 2.3.1). Unforeseen changes in the terrain or misjudged actions that result in abnormally large forces being transiently exerted on bones and tendons seem to be common causes, as well as injuries from predators and potential prey.

■   Are healed bones and tendons 'as good as new'?

Not always. In the case of bone, the regenerated tissue itself may be quite strong (Section 2.3.1), but displacement or distortion of components may greatly weaken the whole structure. For example, the fracture of the sacral vertebrae (probably caused by collision with a motor vehicle) of the badger shown in Figure 3.8 had healed (Figure 3.8a) but its joint with the other hip bones was badly misaligned and the openings through which nerves pass were occluded (Figure 3.8b). The badger almost certainly limped, and its whole hip joint was weakened. Normal movements could have imposed abnormally large or misdirected forces on the back and the other limbs. Injured or aged tendons are mechanically weaker and less resilient than normal ones of similar size (Sections 4.5.2 and 7.2).

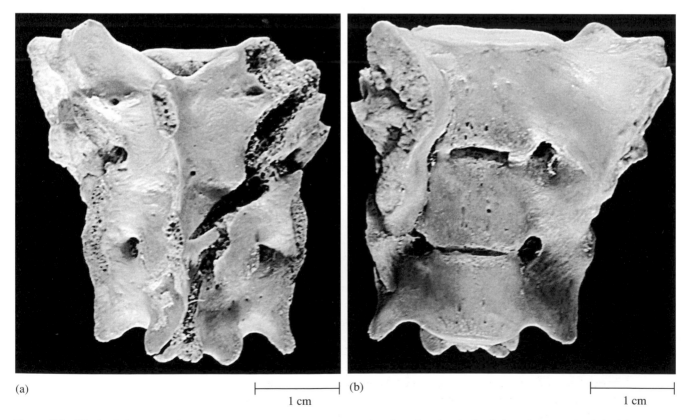

(a)   ⊢————————⊣   (b)   ⊢————————⊣
                                                    1 cm   1 cm

Figure 3.8   The healed sacrum of a wild badger (*Meles meles*). (a) Dorsal surface showing the healed crack across the right side of the three sacral vertebrae. (b) Ventral view showing that the sacro-iliac joint which, in the intact animal, abuts onto the pelvis, is badly displaced and distorted.

Tissues that have been weakened by malformed growth or by an imperfectly healed previous injury may function with a much smaller safety factor than is normal for a healthy structure. The animal risks injuring itself again unless it modifies its behaviour until the first injury is completely healed. This badger apparently coped surprisingly well with its disability, probably by adjusting its gait and other activities appropriately: the injury was long healed, and the animal was clearly able to find enough food because it was quite fat when collected after a fatal road accident.

The combination of a good match between normal behaviour and the safety factors of the skeleton and muscles, and the ability of these tissues to repair minor injuries (Sections 2.3.1 and 2.4.2) mean that the durability of mammalian legs compares favourably with that of the most sophisticated and carefully engineered artificial limbs. Prosthetic limbs worn by people undertaking only light exercise rarely last longer than 2–3 years, while natural legs are serviceable for 70-odd years, if used with reasonable care.

3.2.3 The physiology of extinct organisms

A few apparently terrestrial extinct animals, including the dinosaurs *Diplodocus, Camarasaurus* and *Tyrannosaurus,* were exceptionally large, much larger than any terrestrial species now living (although not larger than the blue whale). The habits and physiological capacities of dinosaurs have recently been the subject of vigorous debate. Some experts imagine them as ponderous poikilotherms plodding across open plains; others represent them as high-spirited homeotherms hopping gracefully across hilly terrain. Much of the argument has focused on the physiological mechanisms of heat production and temperature regulation, but equally relevant is the question of how the skeletons of such large animals, some of which were probably bipedal, could have withstood the forces imposed on them by fast movement on land. Clearly, the argument cannot be settled by observation or experiment because these large animals and all their close relatives are extinct, but, by using allometry to guide extrapolation from living organisms, it is possible to make a meaningful guess about their habits from studying the dimensions of their fossilized bones.

McNeill Alexander measured the running speed, stride length and body mass in various living vertebrates, including ostriches, children and small rodents, and used the data to establish the allometric relationship between leg length, running speed and stride length. The stride length of particular kinds of dinosaurs could be measured from fossilized footprints, some of which show details of the shape of the foot sufficiently clearly for the animal that made them to be identified with certainty. The body mass was estimated from the dimensions of the bones, using comparative data such as those in Figure 3.5. These data, together with information about stride length and leg length, were used to calculate their normal speed of locomotion, using the allometric equations derived from the living vertebrates. The estimated maximum speeds of these species of dinosaurs were quite slow, about 1.0–3.6 m s^{-1}. The large dinosaurs, like large terrestrial mammals, probably moved at a sedate pace and so minimized the risk of damaging their skeleton and muscles. It is most unlikely that the adults of the large species galloped, hopped or jumped.

3.2.4 Structural materials in internal organs

A few organs, notably the central nervous system, are almost completely encased in, and hence supported by, the skeleton, but the structural integrity of many others is maintained by materials within the organ itself. The normal function of internal organs such as the guts, kidneys and pancreas has nothing to do with support, but they are subjected to larger mechanical stresses in bigger animals, and hence contain a greater proportion of structural materials.

The liver consists of numerous small cells that are biochemically active but mechanically flimsy (Section 2.2.1). It is anchored by ligaments to the dorsal wall of the abdomen but is nonetheless subjected to large forces, particularly compression, when the animal twists its body or eats a large meal. Its ability to withstand this deformation without permanent damage is due almost entirely to a network of collagen fibrils that permeate the whole organ and determine its gross shape (Section 7.2.1). Figure 3.9 shows the collagen content of the livers of various mammals as a function of the total mass of the liver.

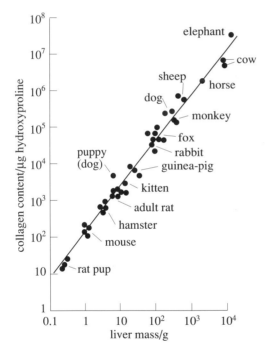

Figure 3.9   Allometric relationship between collagen content and gross mass of the liver of various adult and juvenile terrestrial mammals. Both axes are logarithmic. The straight line represents collagen content $\propto$ (liver mass)$^{1.28}$.

■   Is the allometric relationship between the structural materials of the liver and its gross mass similar to that expected from the geometrical considerations discussed in Section 3.2.1?

Yes. The exponent of allometry (1.28) that fits the data is close to the predicted value of 1.33, suggesting that the mechanical forces applied to the liver of terrestrial mammals are in direct proportion to its size.

■   Would you expect a similar relationship to hold for aquatic animals?

Not necessarily. The collagen content of livers of aquatic species that dive to great depths and/or spend part of their lives on land would be expected to show positive allometry to body mass, because they are subjected to mechanical forces that increase with body size. This relationship would not be expected in neutrally buoyant, slow-swimming fishes that live continuously in an almost weightless environment.

■   Would you expect an increase in collagen content to alter liver function?

No. The main functions of the liver are secretion and the regulation of intermediary metabolism, physiological roles that do not involve structural materials such as collagen. The greater proportion of collagen makes the liver mechanically more robust, but does not imply any differences in its metabolic functions.

■   Would the increase in collagen content alter the palatability of the livers of meat animals?

Yes. More collagen would make the tissue tough to eat. Most of the liver (and other offal such as kidneys and hearts) sold for human consumption comes from poultry, sheep or young pigs. That of cattle and horses is used for dog food. Mechanical strength of 'soft' biochemically active organs is not a trivial matter. Since wearing seatbelts in cars became compulsory, deaths from head injuries have become rarer, but bursting of the liver, with or without tearing of its supportive ligaments, is now one of the commonest fatal injuries in vehicle accidents. The liver is so richly perfused with blood that unless corrective surgery and blood transfusion can be organized within minutes of the injury, the patient dies from internal bleeding.

The greater collagen content of internal organs of larger mammals should not be confused with the accumulation of collagen due to advancing age to be discussed in Section 4.5.2. So far as it is known, the two processes are not controlled in the same way, although larger animals are very often older by the time they reach adult size.

Summary of Section 3.2

There are small differences in the mechanical properties of bone in mammals of different body mass, but the most extensive adaptations of the skeleton to larger body mass are the changes in its gross dimensions. The mass of the skeleton is proportionately larger in larger animals but the exponent of allometry is not as large as would be expected from geometrical analysis. Large animals avoid movements that would impose very large forces on the skeleton. The safety factor is the ratio of the strength of the skeleton to the maximum forces it would normally sustain. Human athletes and specially trained animals can exert forces that are almost sufficient to damage their skeleton or tendons, but the safety factor for the musculo-skeletal elements in normal movements of most animals is greater than 2. Allometric analysis of the stride length and dimensions of the skeleton of large dinosaurs indicates that their normal running speed was slow. The structure of internal organs such as the liver is maintained by a framework of collagen, the mass of which increases with liver mass in accordance with the theoretical predictions.

3.3 Physiological allometry

Just as the study of allometry of skeletons and other structural materials helps us to explain body proportions and what animals can (and cannot) safely do, physiological allometry can account for size-related changes in cellular structure, metabolism and the speed and endurance of animals' locomotory performance. Of course, physiological allometry is somewhat more difficult to study than structural allometry, because most of the measurements have to be made on intact living organisms rather than dead, isolated tissues, and there are a great many biochemical parameters to choose from.

3.3.1 Kleiber's rule

A clear relationship between basal metabolic rate (BMR) and body mass in adult dogs of different breeds was first noticed by the German physiologist, M. Rubner, in the late 19th century. The American biologists Max Kleiber in 1932, and, independently, Samuel Brody in 1945, made similar measurements on a much wider range of organisms and proposed a general formula, now known as **Kleiber's rule**, that relates metabolic rate per unit body mass to total body mass. The data in Figure 3.10 are measurements of the metabolic rate of various organisms ranging in size from bacteria to elephants. Separate regression lines have been drawn for unicellular organisms, poikilothermic multicellular organisms and homeotherms.

■ Why should homeotherms have higher metabolic rates than poikilotherms of similar body mass?

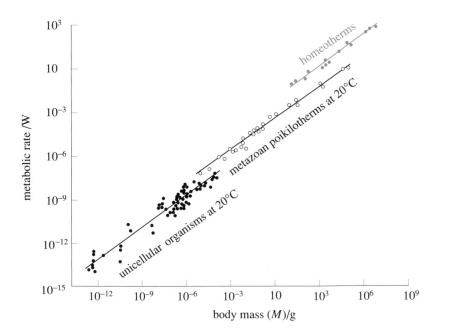

Figure 3.10 Allometric relationship between metabolic rate (in watts) and body mass for three categories of unicellular and metazoan organisms ranging in size from bacteria to elephants. Both axes are logarithmic. The slopes of all three lines are 0.75, i.e. the data fit the equation: metabolic rate $\propto M^{0.75}$.

As you should remember from Book 2, Chapters 1 and 2, the metabolism of homeotherms generates larger quantities of heat than that of poikilotherms, and many biochemical reactions proceed faster at higher temperature. There is also a larger difference between body temperature and that of the environment in the warmer homeotherms so, even with good insulation, cooling is faster. All these effects increase the rate of energy utilization in homeotherms.

However, all three regression lines correspond to the equation: metabolic rate $\propto$ $M^{0.75}$, which indicates that, within each category, metabolic rate per unit body mass is proportionately lower in larger organisms. It is not immediately obvious why the metabolism of a group of small cells in a poikilothermic multicellular organism should be higher than that of a poikilothermic unicellular organism of equivalent mass at the same temperature, nor why the metabolic rate of larger individuals should be lower per unit mass than that of smaller ones.

■   Is 0.75 the exponent of allometry that you would expect if smaller organisms had a higher metabolic rate because their surface area was proportionately larger?

Not for a theory based upon conventional geometry. the surface area should increase in proportion to [volume (i.e. mass)]$^{0.67}$ (Section 3.1.1). In spite of the scatter of points about the regression lines, the exponents of allometry that fit the data in Figure 3.10 are very significantly different from 0.67. However, as discussed in Section 3.1.1, the area of biological surfaces across which heat and metabolites (e.g. oxygen) pass is better regarded as a fractal surface. If so, the expected exponent would be $2.17/3 = 0.723$, which is closer to that which fits the data. Indeed, the data from Brody's extensive study of mammals (mainly domestic livestock, and companion and laboratory species) did fit the equation: metabolic rate $\propto M^{0.73}$.

■   How could the allometric relationship between skeleton and body mass (Section 3.2.1) affect the BMR of the whole body?

The skeleton accounts for a greater fraction of the total body mass in larger species. Furthermore, because only a small fraction of the mass of mature bone is cellular (Section 2.3), the tissue as a whole should have a low metabolic rate. Bodies that contain proportionately more such tissues would have a lower overall BMR.

The liver, kidneys and gut are among the most metabolically active tissues. The relative size of the intra-abdominal viscera depends partly upon diet: the stomach and intestine, and in many cases the liver, are relatively larger in ruminants than in non-ruminant herbivores or omnivores. The Carnivora are a convenient group in which to study changes in the proportions of these organs with body size because they are generally similar in body form, and range in body mass from about 0.1 kg (stoats and weasels) to more than 500 kg (large male polar bears). In a sample of 44 randomly obtained adult Carnivora of various sizes, the mass of the intra-abdominal viscera (excluding the adipose tissue and reproductive organs) was found to be proportional to (lean body mass)$^{0.76}$. Thus in a large polar bear, the entire contents of the abdomen (except the adipose tissue) was found to be only 4.3% of the lean body mass (3.5% of the total body mass), compared to about 30% of the lean body mass in a stoat.

The exponent of allometry relating the gross mass of the liver alone to body mass in mammals is 0.89, so that of the gut (which is by far the largest of the abdominal viscera) must be somewhat less than 0.76.

■   How can the allometric relationship between BMR and body mass explain the decrease in the relative size of the viscera with increasing body mass?

The two exponents of allometry with body mass are about the same (0.75), so BMR and viscera size scale approximately isometrically to each other. A shorter gut with a smaller surface area is needed to secrete digestive enzymes and absorb nutrients in animals whose whole body uses proportionately less energy.

During ontogenetic (i.e. within the life cycle) growth, there are also changes in the relative sizes of organs and hence their contributions to the BMR of the body as a whole. Table 3.1 shows the relative masses, and Figure 3.11 the contribution to basal metabolic rate, of some organs and tissues in boys and men. In human neonates, the brain uses a large proportion, nearly 45%, of the body's total energy expenditure, although it accounts for only 12.2% of the body mass. This organ still accounts for a disproportionate share of energy expenditure in young adults, in whom it is only 2.2% of the body mass but uses 20% of BMR. The muscles, which in healthy young men are 45% of the body mass, use a further 20% of the BMR. The liver, kidneys and heart are all relatively larger in infants (see Table 3.1) than in young adults, but these organs do not use disproportionately more energy. On the contrary, the heart's share of BMR gets significantly greater with age, probably because it is working harder to pump blood through a larger mass of muscle and other peripheral tissues.

Such ontogenetic changes in the relative masses of metabolically active tissues (such as brain, liver, kidney, muscle, glands) and more inert tissues (e.g. bone, tendon, skin, adipose tissue) go a long way towards explaining the changes in BMR during the life history of a single species such as humans. They also account, at least in part, for many interspecific differences. For example, koala bears have a much lower BMR than other mammals of similar size, and the brain is proportionately very small (much smaller than it seems from the size of the skull, which contains large air cavities): they are also incapable of fast movement and, for a mammal, seem slow and unintelligent. These features apparently evolved as adaptations to a diet of nutrient-poor eucalyptus leaves in an almost predator-free environment: a high BMR could not be sustained on the poor diet, and a large brain is not necessary.

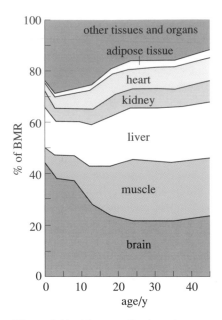

Figure 3.11   The contribution of some organs and tissues to basal metabolic rate of boys and men aged 0.5–45 y. Nearly all the tissues were obtained from people who died suddenly in accidents.

Table 3.1   Proportions (as a percentage of total body mass) of various organs and tissues in boys and men

Age/y	Brain	Liver	Kidney	Heart	Muscles
Birth	12.2	4.53	0.82	0.68	21.3
1–5	8.3	3.45	0.54	0.56	n.d.
6–10	6.7	3.05	0.54	0.60	n.d.
11–15	3.7	2.63	0.45	0.51	36.2
16–20	2.6	2.55	0.46	0.54	n.d.
21–40	2.2	2.51	0.46	0.54	45.2
41–60	2.35	2.49	0.46	0.57	40.2
61–70	2.7	2.14	0.41	0.63	33.9
70+	2.3	2.03	0.41	0.60	27.0

n.d., no data.

However, such differences in body proportions cannot fully account for Kleiber's rule over the whole spectrum of species (Figure 3.10). Comparisons *in vitro* of tissues from large and small animals indicate that many, perhaps all, of the physiological and biochemical processes that contribute to metabolism proceed more slowly per unit mass in larger organisms.

■   What light does Kleiber's rule shed on the allometric relationship between heart size and body mass (Section 3.1.3)?

The hearts of larger animals have to supply blood to a greater bulk of tissue, and more of the tissue is further away from the heart, so one might expect there would be a positive allometric relationship between heart mass and body mass. But Kleiber's rule predicts negative allometry between the two variables, because the metabolic rate of tissues in larger animals is lower than that of smaller ones, so their blood supply requirements are also lower. These two effects cancel each other out and the relationship between heart mass and body mass turns out to be approximately isometric (see Figure 3.1).

■   Can you suggest some physiological or genetic mechanisms by which substantial changes in the relative sizes of organs could have evolved?

Deficiency or excess of paracrine IGFs (Section 1.4.2 and Figure 1.9) and/or of hormones such as thyroxin (Section 1.4.3 and Figure 1.10) cause disproportionate growth, or selective growth retardation, of certain organs and tissues. It is thus in principle possible that species differences in the relative magnitudes of limbs, organs, tissues, cells or even single metabolic pathways could arise by duplication or deletion of genes for such locally acting growth factors or their regulators, binding proteins or receptors.

3.3.2 Locomotion and body size

Animal movement is full of paradoxes that seem to defy physiological explanation: tiny birds (e.g. humming-birds) migrate hundreds of kilometres, but similar-sized mammals such as mice and shrews become exhausted after running less than 0.1 km. There have recently been many experimental and conceptual advances in the study of all aspects of locomotion from gross anatomy to enzyme kinetics, many of which were stimulated by studies of the allometry of animal performance (see Chapter 8).

The energy consumed during locomotion can be measured using apparatus similar to that used for measuring resting metabolic rate while the animal is running on treadmill. By adjusting the speed of the treadmill, the energy used during locomotion at different speeds can be calculated. Figure 3.12 shows some such measurements of the net energetic cost of transportation for various mammals. The energy required to move 1 kg of a mouse-sized mammal *(M* = around 10^1 g) through 1 km is more than fifty times ($10^{3.5}/10^{1.8}$ = 3 162.3/63.1 = 50.12) greater than that needed to move 1 kg of a horse-sized mammal *(M* = around 10^5 g) over the same distance.

Figure 3.13 shows the energy used (in watts per kilogram body mass) by various mammals moving at as wide a range of speeds as they can. As expected from Figure 3.12, the energy used by the mouse is much greater than that of the dogs when both are moving at 1 km h^{-1}, but the rate at which the energetic cost of

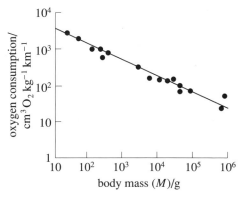

Figure 3.12   The energetic cost of transportation per kg body mass per km travelled as a function of body mass. Both axes are logarithmic. The net cost of transportation was calculated by measuring metabolism during running and subtracting the BMR. 10^6 g = 1 000 kg, approximately the size of a large elephant.

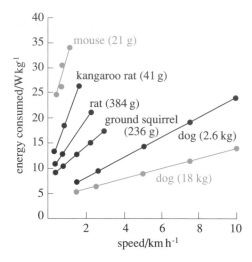

Figure 3.13   The energy consumed by various mammals of different body mass (shown in brackets) while moving at various speeds.

locomotion increases with increasing speed is also much greater for the small mammals than for the larger species. As a result, the metabolic rate of the largest dog for which data are shown in Figure 3.13 more than doubles [from $5\,\text{W}\,\text{kg}^{-1}$ to about $13\,\text{W}\,\text{kg}^{-1}$, a 160% increase, $(13 - 5)/5 = 1.6$], as it accelerates from $1\,\text{km}\,\text{h}^{-1}$ to its maximum speed, whereas that of the mouse, for which any kind of locomotion uses much more energy ($25\,\text{W}\,\text{kg}^{-1}$ for the slowest recorded speed, compared to $5\,\text{W}\,\text{kg}^{-1}$ for the large dog), increases by only about 42% [from $24\,\text{W}\,\text{kg}^{-1}$ to $34\,\text{W}\,\text{kg}^{-1}$; $(34 - 24)/24 = 0.42$] as it goes from its slowest to its fastest speed.

Thus, larger mammals undergo greater net increases in energy expenditure when they run at their fastest speed, but smaller mammals, for whom locomotion of any kind (Figures 3.12 and 3.13) and resting metabolism (Figure 3.10) involve expending energy at a higher rate, can achieve their peak running speed for a smaller *increase* in energy expenditure. The effect is a direct result of differences in body mass, and is not simply a result of morphological differences between species. You have probably noticed that small animals such as piglets, lambs and children run or gallop much more readily than sows, ewes and human adults. This conclusion may surprise you because the basic apparatus of locomotion, the bones, muscles and tendons, is more or less similar in all mammals; some explanations for the phenomenon are discussed in Chapter 8.

3.3.3 Locomotory habits

In Section 3.2.1, it was suggested that the apparently reckless gymnastic feats of small mammals and the sedate, cautious habits of elephants were a direct result of differences in the strength of their skeletons relative to the forces imposed on them during movement. Everyone has noticed that small animals such as insects, squirrels and birds can ascend steep slopes and vertical tree trunks at top speed, but sheep, people and horses are reduced to a slow walk by any gradient steeper than about 30°. The following calculations show how these familiar differences in such animals' habits can be explained as a direct result of the effect of body size on the energetic cost of locomotion.

If the energetic cost of running for a fixed distance on a horizontal surface is E then the energetic cost of running uphill for the same distance $= E + (Mgh)/c$, where M is the body mass of the animal, h is the vertical distance travelled, g is the acceleration due to gravity ($9.8\,\mathrm{m\,s^{-2}}$) and c is the efficiency of conversion of metabolic energy into mechanical work (approximately 25%, see Section 6.3.2). As explained in Section 3.3.2, when M is small, E per kilogram body mass is large. But the term $(Mgh)/c$ is simply proportional to the body mass M: the efficiency of *vertical* motion, doing work against gravity, does not change with body mass. So the additional energy needed by small animals to perform work against gravity when running uphill is relatively small compared to the energetic cost per gram body mass of locomotion on level ground, which, because of their small size, is large.

■   Using the data in Figure 3.13, calculate how much extra energy a small mouse and a large dog use when running at maximum speed for 10 s up a slope to a height of 10 m compared with running for the same period of time on level ground.

The 21 g mouse uses $0.021\,\mathrm{kg} \times 34\,\mathrm{W\,kg^{-1}} \times 10\,\mathrm{s} = 7.14\,\mathrm{J}$ while running at maximum speed for 10 s ($1\,\mathrm{W} = 1\,\mathrm{J\,s^{-1}}$). The additional energy needed to raise this mouse through a vertical distance of 10 m is $(0.021 \times 9.8 \times 10)/0.25 = 8.23\,\mathrm{J}$, an increase of $(8.23/7.14) \times 100 = 115\%$ over the energy needed to run for the same time on level ground. The 18 kg dog uses $18 \times 13 \times 10 = 2\,340\,\mathrm{J}$ while running at full speed for 10 s. The energy needed to raise the dog through 10 m is $(18 \times 9.8 \times 10)/0.25 = 7\,056\,\mathrm{J}$, so running uphill at top speed means the dog must increase its energy expenditure by $(7\,056/2\,340) \times 100 = 302\%$, i.e. an increase of more than three-fold. In an even larger animal such as a horse or a person, the power needed for running uphill can be many times greater than that of running on level ground.

The cardiovascular system and the energy-generating metabolic pathways are already working almost maximally during sustained fast running; the additional demands for energy during running uphill must be met either from increasing the energy supply, or by a drop in the running speed. Much of the additional energy comes from anaerobic metabolism which, in most mammals, cannot continue at maximum rate for longer than about a minute before the accumulation of lactic acid becomes dangerously high (see Book 2, Chapter 8). As you probably know from personal experience, large mammals (such as humans) cannot sustain the necessary doubling or tripling of metabolic power output, and quickly become hot and exhausted unless they slow down when going uphill, and/or pause frequently to rest.

The slopes of the regression lines in Figure 3.13 are much steeper for small mammals than for large mammals; so large mammals must slow down a lot to achieve a saving of energy sufficient to meet the demands of running uphill, whereas in a small mammal a small drop in running speed would substantially reduce the energetic cost of locomotion. This situation, combined with the fact that the extra energy needed to run uphill is relatively smaller in small mammals, explains why they can ascend vertical tree trunks with enviable ease while all but the fittest adult humans become fatigued and breathless just from running upstairs. You can verify this effect for yourself using any suitable combination of large and small animals, such as a big dog and a small cat, or a human adult and a child.

The *total* cost of locomotion is still greater for a larger animal, because its body mass is greater; so what are the advantages, from the point of view of locomotion, of large body size? Referring again to Figure 3.13, you can see that, in general, larger mammals can run faster (on level ground).

■   Would you expect the maximum running speed to increase in simple proportion to body mass over the whole size range of terrestrial mammals?

No. The very largest mammals would be expected to run more slowly than those of intermediate size, because the skeletons of smaller mammals operate with larger safety factors (Section 3.2.2). This expectation is indeed fulfilled: among the fastest mammals are the cheetah and certain species of deer, antelopes and kangaroos, which weigh 50–100 kg as adults.

Another advantage of large size concerns the quantity of energy that can be stored in the body, and hence the distance that the animal can travel without stopping to eat. In vertebrates, energy is stored as glycogen in the liver and muscles, and as lipids in adipose tissue.

■   What is the allometric relationship of these tissues to total body mass?

The mass of the muscles is approximately isometric with the total body mass of adult mammals (Section 3.1.3), and that of the liver is proportional to $M^{0.89}$ (Section 3.3.1). Therefore, the glycogen storage capacity of the mammalian body scales to body mass only a little less than isometrically, but the rate at which energy is used is proportional to $M^{0.75}$ (Figure 3.10). There are not enough data from which to determine the allometric relationship between body mass and adipose tissue mass. The lower mass-specific energy cost of locomotion, combined with the greater energy storage capacity of larger animals means that they can travel further between meals, and hence forage over a wider area.

3.3.4 Physiological allometry of respiratory structures

The higher mass-specific metabolic rate (Kleiber's rule, Section 3.3.1) and the higher mass-specific energy cost of locomotion (Section 3.3.2) in smaller animals have important implications for all components of the respiratory system. All components of the respiratory and circulatory systems must be able to take up, transport, deliver and metabolize oxygen faster in smaller organisms. Professors Richard Taylor of Harvard University (Massachusetts, USA) and Ewald Weibel of the University of Berne (Switzerland) decided to find out how the mammalian respiratory and circulatory systems were adjusted to function in mammals of widely different body sizes. They planned to measure the anatomical structures and biochemical processes that supply oxygen to the muscles working at their maximum rate of aerobic metabolism because anaerobic metabolism, by definition, does not involve simultaneous utilization of oxygen. Therefore, the first step in the analysis was to develop a method for measuring the maximum sustainable aerobic metabolism, $\dot{V}_{O_2 \, max}$ (also called the aerobic capacity) in as wide a variety of mammals as possible.

Africa offers a much wider range of mammals of different body mass than either Massachusetts or Switzerland, so Taylor and Weibel set out for Nairobi, where their Kenyan colleagues could advise them on the capture, maintenance and training of suitable wild African mammals. As pointed out in Section 3.2.2, it is usually very difficult to study running at top speed in large wild animals in the laboratory, so the scientists trained tame individuals to run on a treadmill while wearing a mask through which respiratory gases could be monitored.

They made the animals run faster and faster by gradually increasing the speed of the treadmill, and noted the point at which further increase in the power output of the muscles was no longer accompanied by increased oxygen uptake. It was assumed that beyond this point, the energy supply for any further exertion was derived from anaerobic metabolism. Their data for $\dot{V}_{O_2 max}$ of various mammals are shown in Figure 3.14. The data are fitted by the allometric equation $\dot{V}_{O_2 max}$ μ $M^{0.81}$ so the maximal capacity for sustained aerobic metabolism is proportionately smaller in larger mammals.

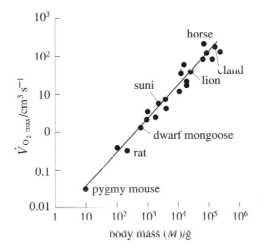
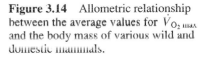

Figure 3.14   Allometric relationship between the average values for $\dot{V}_{O_2 max}$ and the body mass of various wild and domestic mammals.

■   What features of an organism's anatomy and physiology could account for these observations?

An explanation could lie in the structure or properties of any of the organs and organelles involved in aerobic metabolism, including the lungs, the circulatory system and the mitochondria in the muscles themselves. Starting with the lungs, Weibel and his colleagues measured total lung volume, alveolar surface area and the density of capillaries in the lung epithelium.

■   Would such measurements be confounded by the fractal problems mentioned in Section 3.1.1?

Yes, but the inaccuracies would be quite small because all the species compared were adult mammals, whose lungs are of similar shape, structure and composition.

The investigators found that all three aspects of lung anatomy scaled to body mass with the exponents of allometry between 0.95 and 1.06, which are not significantly different from isometry.

■   Can the scaling of $\dot{V}_{O_2 max}$ to body mass be attributed to these properties of the lungs?

No. If the structure of the lungs were the main cause of the change in $\dot{V}_{O_2\,max}$ with body mass, one would not expect it to change isometrically with body mass, unless the larger mammals do not use their lungs to full capacity even during maximum exercise, or the tissues of the smaller species have more oxygen available to them than they actually utilize. Neither suggestion seems very plausible.

The investigators then tried to quantify tissue respiration in the locomotory muscles by measuring the relative abundance of mitochondria. Because of the extensive technical work involved, only three species were studied in detail: the dwarf mongoose $(M = 0.5\,\text{kg})$, and two kinds of antelope, the small suni $(M = 3.3\,\text{kg})$ and the large eland $(M = 240\,\text{kg})$. Figure 3.15 shows electron micrographs of cross-sections of the semitendinosus muscle in the hindleg of each species. The structure of the contractile components of muscle (grey speckled areas) are described in greater detail in Chapter 5. The important structures from the point of view of tissue respiration are the darkly stained mitochondria. Although there was little difference in the abundance of mitochondria in the middle of the muscles of the three mammals, mitochondria near to the outer membrane in mongoose muscle were significantly more numerous (see Figure 3.15a); the effect is less noticeable in the suni (Figure 3.15b) and absent in the eland (Figure 3.15c). The fraction of the volume of a whole muscle occupied by mitochondria was found to be proportional to $M^{0.23}$. The scaling of the mass of the whole musculature to body mass is approximately isometric (Section 3.1.3), so the total mass of muscle mitochondria in the body would scale as $M^{1.00}/M^{0.23} = M^{1.00\,-\,0.23} = M^{0.77}$.

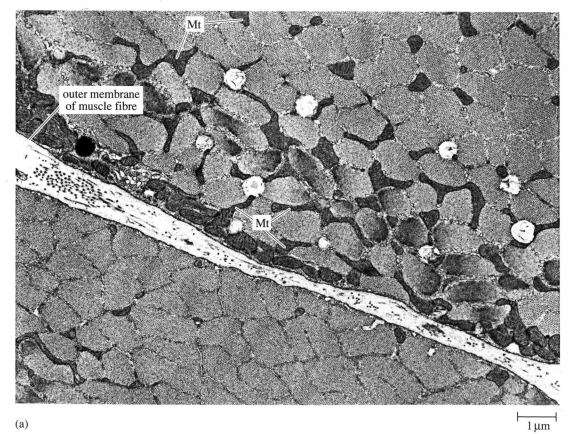

(a)

1 μm

Figure 3.15   Electron micrographs of cross-sections of the semitendinosus muscle in the hindleg of (a) dwarf mongoose; (b) suni antelope, *opposite, above,* and (c) eland, *opposite, below.*

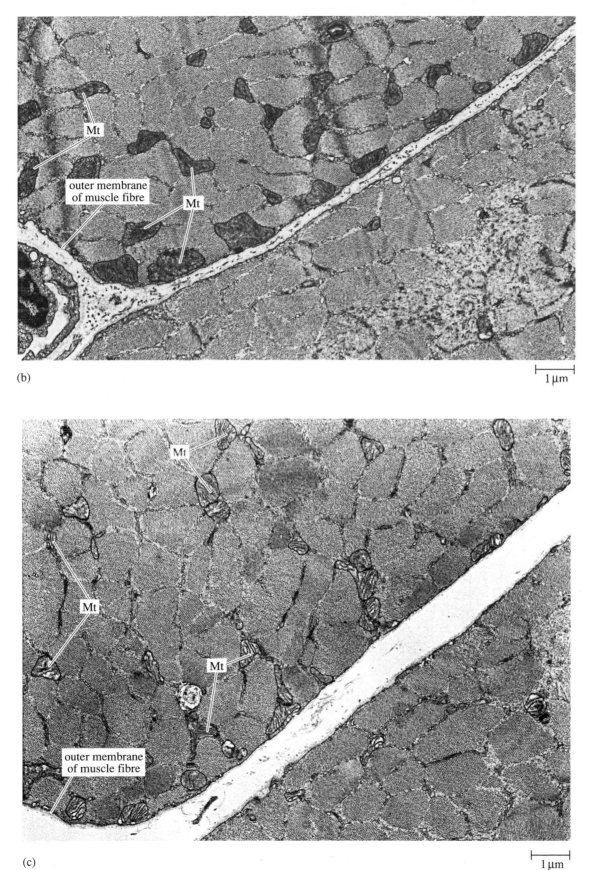

(b)

1 μm

(c)

1 μm

■ Do these observations help to explain the data in Figure 3.14?

Probably. The exponent of allometry relating $\dot{V}_{O_2\,max}$ to body mass is 0.81, which is quite close to 0.77. So the allometric relationship between mitochondrial density in the muscles and body mass suggests that the abundance of these organelles is the main factor responsible for the decrease in maximum sustainable aerobic metabolism in larger mammals. The investigators also found that capillaries were more dense in the muscles of the mongoose than in those of the eland.

Thus Weibel and Taylor showed that the main factor that limits the maximum rate at which oxygen is used by the muscles of mammals of different sizes is the relative abundance of mitochondria. Their studies on lung morphology failed to reveal which features set a limit on the maximum rate of oxygen uptake. In fact, this study of the allometric relationships within the respiratory and cardiovascular systems has prompted physiologists to rethink the whole question of what factors actually determine the maximum rate of flow of gases between the air and the lungs.

Summary of Section 3.3

Kleiber's rule states that basal metabolic rate is proportional to $M^{0.75}$ and applies to all organisms from bacteria to whales. Homeotherms have higher metabolic rates than poikilotherms of similar size, but the exponents of allometry are similar across more than 20 orders of magnitude. Much of the ontogenetic change in BMR can be explained by the changes in the relative masses of metabolically active tissues (such as brain, liver, kidney, muscle, glands) and metabolically sluggish, mainly extracellular tissues (e.g. bone, tendon, skin, adipose tissue). Differences in body proportions also account for some of the interspecific differences in BMR, but the rate of energy utilization is also higher in tissues from smaller organisms.

The energetic cost of transport per kg body mass per km is higher in smaller mammals; the energy expenditure increases more slowly with increasing running speed in larger mammals. Smaller animals can ascend steep slopes with a smaller increment in energy expenditure and/or a smaller decrement of running speed, but larger animals can often travel further without pausing to eat. Changes in the density of mitochondria in the locomotory muscles is the chief means by which the mammalian respiratory system scales to body mass.

3.4 Ontogenetic changes in body size

All multicellular organisms grow from a small egg to an adult, and so change in size during their lifetime. Many scale effects, such as the relative mass of structural materials (Sections 3.2.1 and 3.2.4) and size-related changes in the energetics of locomotion (Section 3.3.2) apply equally to interspecific differences and ontogenetic changes in body mass. This section is about some of the consequences of size that specifically affect organisms that undergo large changes in body size during their lifetime.

3.4.1 Diet and habits in relation to body size

Ontogenetic changes in body mass are quite modest for small animals such as *Drosophila* and *Caenorhabditis* but may span many orders of magnitude in the case of large species, such as humans. The juveniles of very large animals can be so much smaller than their parents that, if they were a separate species, they would probably have completely different diets and habitats. How do such species adapt their habits and habitat to their changing body size?

In large reptiles (except viviparous snakes and lizards), the hatchlings are very small compared to the adults and they grow relatively slowly in the wild (Section 1.5), so a large part of any individual's life is spent being much smaller than the adults. Reptilian parents do not feed their offspring, although some may protect the hatchlings from predation for the first few weeks. The juveniles function as free-living organisms throughout the growth period and have to find, subdue and digest all their food for themselves. Crocodiles and alligators grow from tiny hatchlings, weighing less than 100 g, to large adults of more than 200 kg. Although all growth stages share the same habitat, slow-flowing tropical and semi-tropical rivers, lakes and swamps, their diets are quite different.

The data in Figure 3.16 were obtained in the 1950s from examination of the stomach contents of different-sized specimens of the African crocodile, *Crocodylus niloticus,* shot in the wild in Uganda and Zambia. No item of diet is eaten by crocodiles at all growth stages, and mammals do not constitute major items of diet until the crocodiles are about 3 m long, about the size at which they start breeding.

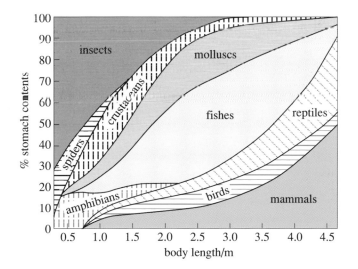

Figure 3.16 The proportion of different food items found in the stomachs of wild-caught crocodiles of various body lengths.

Small crocodiles are easy prey for large fishes, various predatory birds and mammals, and larger individuals of their own species; as they grow larger, fewer predators can successfully tackle them, and their survivorship increases (Section 4.3.1). Large crocodiles have no natural enemies except humans and can live for many years. But if there is insufficient food for juveniles of any particular size, their rate of growth slows and attainment of sexual maturity may be delayed, or even postponed indefinitely (Section 1.5). If growth is slow, the juveniles are small, and hence vulnerable to predation for longer. A permanent breeding population of such large reptiles can be established only where there is sufficient food suitable for *all* the growth stages.

In many of the places where, until recently, crocodiles bred successfully, there is still a large population of adults, and most of the mature females lay eggs, but habitat disturbance has caused many food items normally eaten by the juveniles to become very scarce, so very few hatchlings grow large enough to reach breeding size.

■   What is likely to happen to this population in 50–100 y from now?

It will be extinct. Such 'bottlenecks' in food or habitat for juveniles are behind the abrupt decline or extinction of apparently prosperous populations of large fish, reptiles and birds.

The allometric growth of body parts has been studied in detail in the American alligator, *Alligator mississippiensis,* whose diet and habits are similar to those of the African crocodile. These reptiles grow from about 32 g at hatching to a maximum body mass of over 1.4×10^5 g, an increase of more than 4 000-fold. Growth of the limbs shows negative allometry to that of the trunk; although the skull as a whole grows isometrically with the rest of the body, the snout becomes longer relative to the back of the skull as the animal gets bigger.

■   From your own observations, and data in Section 1.2.3, how do these changes in alligator body proportions compare with those of humans at different growth stages?

They are quite different. The legs of a newborn infant are very short relative to the trunk, but they grow faster than the body as a whole, and account for almost half the length of the body by sexual maturity. The mammalian skull grows very fast just after birth, so the head is large relative to the body in infants, but after the age of weaning it grows more slowly and becomes proportionately smaller in adults.

3.4.2 Viviparity and parental feeding as adaptations to large adult body size

The diet and habitat requirements of the juveniles of large reptiles discussed in Section 3.4.1 were so different from those of the adults that the species could only breed successfully in a varied habitat in which many different items were available as prey. Almost all the very large reptiles which have ever lived (dinosaurs, giant tortoises and other Mesozoic reptiles) are now extinct, and the few survivors (such as big snakes and crocodiles) are most abundant in tropical forests and other ecologically complex habitats, or on remote islands. Their nearest living relatives, the birds, although very abundant and successful, are mostly small. But there are many kinds of large mammals that live permanently at high latitudes and in other ecologically homogeneous environments where there is little variety in the food available.

Mammals do not forage for themselves while they are very small; their food is supplied by the mother, first via the placenta and then in the form of milk. By the time the young mammal is weaned and has to start to find its own food it is at least 10%, and in some species more than 50%, of the size of the adults, and is hence equipped to deal with the same diet as its parents. For example, the body mass of humans increases less than ten-fold between nutritional independence from the parent at weaning (at 8–12 kg body mass) and sexual maturity (60–

80 kg). Thus the unique reproductive system in mammals, viviparity followed by lactation, emancipates them from many of the ecological problems associated with large adult body size: their rapid post-natal growth (Section 1.5) is supported by food obtained and processed by their (larger) parents, so they reach adult size at an early age, and spend most of their lives as full-sized organisms.

Birds lay relatively large eggs, rich in nourishing yolk, and the chicks grow very fast (Section 1.5), supported by the food that the parents bring to the nest. But food for nestlings cannot be stored, and with the possible exception of pigeons and penguins, the parents cannot draw on their own physiological reserves of energy, protein or minerals to feed their offspring. Therefore most birds are restricted to breeding in places where all the dietary needs of the nestlings can be obtained by the parents in the required quantities in the vicinity of the nest.

■   Would young birds be able to extract proteins and minerals from foods that consist largely of carbohydrates and fats as efficiently as young mammals can?

Altricial birds use nutrients very efficiently as long as the diet is reasonably well-balanced (Section 1.5). However, birds do not have brown adipose tissue (Book 2, Chapter 4), which, in mammals, can adjust the relationship between energy intake and energy utilization by facultative thermogenesis. Most birds are unable to take any exercise while confined to the nest, so, unlike young mammals, they cannot 'burn off' excess energy by increasing either thermogenesis or movement. Thus nestlings that are fed on a diet that is rich in energy but poor in protein and calcium may become very obese. For example, the Venezuelan oil bird, *Steatornis caripensis*, lives entirely on fruit that contains only about 1% metabolizable nitrogen (i.e. proteins). The chicks are fed large quantities of such fruit and are obese at fledging, weighing up to 57% more than their parents, because they are unable to burn off the excess energy that they ingested to obtain enough protein to sustain the growth of their lean tissues. Frugivorous bats may be able to live on fruits with a lower nitrogen content than frugivorous birds because they (and other mammals) can dispose of excess energy more efficiently, thereby extracting the protein and minerals and avoiding obesity.

Diets that are adequate for adults are often quite unsuitable for chicks of the same species, because the growing birds require much more protein and minerals. In many bird species, the nestlings' diet is quite different from the adult diet and the requirements of the chicks for a nutritionally balanced diet is the main reason that many birds migrate and breed in areas that provide food items, such as insects, small vertebrates and plant buds, suitable for nourishing growing nestlings.

Most mammals can deplete their own physiological reserves of fats and other nutrients when lactating; the milk may be synthesized from precursors that have been stored in the body and which are derived from foods eaten in a distant place and some time ago. Thus, neither the mother nor the neonate is absolutely dependent upon the continuous availability of a local supply of suitable food in order to maintain the neonate's growth close to adult size.

In general, the greater the skill and experience needed to obtain food, the larger the fraction of the juvenile period for which the young remain with the mother. For example, in Hudson Bay at the southern edge of the species' range, polar bear cubs forage alone from the age of about 18 months, but at higher latitudes, where locating and catching seals is even more difficult, the mother does not abandon the young until their third summer, by which time the male cubs (which grow to three times average female body mass by the age of 8–10 y) may be substantially larger than she is. Viviparity and parental feeding have obvious advantages for reproduction in disturbed or ecologically uniform environments where only a narrow range of kinds of foods are available to the species.

Summary of Section 3.4

Most of the changes in body structure and metabolism already described in species with different adult body sizes also occur during ontogeny as the juveniles of species with large adult body sizes grow to maturity. The diet, and hence the habitat, change greatly as the young grow; animals in which the parents do not feed the young can only establish a permanent breeding population in environments in which there is suitable food for all growth stages. Mammals avoid most of the problems associated with growth to large adult body size because the young are nourished *in utero* or by milk, the nutrients for which are derived from the mother's food supply or from her own energy stores. Most young mammals are large enough to find, subdue and digest the same food as the adults by the time they become nutritionally independent.

3.5 Conclusion

The study of the anatomical and physiological consequences of size is still in its infancy although the subject has made important advances in the last decade. As the examples discussed in this chapter show, anomalies and discrepancies can arise from erroneous assumptions or misunderstandings in formulating predictive theories, as well as from inaccuracies in measurements.

The effects of body mass cannot be ignored when making comparisons between physiological processes in different species, or when extrapolating experimental results from one species to another. This chapter has stressed the *variety* of ways in which an organism's body size affects its anatomy, physiology, habits, behaviour and life history. Some of these effects were predicted from simple geometrical considerations; the origin of others still cannot be explained completely. Although many anatomical structures and physiological mechanisms are qualitatively similar in all growth stages and in taxonomically related animals of different adult body mass, the details are specific to the size and habits of the individual.

Objectives for Chapter 3

When you have completed this chapter, you should be able to:

3.1   Define and use, or recognize definitions and applications of each of the **bold** terms.

3.2   Outline the main theoretical and practical advances that led to recognition and measurement of size-related effects in biology.

3.3   Describe three ways in which the structure and function of the vertebrate skeleton is modified according to the size of the animal.

3.4   Explain the concept of safety factor in animal movement and describe what measurements must be made to calculate it.

3.5   Explain how and why allometry enables scientists to make reliable guesses about the physiology of extinct organisms.

3.6   Describe how the structure of soft tissues is maintained in vertebrates of different body size.

3.7   State Kleiber's rule and describe some explanations that have been proposed to account for it

3.8   Describe how body size and terrain affect the energy expenditure during locomotion.

3.9   Describe how the various components of the mammalian respiratory system are adapted to size-related differences in metabolism.

3.10   Contrast the ontogenetic changes in diet and habitat of large mammals and large reptiles, and explain the adaptive significance of viviparity and parental care for organisms that are large as adults.

3.11   Explain how and why many different aspects of an organism's biochemistry, physiology, behaviour and ecology are determined by its body size.

Questions for Chapter 3

(*Answers to questions are at the end of the book.*)

Question 3.1 (Objective 3.2)

For which of the following purposes is allometry a valuable tool?

(a)   Suggesting how the laws of elementary geometry should apply to physiological problems.

(b)   Summarizing trends in anatomical or physiological data from animals of widely different body sizes.

(c)   Establishing taxonomic and phylogenetic relationships between organisms.

(d)   Predicting the expected dimensions of an anatomical or physiological character in a species that cannot be investigated directly.

(e)   Drawing attention to cases in which the empirical data deviate from the theoretical predictions.

Question 3.2 (Objective 3.3)

Which of the following differences would you expect to observe in the adults of large species compared to those of taxonomically related smaller species?

(a)   They are more easily confined by ditches, hedges and fences because they do not readily jump or scramble over obstacles.

(b)   They are less easily panicked into running very fast over unfamiliar terrain.

(c)   Their flesh is tougher and so less palatable.

(d)   The bones are more suitable for making artefacts because they are less breakable.

(e)   There is proportionately more meat on the carcass because the skeleton is relatively smaller.

(f)   There is proportionately more meat on the carcass because the skin area is relatively smaller.

Question 3.3 (Objective 3.4)

How does the concept of 'safety factor' help in establishing: (a) the kinds of movements that an animal normally performs in the wild; (b) the kind of terrain and habitat in which it is adapted to live; (c) whether the specimen's skeleton, tendons or muscles are normal and healthy, or are defective and deformed through abnormal growth, injury or disease?

Question 3.4 (Objective 3.5)

Which of the following are correct explanations of why allometry is a useful technique for establishing the habits and physiological capabilities of extinct animals?

(a)   It is not necessary to make any measurements from the species under investigation.

(b)   The skeleton is the tissue best suited to allometric study, and it is usually only the skeleton of extinct animals which is fossilized.

(c)   Allometry is mainly concerned with large animals and most extinct animals were large.

(d)   Allometry uses the known facts about a species to guide extrapolation of other data from one kind of animal to another.

(e)   Allometry uses geometrical and engineering principles to predict how the proportions of animals ought to change as they become larger.

Question 3.5 (Objective 3.6)

Why do the structural components of most soft tissues increase in proportion to $M^{1.33}$ whereas the exponent of allometry for the mass of the skeleton in relation to body mass is lower?

Question 3.6 (Objective 3.7)

Which of the following statements are true of Kleiber's rule?

(a)   It was formulated from direct observations on living organisms.

(b)   It is easily derived from simple geometrical and engineering principles.

(c)   The BMR of all organisms studied is exactly in accordance with that predicted by Kleiber's rule.

(d)   The coefficients, but not the exponents, of allometry can be different in organisms of widely different structure and metabolism.

(e)   It can be explained partly by differences in the body shape of large and small organisms.

(f)   It can be explained partly by differences in the tissue composition of large and small organisms.

(g)   It means that many biochemical reactions taking place in larger organisms use less energy per gram tissue per hour than do similar processes in small organisms.

Question 3.7 (Objective 3.8)

A small rabbit is surprised at close range by a large dog on a mountainside. On level ground, the maximum running speed of the rabbit is only 70% of the maximum speed of the dog. In which direction should the rabbit run to minimize the chances of being caught?

Question 3.8 (Objective 3.9)

What are the reasons for believing that the major size-related adjustments of the mammalian respiratory system involve modifications of the intracellular structures?

Question 3.9 (Objective 3.10)

Explain how viviparity and parental feeding of the neonates enable mammals to: (a) reduce the fraction of the total lifespan that they spend being below adult size; (b) develop specialized feeding habits and exploit a narrow range of food sources; (c) establish permanent populations in habitats that would not support a breeding population of large reptiles.

Question 3.10 (Objective 3.11)

In which of the following areas of study would you expect to find *no* size-related effects?

(a)   Ecology

(b)   Animal behaviour

(c)   Anatomy

(d)   Environmental physiology

(e)   Organ physiology

(f)   Cellular physiology

(g)   Metabolic biochemistry

(h)   Crystallography of biological molecules

CHAPTER 4   AGEING AND DEATH

4.1 Introduction

This chapter is about growing older: how it is chronicled, how long it lasts, what factors hasten or delay its effects and a little about the mechanisms behind it. Ageing is a topic for which the perspective of the 'whole-animal' physiologist deviates most fundamentally from that of cell and molecular biologists. Many phenomena of whole-body ageing have no obvious counterparts at the cellular level and may seem to be paradoxical. For example, many forms of cell death are actually more common in the very young than in adults or the elderly (except in a dying organism). Old bodies do not necessarily lack newly formed cells, indeed, they may have an excess of them. The study of ageing thus forces us to address a fundamental unsolved issue in physiology: the status and autonomy of individual cells and tissues within a whole body.

Chapter 3 described issues relevant to the basic question: why bother to grow larger? The equivalent questions for growing older and dying are not valid because these processes have not evolved to be adaptive. Natural selection operates only on events leading up to the completion of reproduction, it cannot directly alter situations that do not affect reproductive success. So, in contrast to growth and regeneration, many of the whole organism processes of ageing and dying should not be expected to be strictly functional and adaptive.

Although the topic has been much studied over the last 25 years, the major factors and mechanisms of ageing are far from understood. This chapter describes some well-documented, but in many cases apparently paradoxical experiments whose results must be accounted for in any synthetic theory of ageing. The account may therefore seem bitty and inconclusive, but that is the present state of research on the topic.

4.2 Age determination in wild vertebrates

Young animals can usually be recognized by their small size, lack of secondary sexual characters and, in the case of many birds, juvenile plumage. However, it is surprisingly difficult to tell the exact age of juveniles of slow-growing species such as humans and elephants, or the age of any wild animal after sexual maturity. The study of longevity in natural populations depends upon a simple, accurate means of age determination; this section is about the principles behind some of the more widely used methods.

Apart from ringing, earmarking or tagging young individuals and following their careers by resighting or recapturing them, there are two main methods of age determination. The first involves following the course of growth of some easily measured anatomical parts: the skeleton is the most convenient tissue because its growth is strongly dependent upon the absolute age of the organism, at least in mammals and birds (Sections 1.1.1 and 1.5). The other method is examination of wear and degradation of anatomical parts: the teeth are frequently chosen, because they are easily studied and normally subject to extensive wear.

4.2.1 Age determination in young animals

Bones grow in length at the epiphyses, which can be studied quite easily with X-rays in living animals or by *post-mortem* examination of the bones. The epiphyses gradually close with the onset of sexual maturity (Section 2.3, Figures 2.8 and 2.9), and for a very few species (rats and humans) the relationship between chronological age and the closure of epiphyseal plates of various bones has been thoroughly studied. Studies of this kind have established the concept of **bone age**, the degree of maturation of the skeleton, which, for endocrinologically normal children on an adequate diet, is closely correlated to chronological age. X-ray photographs, particularly of the hand and the hip joint, can be used to determine the age of a child to within an accuracy of a few months.

■   Using information presented in Chapter 1, suggest some obvious limitations of this technique.

Apart from being cumbersome and stressful to the individual, the method has the disadvantage that the child's nutritional history makes a significant difference to age of maturity (Section 1.2.2) and hence to the 'bone age'. A variety of hormone disturbances could also delay or accelerate the maturation of the long bones, and hence give inaccurate results. As will be described in Section 7.3.3 (Figures 7.8 and 7.9), the rate of maturation of bone structure and properties also differs greatly between species of mammals.

The teeth are another tissue whose development, at least in mammals, is closely related to chronological age. Most terrestrial placental mammals have two sets of teeth: deciduous or **milk teeth**, which erupt at or shortly after birth and are shed well before skeletal growth ends, to be replaced by the permanent set. The permanent teeth are usually fully functional by the time the animal is sexually mature and, although the inner (dentine) layer of hard tissue may thicken with time, each tooth cannot grow or be replaced if it is damaged by wear, breakage or disease. The development of the two sets of teeth is therefore an accurate indicator of age in subadult animals but, since the chronological age at which each tooth develops differs between species (depending upon diet and other factors), the method must be carefully calibrated for each species using specimens of known age. A combination of bone and dental methods has been extensively used for archaeological and forensic investigations to determine the age at death of humans from their skeletons.

4.2.2 Age determination in adults

It was emphasized in Chapter 2 that the molecular and cellular components of most mammalian tissues are capable of regeneration following wear or injury, and that newly formed cells are often impossible to distinguish from longer established components. Evidence of wear or damage through prolonged use is thereby destroyed. Obviously, the age of an organism can only be established from examination of a tissue which is either not renewed at all or, if it is renewed, the younger components must be readily distinguished from the older parts. Again, the teeth provide the best indication of age: they are continuously subjected to wear and damage through use, and, in mammals, they are not replaced in adults and have only limited capacity for repair. For example, the teeth of foxes and badgers are abraded through contact with gritty soil and bones, and those of old individuals are always chipped and worn, sometimes to the extent that the big canine teeth, which are sharply pointed in a young animal, become low, blunt cones.

Tooth wear is particularly severe in herbivores, because they chew large quantities of tough plant material, such as grasses and wood. Some long-lived herbivorous mammals such as horses have very long, narrow teeth that erupt slowly over a period of many years. Under normal circumstances, the chewing surface of the tooth is worn away at about the same rate as the tooth erupts. Old horses become 'long in the tooth' because the shape and wear pattern of the incisor (anterior) teeth tilts progressively from the vertical to the horizontal, so the exposed portions of the teeth appear relatively long and the biting surfaces become oblique. The molar (cheek) teeth of very old horses and donkeys can be worn almost flat (Section 4.6.2 and Figure 4.17).

Elephants are another group of long-lived, herbivorous mammals for which tooth morphology has been studied with a view to using it as a guide to age. One factor distinguishing elephants and their kin from other kinds of mammals is that the molar teeth are very large: a single tooth can weigh several kilograms. Each molar or premolar tooth is functional in turn, rather than the whole permanent set being used simultaneously, as in most mammals. The photos shown in Figures 4.1 and 4.2 were taken in Tsavo National Park in Kenya, where scientists have collected the jaws of wild African elephants which died or were culled in the severe drought of the mid-1960s and have used them to develop an accurate method of age determination.

The mechanism of tooth replacement is illustrated by Figure 4.1. The whole surface of the teeth in the front of the jaw is extensively worn because it was the main grinding surface at the time of death. The teeth behind were not yet fully erupted at the time of death and so are not worn. These teeth were gradually moving forwards along the jaw and would have replaced the ones in front at about the time the latter were worn away. This process of tooth replacement continues until old age, with successive teeth becoming more massive as the jaws and heads also grow bigger. However, as in all mammals, there is a

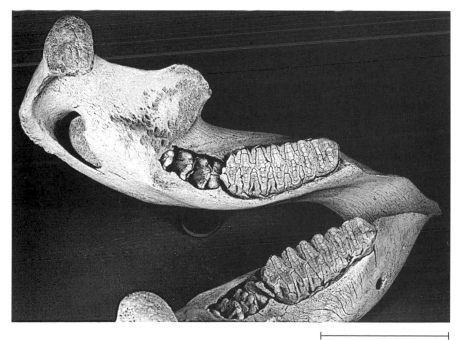

├──────────────────────┤
0.1 m

Figure 4.1   The lower jaw of a subadult African elephant (*Loxodonta africana*). At the time of death, only a single molar tooth in each half of the jaw was in use as a grinding surface. Another tooth is in the process of formation behind each of the functional molars, but in life they were probably not yet erupted through the gum. Further molar teeth are forming in the socket in the back of the jaw that would have replaced these ones as they wore away.

Figure 4.2   The lower jaw of an elderly African elephant with extensively worn teeth. Note that the functional teeth are worn so smooth they would not be efficient grinding surfaces, and that there are no more teeth forming or erupting in the back of the jaw.

maximum number of molar teeth. Figure 4.2 shows the jaw of a very old elephant, perhaps over 50 years old, in which the last molar tooth has been ground to a thin, flat plate. You can see that no more teeth were forming behind the worn ones, as was the case in Figure 4.1. This animal had literally run out of teeth, and it is likely that it had difficulty in chewing its food at the end of its life.

This method of estimating age from dental morphology can be calibrated by following tooth replacement in marked individuals whose exact age is known from birth.

■   What are the limitations of such a method?

Tooth wear depends upon diet as well as upon age, and individuals may also vary in the hardness of their teeth and hence in the rate at which they are replaced. The rate of attrition of the teeth does indeed depend greatly on diet, and there are no reliable means of avoiding this source of inaccuracy in the ageing of many mammals.

Egyptians buried or mummified at the time of the Pharaohs seem to have eaten a very abrasive diet, probably bread made from flour contaminated with sand, because a great many skulls had very worn teeth, often so worn that the soft tissues in the core of the tooth had become exposed and infected, forming large abscesses in the jaw.

■   What errors would be introduced if the same standards of tooth wear were used to age individuals in Egyptian burials and modern populations?

Modern populations would appear to be much younger than the ancient Egyptians because the modern refined diet abrades the teeth very much less than did the diets of our ancestors.

Many mammals, especially arctic and temperate-zone species, grow for only part of the year, or at very different rates according to the seasonal fluctuations of temperature and food supply. Growth under such conditions tends to produce **growth rings**, particularly in hard tissues such as teeth, and the scales, bones and earbones of fishes. Figure 4.3 shows a section of decalcified tooth of the antarctic dolphin *Cephalorhynchus commersonii*. In this species, as in many marine mammals, there is only a single set of teeth, whose growth begins well before birth. Two different components of the tooth are laid down in alternating layers according to the season, giving the distinct 'growth rings'. The dolphin was about 10 years old at the time this tooth was collected.

■   Why are the rings labelled with low numbers more widely spaced than those with high numbers?

Growth is almost always more rapid in young animals than in older ones, and becomes very slow after sexual maturity. The layers formed early in life are therefore thicker than those formed later. The method can be confounded if an individual fails to grow at all in a particularly poor season, or produces two rings in a good year. It is often possible to remove a single scale or vestigial tooth without harming the animal, so this method is not limited to estimating age *post mortem*.

Although the development and attrition of the teeth is a useful guide to age in many mammals, it obviously cannot help in the case of toothless vertebrates such as baleen whales and all birds and tortoises. Toothed reptiles such as crocodiles, snakes and lizards, and most fishes, can replace individual teeth up to fifty times during their lifetime, so tooth wear or tooth rings are at best only a very approximate indicator of age.

The most reliable data on age come from the tagging and ringing of wild animals, and from zoo records. Data from such long-term studies are only now beginning to accumulate, and they have produced many surprises, particularly among birds: some of the albatrosses ringed as chicks when research in the Southern Oceans around Antarctica restarted after World War II are still alive and active. As methods for marking animals and for keeping them in captivity improve, so do our estimates of the maximum possible lifespan, and their average longevity in the wild.

Summary of Section 4.2

Anatomical methods for age determination depend upon following the development of slowly maturing tissues such as bones and teeth, and upon observing attrition in non-replaceable tissues such as teeth. Neither approach is completely accurate, because both the rate of growth and the rate of wear depend upon factors other than chronological age. However, except for marking individual animals and following their careers over a long period, these methods are the only ones available for estimating the age of wild vertebrates.

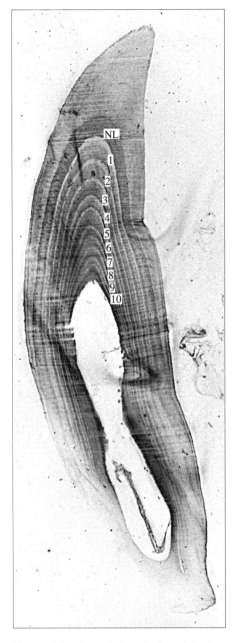

Figure 4.3   Growth rings in the tooth of a dolphin, *Cephalorhynchus commersonii*, shown at about 4 times actual size. Tooth above the neonatal line (NL) was formed during gestation. The inner layers developed after birth.

4.3 Ageing and death

With the doubtful exception of some kinds of unicellular organisms, all animals and plants eventually die. When death occurs after the normal period of reproduction, it is almost always preceded by a period of progressive decline in function of many different tissues and organs; this process is called **senescence**, and it occurs in most multicellular plants as well as in vertebrates and many invertebrates. A finite lifespan and gradual decline in physiological competence and anatomical integrity seem to be almost universal properties of living things, although the potential lifespan may vary from at least 4 500 years in certain trees, such as the bristle cone pines of the Sierra Nevada in the USA and some oriental species of the genus *Ficus* (figs), to less than a week in some insects and lower invertebrates.

Unfortunately, although the process of senescence can be observed almost wherever it is sought, so little is presently understood about the basic mechanism(s) involved that it is impossible to say which phenomena are fundamental and common to all multicellular organisms, and which are merely outcomes of the basic processes. In this respect, the study of senescence is still almost at the stage that the study of other basic biological processes, like respiration, inheritance or muscle contraction, were 100 years ago; there is no neat, clear, universally accepted story. Over the last 30 years, research into ageing as a process has gained momentum and a great deal of descriptive and experimental information is available, but because no general theory exists, it is hard to decide which of the many studies of ageing are relevant to a short, elementary account of the subject. It is an area in which you can be sure that expert opinion will change very rapidly.

4.3.1 Senescence as a cause of death

In many cases, such as when a hedgehog is crushed by a car or a zebra killed by a lion, it is easy to establish the immediate cause of death. Even in such apparently straightforward cases, however, research has shown that among mammals and birds, healthy specimens in the 'prime' of life rarely fall prey to their natural predators. Predation is most successful when the prey are undersized or inexperienced, weakened by disease or senescent. Elderly specimens, particularly of small, solitary species, are very rarely found in the wild because they quickly fall prey to predators. The role of senescence in promoting predation and disease makes it very difficult to pin-point a single, definitive 'cause' of death. For example, typical courses of events leading to the death of a wild elephant might be :

molar teeth worn out → inability to chew tough grasses → dependence on soft, newly-grown grasses → tendency to frequent river banks and marshes → trunk bitten by crocodile → septic wound → blood poisoning → death

molar teeth worn → toothache → loss of appetite → emaciation and muscular wasting → insufficient ventilation of lungs → pneumonia → death

In these cases, was the 'cause' of death crocodiles, pneumonia pathogens or worn-out teeth? It depends upon how much one understands about the physiology of the events leading up to death. Someone who was unfamiliar with the importance of tooth wear in mammals (Section 4.2) would naturally pin the 'blame' on the crocodile or the pneumonia pathogen. The point is that crocodiles and elephants have shared the same habitat for millions of years and there are pneumonia pathogens everywhere most of the time, yet elephants have continued to flourish.

This apparently trivial example illustrates a basic feature of studies on ageing and death: animals and plants, including humans, 'live with' numerous causes of death throughout their lives, pathogens, road accidents, etc., but most individuals do not die from these causes. Death, particularly in large species such as humans, often only occurs after senescence, the internal changes within the organism itself, has made it vulnerable to external agents of death.

Elephants are the largest animals in their habitat, and they live in social groups in which weak members are protected. Consequently, they are among the few mammals other than humans and domestic pets in which senescence is often well advanced at the time of death (e.g. the individual whose jaw is shown in Figure 4.2 lived long enough for wearing out of the teeth to be almost complete). Evidence of heart attacks, strokes and other causes of death common among modern humans is quite frequently found in senior members of elephant herds.

4.3.2 The course of ageing in different tissues

When the bodies of old people are examined thoroughly in the post-mortem room, or by medical students studying gross anatomy, the number and variety of abnormalities in almost every organ are so impressive that one is surprised, not that they died, but that they lived long enough to acquire so many defects. When senescence can be observed in almost every tissue and organ, it is tempting to ascribe its cause to some physiological process affecting the whole organism, such as metabolic rate or nutrition. Another approach is to identify those tissues in which senescence can be soonest detected.

It is a matter of common observation that in humans and other mammals (e.g. dogs) the ageing of the skin, teeth, hair and sense organs, particularly the eye and the ear, begins long before death from old age occurs. The beginnings of senescence can be detected in the human eye and ear before sexual maturity. Degradation of the teeth (Section 4.2) and skin can be attributed to mechanical wear and damage but it is less obvious that the decline in function of the inner ear, or the lens and cornea of the eye, can be simply a result of prolonged use. However, although people (and animals) may become totally blind or deaf at the end of their lives, the decline in function of these organs does not directly cause death, nor is there any fixed connection between senescence in these tissues and ageing of the body overall.

Some data on a few of the many physiological functions that decline with age are shown in Figure 4.4 (*overleaf*). The remarkable thing about these data is the early age from which significant decline is recorded, and the extent of loss of function before about age 75 y, when most deaths now occur. Many people are at their most vigorous and productive well after senescence has set in!

The capacity of the organism to correct and compensate for almost every kind of physiological disturbance also declines progressively with age. For example, the fasting level of blood sugar is the same in healthy young and old, but if blood sugar level is artificially raised, it takes longer to return to normal in old people than in young. Bleeding from a wound stops much more slowly in an old

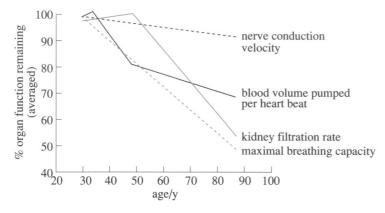

Figure 4.4   Age-related changes in various human physiological functions, expressed as a percentage of the level of function at age 30 y.

individual than a young one, and older animals and people are incapacitated after the loss of a smaller proportion of their blood volume than young ones. Although the normal body temperature is the same in young and old members of the same species, temperature regulation, particularly the ability to produce more heat after cooling of the body, is slower and less efficient in older specimens. So wounds or sudden changes in body temperature become increasingly more likely to cause serious damage to tissues and physiological systems.

The decline in breathing capacity and cardiac output are two symptoms of the general reduction in distensibility and resilience of the ribs and lungs. Muscle strength also starts to decline early in adulthood and, especially in women, becomes noticeable in middle age as a more stooping posture and a weaker grip. The mean area of muscle fibres decreases by about 25% between the ages of 25 and 80 years, but the total mass of skeletal muscle declines to half, so some muscle fibres must disappear completely, possibly following the death of their nerve supply. Frequent, strenuous exercise cannot stop these processes, though it may help to delay them. Recently, evidence has emerged that skeletal muscle strength correlates with levels of circulating oestrogen, possibly by a direct action on the contractile proteins themselves (described in Section 5.2.1).

At the same time as muscle declines, adipose tissue expands, especially that in the abdomen and around the midriff. It has recently been found that the tendency to lose muscle and gain adipose tissue can be arrested, and to some extent reversed, by administering growth hormone, GH (Section 1.4.1), to elderly people.

■   What known actions of GH could account for these effects?

GH and IGFs stimulate muscle growth and oxidation of fat.

Stronger muscles make people thus treated feel healthier, but side effects such as hyperglycaemia may be harmful over a long period. Other hormones, particularly oestrogen, are used to ameliorate some of the more tiresome metabolic and structural changes that menopausal women experience (though they do not restore fertility). However, there is a fine line between relieving symptoms of ageing and trying to delay ageing itself.

4.3.3 Age at death

Death from some external cause (such as a road accident) can occur at any age but, as stressed in Sections 4.3.1 and 4.3.2, senescence is progressive and closely related to age. To study the role of senescence as a cause of death, it is first necessary to establish the age at which members of a particular population die. As explained in Section 4.2, it is often extremely difficult to establish the age of a wild animal, and the diet and exercise regimes of captive specimens are inevitably so different from those of wild specimens that inferences from zoo animals are also fraught with difficulties. Reliable information about the longevity of large populations is really only plentiful for a few short-lived species which can be maintained in captivity, such as *Drosophila,* houseflies, rats, mice, hamsters and domestic livestock, and one kind of long-lived animal, *Homo sapiens.*

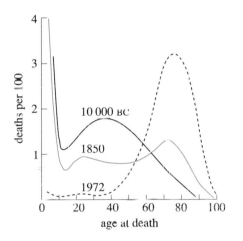

Figure 4.5   The age of death of humans living in three historical periods.

Figure 4.5 shows some data for the age of death of men and women living in England during various historical periods. Data for 10 000 BC were obtained by studying graves, using the techniques outlined in Section 4.2. Its compilation assumes that the whole population was buried in similar sites, regardless of age, sex or social status, and, of course, it is not certain that this assumption is justified. The modern data are more accurate and more comprehensive because of compulsory registration of births and deaths since early in the 19th century.

From Figure 4.5, it is clear that death before the age of 10 y was very common from prehistoric times until this century. In both the prehistoric and the 19th-century samples, deaths of people aged between 10 and 65 y constituted an almost constant proportion of the deaths in any single year group, although by 1972, death in people under 40 y was a rare event. People aged 70–80 y constituted a large proportion of the undertaker's business in 1972 and also in 1850, but the oldest recorded age is similar in all three groups. In other words, the main reason why the *mean* longevity of humans has increased over the last 10 000 y is that fewer people now die prematurely. The *maximum* recorded lifespan has hardly changed at all.

Data similar to the 1972 sample, but this time including infants, are plotted in two different ways in Figure 4.6. Survivorship (*L*) is the number of any organism (in this case people) alive at the beginning of each time interval; clearly all of them were alive at the beginning of the period, and none of them at

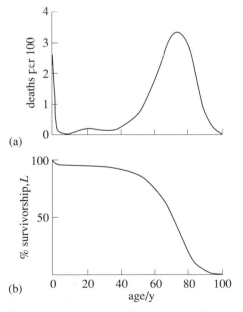

Figure 4.6   Two ways of plotting data for the deaths of male humans in England during 1960–2. (a) The distribution of ages at death (similar to Figure 4.5). (b) Survivorship curve: the proportion of individuals alive at the start of each year.

the end. The graph shows that the rate of loss from the population is much greater after the age of 50 y. Plotted in this form, the data for humans can be compared to those obtained from other animals. Figures 4.7 and 4.8 show data plotted in the same way as Figure 4.6b, for male *Drosophila* raised in milk bottles in the laboratory and for Dall mountain sheep in northwestern Canada and Alaska, respectively. The time-scales are clearly different but the curves are strikingly similar in shape, in spite of the fact that predation by wolves was the most frequently recorded immediate cause of death in sheep, and strokes, heart attacks and cancer the main causes of death in humans. The immediate causes of death in the flies were not determined, but clearly they were unlikely to have been either wolves or heart attacks.

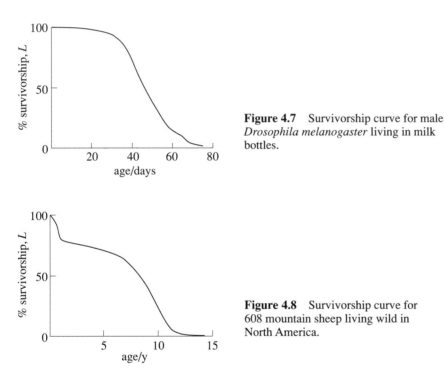

Figure 4.7   Survivorship curve for male *Drosophila melanogaster* living in milk bottles.

Figure 4.8   Survivorship curve for 608 mountain sheep living wild in North America.

The data in these Figures illustrate an important and, as yet unexplained, phenomenon in the study of senescence: most species have a well-defined maximum lifespan in the 'wild' as well as under 'laboratory' conditions, about 7 weeks in *Drosophila* and over 100 years in humans. Beginning at about half the maximum age, mortality starts to increase, in spite of the fact that the agents of death (wolves, etc.), are present throughout life. Such populations show a marked senescent phase.

However, in other wild populations, particularly those of many fishes, small mammals and small birds, the probability of dying from accident or predation is almost independent of age and senescence plays a minor role in determining the age at which most deaths occur. In such populations, the relationship between the number of survivors and age is a negative exponential. The data shown in Figure 4.9 were obtained from lapwings ringed as nestlings in Britain; their age when found dead was recorded. The numbers in the marked population simply declined with time and there is little suggestion in these data that the probability of dying changes with age. One could conclude from such a study that

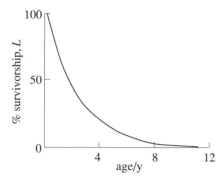

Figure 4.9 Survivorship curve for 460 lapwings living wild in England.

senescence does not occur in lapwings. However, in captivity, these birds live up to 10 years and elderly specimens show typical old-age degeneration before they die. In this case, senescence seems to be a 'laboratory phenomenon': a condition easily produced under artificial conditions, but having little to do with the natural composition of wild populations.

There are sufficient data on longevity in both wild and captive specimens for only very few species, but such comparisons indicate that, in general, animals live longer in the less strenuous conditions that captivity provides. For example, in a study of 316 wild polar bears in the Canadian Arctic, only 30 (9.5%) were aged by tooth rings as more than 20 years old, only 6 (2%) were aged 25–27 and none was estimated to be over 27 years. In zoos, nearly all bears that reach adulthood live to be 25, and at least one has reached the age of 33 y, a lifespan nearly 25% longer than the maximum observed in the wild sample. It is impossible to say that bears never reach this age in the wild, but in view of the large sample size studied, such longevity must be very rare.

Whether or not senescence plays a significant role in determining the age at which members of a natural population die, one of the few absolutely consistent features of the process is that it is progressive, and often begins long before most deaths occur. It is therefore possible to study the process of senescence without worrying about the details of what was the immediate cause of death in each animal. A first step towards an explanation for senescence is to look for correlations between anatomical features and events early in the animal's life and its longevity (Section 4.4).

Summary of Section 4.3

Senescence is a progressive decline in the functional efficiencies of an organism which makes it more vulnerable to external agents, such as disease or predators, which can bring about death. Senescence occurs in almost all plants and animals and affects most, if not all, tissues and physiological systems. In humans, senescence can be detected long before the probability of adults dying increases substantially, and is particularly evident in the skin and sense organs. Many physiological processes decline to two-thirds or less of their peak values before most deaths occur. Populations in which senescence is a major factor in determining the age of death have sigmoidal survivorship curves: mortality is low among young adults and a high proportion of the population die at about the same age. In some wild populations, the probability of death is not related to age: senescence can be observed in such populations if they are artificially protected from the 'agents of death' which normally kill them.

4.4 The determinants of longevity

Table 4.1 shows some data on the maximum recorded lifespan of various animals, most of them captive specimens. Among the first workers to collect such data was Major S. S. Flower who, on his retirement from the British Army early in the 1920s, organized the Cairo Zoo in Egypt. Major Flower went to very considerable lengths to ensure that the figures he quoted were authentic because, as he himself pointed out, it is very tempting to substitute a younger animal for an old and sick specimen in a zoo exhibit, and the longevity of 'celebrity' animals is easily exaggerated. In Table 4.1 the organisms within each taxonomic group are arranged according to adult body mass; you can see that, although in general, larger animals live longer than small ones, there are many glaring exceptions. Freshwater mussels, wasps, tortoises, newts, eels, bats, echidnas, owls, parrot-like birds (cockatoos, macaws, etc.) and humans seem to live an exceptionally long time for their size. Ignoring these exceptions, there have been two main types of theory put forward to account for these data.

The first kind of theory proposes that longevity is somehow related to the rate of living: faster 'rate of living' promotes a shorter lifespan, but a less energetically demanding life-style permits greater longevity. Two aspects of 'rate of living' have been considered: growth rate and metabolic rate during juvenile and adult life. Lower metabolic rate helps to explain why many poikilothermic fishes, amphibians and reptiles live longer than homeothermic mammals of similar body size. Many insectivorous bats, which undergo diurnal and annual cycles of torpor, live much longer than similar-sized non-hibernating mammals, and the proverbially unhurried tortoises often live much longer than the more active snakes and lizards.

■   Which data in Table 4.1 clearly cannot be explained in terms of an inverse relationship between metabolic rate and age?

The difference between birds and mammals. Birds such as owls and parrots with body masses around 1 kg live much longer than mammals of similar size, in spite of the fact that all are homeothermic as adults and birds' body temperature is as high or higher than that of mammals. Nor do strenuous activities such as prolonged flight impair longevity; the maximum longevity of flightless ostriches is substantially less than that of most other smaller flying birds. Furthermore, although most elderly mammals can be identified as such by paler fur or hair and less robust muscles, old birds are almost indistinguishable from young adults, to our eyes at least: for example, on a good diet, the appearance and behaviour of grey parrots hardly changes over several decades.

The other kind of theory to account for species differences in maximum longevity places emphasis on the organism's ability to renew tissues during its lifetime. *Caenorhabditis* (Section 2.1.1) grows in a determinate way and hence has little, if any, capacity for renewal of worn or defective components. Its lifespan is indeed very short: at 20 °C, *Caenorhabditis* takes about 3.5 days to grow from a zygote to sexual maturity and has a maximum total lifespan of about 14 days. However, other species of nematodes whose development and growth processes are apparently very similar to those of *Caenorhabditis* live very much longer at the same temperature.

Table 4.1   Some longevity records for animals of various sizes. These figures are examples only and are not intended to be comprehensive or exhaustive. All ages are in years. + indicates that the figure quoted is the period for which a specimen has been observed to live. Actual maximum longevities may be greater.

Average adult body mass/kg	Invertebrates		Fishes and amphibians		Reptiles		Birds		Mammals	
less than 0.1	freshwater mussel	80	guppy	6	sand lizard	8+	chaffinch	29	house mouse	3
	earthworm	6	stickleback	5	spotted gekko	9+	humming-bird	8	wood mouse	6
	wasp (queen)	19	common newt	25	spiny lizard	9+	robin	11	bat (*Myotis*)	20
	flour beetle	1.5	tree frog	16			goldfinch	16	shrew	1
0.1–1.0	termite (queen)	25	goldfish	30+	stinkpot turtle	52	herring gull	36	hedgehog	4
	crayfish	25	salamander	24	slow worm	33	pigeon	30	brown rat	4.5
	limpet	15	common frog	12	box tortoise	118+	grey parrot	49+	guinea-pig	7.5
	sea anemone	90	clawed toad	15	glass lizard	11.5	starling	18	fruit bat	22
1.0–10	squid	4	herring	25	Greek tortoise	105	golden eagle	46	rabbit	13
	lobster	50	eel	55	pond tortoise	120	cockatoo	56	fox	15
	ormer shell	13	trout	18	gila monster	20	Canada goose	33	cat	31
	tapeworm	35	bream	15	tuatara	28+	macaw	43	echidna	49
10–100	coral (colony)	100	cod	20	anaconda	29	eagle owl	68	human	120
			pike	14	rainbow boa	27	condor	52	baboon	30
			giant salamander	52+	Chinese alligator	52+	ostrich	27	goat	18
			sting ray	21	Marion tortoise	152+	domestic goose	35	otter	14.5
over 100			halibut	60+	Galapagos tortoise	100+			elephant	70
			sturgeon	82	loggerhead turtle	33			hippopotamus	51
			catfish	60					elephant seal	20
			tuna	15	snapping turtle	58			rhinoceros	49

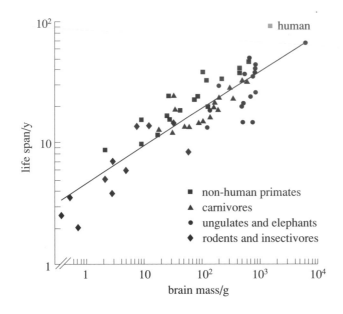

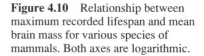

Figure 4.10 Relationship between maximum recorded lifespan and mean brain mass for various species of mammals. Both axes are logarithmic.

The proliferation and growth of neuroblasts (cells that mature to become neurons) occur very early in development in mammals (and in other vertebrates) and are often almost complete shortly after birth. Throughout life, neurons in the brain disintegrate and disappear, but are not replaced because there are no stem cells for neurons. Because the brain seems to be non-renewable and to decline with age, investigators have sought a relationship between its mass and maximum longevity in vertebrates, particularly mammals.

Some data from various mammals are shown in Figure 4.10. You can see that there is a reasonably close fit but, perhaps surprisingly, the maximum lifespan of most primates is longer and that of most rodents shorter, than would be expected from the masses of their brain. Humans, in spite of their relatively enormous brain, still live longer than would be expected from the allometric relationship derived from data from other mammals. Interesting though this association is, it is impossible to manipulate the size of the brain or bring about renewal of other tissues without major trauma, so an experimental approach to the problem is precluded.

4.4.1 Ageing and 'rate of living'

One attractive suggestion for the determinants of an organism's lifespan is to propose that it has a certain 'potential for living', which may be expended at a higher rate for a shorter time or at a lower rate for a longer time, rather like a torch battery. Senescence and death may be compared to the waning and extinction of the current produced by the battery, the 'life' of which may be prolonged by using it less frequently and by drawing current from it at a lower rate. The longevity of poikilothermic organisms living at different temperatures is an obvious means by which to test such theories. Metabolic rate depends partly upon temperature (see Chapter 3) and in small species such as insects and most fishes, the body temperature is the same as that of the environment.

In captivity, populations can be kept free from predators and infectious or nutritional diseases, thus ensuring that senescence and endogenously produced diseases (e.g. some forms of cancer) are the major factors bringing about death.

Table 4.2 Temperature effects on the lifespan of *Cynolebias bellottii*.

Temperature	Number of fish	Lifespan/months (mean ± standard errors)	Maximum lifespan
Continuously at 20 °C	25	14.0 ± 3.9	21
15 °C for 8 months, 20 °C thereafter	54	15.2 ± 4.4	26
Continuously at 15 °C	52	18.9 ± 5.5	32
20 °C for 8 months, 15 °C thereafter	14	23.5 ± 9.1	38

Experiments on *Drosophila* show that flies that spend their post-larval lives at 26 °C die younger than those kept at 20 °C. However, if the flies are transferred to the cooler environment after spending about half their adult lives in the warmer conditions, they have the same lifespan as those which had been at 20 °C all the time. These experiments suggest that the factors that determine the course of senescence are established during the second half of the adult lifespan.

More thorough experiments (Table 4.2) on the small teleost fish *Cynolebias bellottii* confirm this conclusion. The fish that lived longest were warm for the early part of their lives and later transferred to cooler conditions. Those which were kept cool for the first 8 months of their lives did not live significantly longer than those which had been kept warm throughout their lives. All four groups of fishes grew equally fast and were equally active at the different temperatures.

■   Why is it important to check on growth rate and activity levels in this experiment?

Because the experiment is aimed at exposing the effect of temperature on natural longevity: if the fish were 'ill' and ate less, grew more slowly or were sluggish, it would not be surprising that they also died sooner.

These experiments seem to suggest that whatever determines longevity acts only in the second half of the lifespan: the experiences of youth have little impact on the length of life. However, other kinds of experiments point to the opposite conclusion: conditions during the animal's youth, particularly its diet, are a major factor in its longevity.

4.4.2 Nutrition and longevity

Better nutrition promotes faster growth and, to a modest extent, hastens sexual maturity (Section 1.2). Does better nutrition also prolong life? Do animals live longer when free to choose how much they eat? Both propositions seem intuitively reasonable, but the experimental data in Figure 4.11 (*overleaf*) suggest otherwise. In both hamsters and mice, those that ate as much as they liked all their lives had the shortest lifespans. Next shortest lifespans were observed in those receiving only half the full diet from weaning onwards. Those that lived the longest, almost 50% longer than the unrestricted animals, ate less when young and as much as they liked when older. Similar experiments on rats and other species have also shown that individuals whose youth was similar to that of Oliver Twist consistently outlived those that had enjoyed a life of gluttony from the start.

■   Can you suggest any problems in interpreting this experiment in relation to wild populations of mice and hamsters?

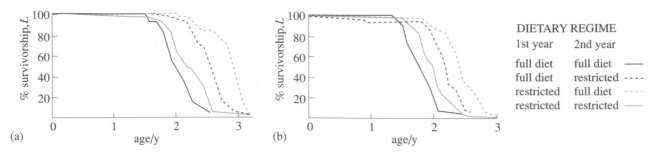

Figure 4.11   Survivorship curves for (a) non-hibernating golden hamsters and (b) laboratory mice, fed on four different dietary regimes over a period of 2 y while living in captivity, where they were free from all predators and most pathogens.

Without information about the diet, growth rate and longevity of wild populations, you cannot decide which group is receiving a diet most similar to that which the species is adapted to eat in the wild. If the wild population normally eats, and hence is adapted to deal with, a sparse diet from weaning to maturity, then the animals on the continuously restricted diet are the 'controls' in the sense of experiencing the conditions to which they are most completely adapted. The unrestricted animals may be the ones receiving the 'unnatural' treatment and, hence, not surprisingly, live for the shortest time.

These experiments suggest that dietary restriction during the growing phase and during young adulthood prolongs life. Further experiments in which rats were so severely undernourished that the onset of sexual maturity was delayed by two years confirm the suggestion that the onset of senescence is related to the age of sexual maturity. These 'Peter Pan' animals also had long total lifespans, suggesting that the processes which eventually lead to senescence are not started until adulthood.

However, the conclusion that there is a causal relationship between total lifespan and the fraction of it taken up by juvenile growth is not confirmed by experiments in which growth is accelerated. Rats that are made to grow faster and for longer by administration of hormones such as GH early in their lives (Section 1.4) become larger but live for the same length of time as untreated controls. The relationship between absolute age and senescence is unchanged by this experiment, in spite of the fact that a greater proportion of the lifespan was spent growing and a smaller proportion as a mature adult.

4.4.3 Reproduction and longevity

This section is about the role in longevity of the activity to which most of the middle period of an animal's life is devoted: sexual reproduction. In mice and humans, females that have never reproduced live slightly longer than those that have borne and raised offspring. It could be suggested that the shorter lifespan is due to the extra physiological stress incurred by females during pregnancy and lactation. However, in most species that have been thoroughly studied, the males have shorter lives than both reproductive and non-reproductive females. The generalization is true even for people in underdeveloped countries where the women have numerous children and perform strenuous physical work throughout their lives. Although signs of senescence such as menopause and atrophy of the skeleton (Section 7.3.4) appear earlier in women, men die at a younger age. In Britain at present, more than three-quarters of those aged 100 years or more are women, and, although the number of centenarians is increasing rapidly, the proportion of men among them is not.

As the data in Figure 4.12 show, the sex difference in longevity in houseflies is even more impressive. So a paradox emerges: the 'weaker sex', which contributes the most physiological effort to reproduction, has a longer lifespan than males which, in humans at least (Section 1.1 and Figures 1.1–1.3), grow for longer and are larger as adults.

It has been suggested that the exertion of courtship, male–male combat and territory defence may be the main reason why males have shorter lifespans. This theory may account for the short lives of strongly territorial species such as deer and sea-lions, but experiments in which the longevity of unmated male rats was compared with the longevity of those co-habiting with a female showed that the latter outlived the former by about 6 months. These data seem to suggest that the exertions of courtship and mating prolong the life of male rats; but it would be equally consistent with the facts to say that the inactivity of bachelorhood shortened the lifespan. The eminent gerontologist, Professor Alex Comfort, is fond of pointing out that the continuation of sexual activity into old age is strongly correlated with both vitality and longevity in humans of both sexes.

Taken together, these experiments suggest that there is an intrinsic difference in the potential longevity of males and females of the same species, and that, at least in males, the exertions of mating, reproduction and rearing the young do little to hasten the onset of senescence. On the contrary, the fulfilment of all normal life functions seems to promote longevity. However, only 'natural' physiological stresses, such as courtship and mating, have been discussed. The role of physiological stresses to which the species has *not* been exposed during its evolutionary history in promoting premature ageing is a different matter entirely.

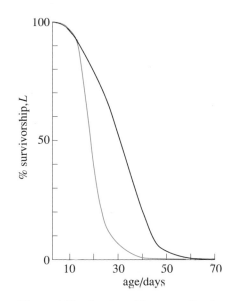

Figure 4.12   Survivorship curve of male (blue) and female (black) houseflies in captivity.

Summary of Section 4.4

The maximum and average longevity of different species is extremely variable and it is difficult to establish the cause of the variation either by correlations between longevity and anatomical characters such as brain mass, or by experimental manipulation of physiological variables such as growth rate, body temperature and diet. Some experiments suggest that events early in life are major determinants of longevity, others point to the opposite conclusion. Males of a wide range of species have shorter lives than females of the same species, even though the physiological strain of reproduction is greater for females.

4.5 Cellular mechanisms of ageing

It is clear from Section 4.4 that, in spite of its universal occurrence, senescence is remarkably difficult to identify with a single system or process in the whole organism. Little is revealed about the basic mechanism(s) of senescence from the study of factors that affect all body processes, such as growth rate, metabolic rate or reproductive or nutritional status. Attention has therefore turned to the course and mechanisms of senescence in particular kinds of cells, both *in vivo* and *in vitro*.

In Sections 2.1.1, 2.4 and 2.5, it was pointed out that some types of cells, notably those in the brain, muscle and adipose tissue, endure for most of the animal's lifetime, while others are continuously replaced. The possibility that long-established cells degrade or that the capacity for cell replacement wanes seem to be promising lines of investigation. A third line of inquiry is suggested by the early onset and, in mammals, almost universal occurrence, of age-related changes in the skin, joints, structural components of the eyes and teeth. All these tissues have a very high proportion of collagen, so changes in the abundance and chemical organization of this molecule have long been a focus of study. Finally, anxiety about radiation and the observation that some features of senescence can be stimulated by radiation-induced DNA damage have focused attention on damage to the genetic material as a cause of ageing.

4.5.1 Cell division, replacement and longevity

It was pointed out in Chapter 2 that one of the ways in which large, long-lived organisms sustained their normal structure in the face of disease, injury and the vagaries of food supply was by cell replacement 'as required', within a framework of determinate growth. Some organs in which the tissue mass was constantly 'under review' were discussed in Sections 2.2, 2.3.1 and 2.4.1. In many such tissues, there is constant turnover of cells and molecular components even without damage or functional overload. Under constant conditions, the rate of production of new cells is finely balanced to the rate of elimination of the old cells.

The cells lining the small intestine are convenient for study because their lifespan lasts only a few hours, even in large mammals. Division of the stem cells takes place in the 'crypts' of the villi, and mature cells move to the surface of the villi, where they become functional and die, eroded by the gut contents as they pass by (Section 2.1.1). These cells are easily labelled by injecting mice with radioactive thymidine which is incorporated into newly synthesized DNA. In such experiments, the mice were killed at various times after the injection and the tissue examined for mitotically dividing cells. Autoradiography was used to follow the careers of cells that were formed while the labelled DNA precursors were available. Such experiments show that the lifespan of the duodenal crypt cells is variable, but it increases from an average of 10.3 h in mice aged 55 days (young adult) to 15.6 h in mice aged 3 years, a very great age for a mouse (Table 4.1).

■ Does cell division slow with age in any other mammalian tissues?

Yes. The maximum incorporation of DNA precursors is both reduced and delayed in older rats compared to weanlings (Figure 2.2, Section 2.2.1), implying that cell division is taking place more slowly, and that fewer cells divide in the course of regeneration. Although the regeneration of tissue mass following removal of kidneys is about the same in rats (and humans) of all ages, the formation of additional cells predominates in younger specimens, whereas in older animals enlargement of existing cells is the chief means by which the tissue grows. No differences in kidney function have been detected; growth mainly by cell enlargement generated organs that worked as well as those that contained more cells. However, these experiments suggest that the cells' capacity for division wanes sooner and to a greater extent than their ability to enlarge or their normal metabolism.

Observations on serial transplants of tissues into progressively younger hosts and on cells in tissue culture point to similar conclusions. Some normal skin cells have been induced to outlive their original (mouse) donor by several years by transplanting them into younger hosts.

Many different kinds of cells can now be maintained in culture for weeks or months if fresh culture medium is provided and the new generations of cells are removed to prevent overcrowding. With few exceptions, however, frequent cell division seems to be essential for a vigorous colony, and all cell lines die out eventually. At first it was thought that death was the accidental result of contamination or improper handling, but careful analysis of laboratory records showed that almost all lineages of human origin died out after 40–60 divisions.

■   Assuming that every cell grows satisfactorily and none dies, what is the mass of a culture descended from a single cell, after the 50th generation of cell division? Assume that each cell weighs 10^{-7} g and there is unlimited space and nutrients.

112 600 kg, about the mass of 100 elephants. On the 50th generation, there will be $2^{50} = 1.126 \times 10^{15}$ cells, or 1.126×10^5 kg of cellular material. Clearly, any one cell lineage has the potential to produce more than enough cells to last the lifetime of its owner and it is unlikely that death comes about solely because the supply of new cells is insufficient.

Although the average time between divisions differs greatly with the kind of tissue used, it almost always becomes longer and longer as the cell culture approaches the point at which division fails completely. This information has been taken to indicate that senescence is a cellular process, which takes place whether cells are in contact with other cells inside the animal or not. Since these original observations in the 1950s and 1960s, the addition of various vitamins and hormones, even of other kinds of cells, has been shown to extend slightly the lifespan of some normal cells in culture. But the only kinds of cells definitely known to divide and grow with undiminished vigour over many years are those derived originally from cancerous tumours.

Do cells from species with very different longevities, or cells from older or younger members of a population of known longevity, differ in their ability to divide further when cultured? Table 4.3 shows some data on cultured fibroblasts taken from adults of various vertebrates of widely different longevities.

■   How do these data compare with those for the longevity of the animals from which the cells are derived (see also Table 4.1, Section 4.4)?

In general, longer-lived animals are found to be composed of cells which themselves survive longer in culture. But the differences are slight and not sufficient to explain the longevities of the whole organisms: human cells live for only three times as many generations as mouse cells, although people live 30 times as long as mice.

Table 4.3   The number of divisions that lineages of normal fibroblasts derived from various vertebrates can support in tissue culture.

Species	Generations of cell division	Maximum lifespan/y
Galapagos tortoise	90–125	100+
Human	40–60	120
Mink	30–34	10
Chicken	15–35	30
Mouse	14–28	3

Figure 4.13 shows a weak inverse correlation between number of cell generations in culture and the age of the person from whom the skin fibroblasts were derived initially. The vertical bars show the range of observations in each age group; although the mean rate of division declines slightly with age, as with many aspects of ageing, there is very wide variation between individuals. Although the decline and eventual demise of cell lines in culture show several parallels with senescence in whole organisms, there is no direct evidence that the timing and course of ageing in organisms is a simple consequence of ageing in any particular cell or tissue so far identified.

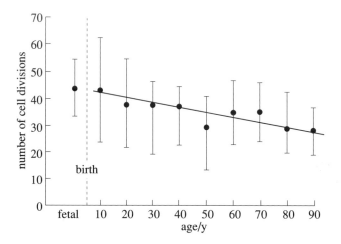

Figure 4.13   The number of divisions in culture before the cell line dies out for skin cells from human donors of various ages. The mean and the range of all observations for each age group is shown.

Many cells, including neurons and many skeletal and blood cells, never divide *in vivo* once they become functionally mature. Most such cells are inaccessible or live for many years so it is impractical to study their longevity *in vivo*, but the lifespan of erythrocytes (red blood cells) is conveniently short and relatively easy to follow. In humans, each erythrocyte circulates for about 120 days before being broken down and many of its constituents, particularly the iron in its haemoglobin, are reused for the formation of new cells. Data from human blood transfusions show that the age of the stem cell population from which the new erythrocytes arise has no bearing on their longevity: even when the difference in age of the blood donor and that of the recipient is very large, the erythrocytes last for the same time.

■   Why should the lifespan of human erythrocytes be so short?

Although they are not subjected to as much wear as epidermal or intestinal cells, all mammalian erythrocytes lack a nucleus and the machinery of protein synthesis, so defective enzymes and other proteins cannot be replaced. There is, however, little evidence that this lack of protein turnover (Section 2.1.2) impairs function: careful measurements of the oxygen-binding capacity of marked populations of erythrocytes show that their capacity to deliver oxygen to tissues does not decline significantly as they approach the end of their lifespan.

■   Do these observations show that senescence does not occur in erythrocytes?

No. A more likely hypothesis is that the phagocytes in the liver, spleen and bone marrow that destroy the erythrocytes respond to very early signs of senescence, and break them down before any impairment in their efficiency as oxygen carriers can be detected by laboratory measurements.

■   How would such a property *benefit* the organism as a whole?

Prompt destruction and replacement of erythrocytes reduce the risk of damage from anoxia to other important tissues (e.g. the brain and the kidneys). In general, the health of the body as a whole is maximized by ruthless extermination and replacement of all slightly abnormal or substandard cells.

■   If the time for which a mature cell remains in peak condition does not change with the age of the organism, but the rate at which new or replacement cells form does decline with age, what can you conclude about the composition of the body of old or young animals?

Older animals must contain a higher proportion of worn-out cells which are ripe for replacement. Either such old animals must be retaining replaceable cells beyond their normal functional lifespan, or the total tissue mass slowly declines as cells and cell components are replaced more slowly than they disappear.

In fact, both processes happen. All mammals that have been studied lose weight in extreme old age; the mass of the muscles and abdominal organs, in particular, declines extensively as replacement of cell components and whole cells fails to keep pace with tissue breakdown. At the same time, the retention 'in office' of cells which, in a younger organism, would have been replaced by others, may be behind the slow but relentless decline in almost all physiological functions noted in Section 4.3.2 (Figure 4.4).

Put together, these observations suggest that mitosis may be among the first functions to slow down. The transplantation experiments and tissue culture data suggest that the decline in capacity to divide is an inherent property of the cell line, and that it can be slightly delayed, but not halted by changing the environment. Perhaps animals 'economize' on cells as they approach the end of their lifespan because the cells can only divide a limited number of times. However, observations on regenerated organs indicate that these age-related changes do not significantly impair function, at least in their initial stages, i.e. they do not contribute to senescence.

Comparison between the age of organisms and the age of the cells of which they are composed produces a paradox: in tissues that depend upon cell turnover, there is more cell death and the average lifespan of the cells may be shorter in younger animals because, with advancing age, slightly defective cells remain functional for longer before being replaced.

4.5.2 Ageing in the extracellular matrix

It is clear from the previous section that the ageing of organisms cannot be completely explained by the behaviour of cells themselves, so attention is turned to the extracellular matrix.

■   Why would extracellular structural proteins such as collagen be a better material in which to look for signs of ageing than enzymes?

Because such proteins turn over much more slowly (Section 2.1.2). Most intracellular proteins do not 'live' long enough to acquire detectable signs of ageing.

In vertebrates, collagen (Section 7.2) is the major extracellular component of connective and skeletal tissues such as the skin, bones, joints, tendons, arteries and many other tissues in which senescence is pronounced and begins quite early in life. It occurs in smaller quantities in many other tissues and is the major determinant of their mechanical properties (Sections 3.2.4, 5.3.1 and 7.1).

The collagen content of muscles increases steadily with age in rats, humans and, as those who eat meat know well, in sheep and cattle. It is not known how this change affects muscle performance. Such changes, known as fibrosis, occur in many other tissues, particularly at the sites of infection, inflammation and wounds. One of its commonest and most debilitating manifestations is fibrosis of the lungs which is often exacerbated by prolonged exposure to toxins such as tobacco smoke. The soft, permeable tissues of the lung alveoli are gradually replaced by tough, inextensible collagen which prevents normal inflation and deflation of the lungs, and through which, not surprisingly, gases cannot pass.

For collagen-rich tissues, e.g. tendons, the lens of the eye, skin, etc., the *quantity* of structural protein does not change very much but, beginning at an early age, the polypeptide subunits of which the proteins are composed become more extensively cross-linked. This process, which alters the molecule's tertiary structure and makes it less flexible, may be due to the formation of additional strong bonds between amino acids and/or to **non-enzymic glycosylation**, the incorporation of sugar molecules, such as glucose, into fully-formed proteins. As the name implies, such bonds form spontaneously, without the help of enzymes or metabolic energy.

■   How is this process relevant to interpreting the effects of nutrition on longevity (Section 4.4.2)?

Underfeeding keeps the blood glucose level continuously low, which would reduce opportunities for proteins to be damaged by glycosylation, thereby delaying ageing. The process, which affects all proteins, is hastened by chronic hyperglycaemia and is thus worse in poorly controlled diabetics and very obese people.

Cross-linking makes the connective tissues of older animals less extensible, less elastic and less easily digested by protease enzymes than those of younger individuals. The increased cross-linking within collagen macromolecules is believed to underlie such familiar changes as the formation of lines and wrinkles in the skin, reduced capacity for deformation, and hence for optical accommodation by the lens of the eye, and reduced compliance of joints and tendons. The complex tertiary structure of many non-living macromolecular materials (e.g. rubber, polyurethane foam) also gradually changes with time. It is not clear, however, why cross-linking in collagen molecules should have progressed as far in a mouse after about 30 months, as in a human after about 70 years.

■   What is the most usual non-biological factor that controls the rate of chemical reactions?

Temperature; but since most mammals, including rats and humans, have the same body temperature, such a huge difference in the rate of the reaction cannot be a temperature effect. Progressive cross-linking cannot be due simply to the physical chemistry of the collagen itself; the process must be under active physiological control.

Further evidence that the process is regulated by biological, rather than physical, factors comes from the studies on 'Peter Pan' rats, mentioned in Section 4.4.2. Underfeeding severely retarded growth and delayed sexual maturity, and these rats retained collagen of youthful chemical organization well beyond the age at which cross-linking is extensive in well-fed rats. Because changes in collagen parallel so closely changes in longevity, it is often used as an index of senescence, but the fact that changes in collagen proceed at such very different rates in animals of naturally different longevities strongly suggests that they are following a genetic programme.

4.5.3 Subcellular processes of ageing

The data presented in Section 4.5.1 point firmly to the conclusion that cell division is one of the first processes to decline as senescence proceeds. Damage to chromosomes and genes often prevents successful cell division, even if the somatic functions of the cell are unimpaired, so the genetic material and its chromosomal organization has long seemed promising as the key to senescence in cells and tissues.

Many, although by no means all, of the alterations to genes and chromosomes take place during chromosome replication before mitosis. Alterations to the DNA in the genes involving substitution of one nucleotide base by another, or the rearrangement of groups of nucleotides, are called mutations. All other kinds of alterations to DNA are referred to as DNA damage, and include modifications of the chemical structure of the nucleotides themselves, their double helix arrangement or their relationship to the protein components of the chromosomes. Many kinds of DNA damage can be repaired by enzymes, the activity of which can be studied *in vitro*. Figure 4.14 shows that there is a good correlation between the normal lifespan of a species and the capacity of its DNA to repair itself.

■ What information in Figure 4.14 indicates that DNA repair capacity is related to potential lifespan (see Table 4.1), not to the number of times that cells divide during growth?

The repair of DNA is more extensive in hamsters than in rats, and in humans than in elephants, although rats are three to five times the size of hamsters (and so have about three to five times as many cells) and elephants are more than ten times the size of humans.

Even quite high rates of DNA damage may continue without DNA repair for quite a long time before there is a detectable impact on the viability of the cell. The commonest kinds of damage to DNA are the conversion of the nucleotide cytosine into uracil (which is not transcribed) and the removal by hydrolysis of the purine or pyrimidine portions of the nucleotides from the sugar–phosphate 'backbone'. The hydrolysis of purines (adenine and guanine) proceeds faster at normal temperatures than the hydrolysis of pyrimidines (thymine and cytosine). Normal mammalian cells at 37 °C lose about 500 purines and about 25 pyrimidine bases each hour. At this rate, about 3×10^8 bases would be lost in 75 years, the equivalent of about 3% of the total number of bases in the DNA complement of a long-lived cell such as a human brain cell. In normal animals, the repair enzymes reform the bond between the base and the other components of the nucleotide but, as you can see from the above calculation, even if repair

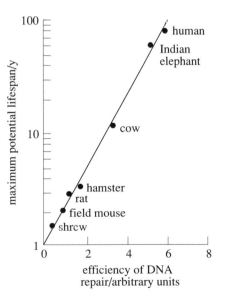

Figure 4.14   The efficiency of DNA repair in mammals of different maximum longevity. Note that the *y*-axis is on a logarithmic scale.

did not take place, only a small fraction of the DNA would be unserviceable after a long period of time. Thus DNA repair mechanisms maintain the integrity of the genes in long-lived, non-dividing cells. But mutations in dividing cells, whether in somatic cells (somatic mutations) or germline cells, can be successfully transmitted to daughter cells, and can thus give rise to whole clones with altered genotype.

■ In which kinds of somatic tissue would you expect DNA damage or DNA mutations to be most important?

DNA damage is likely to affect tissues such as liver, muscle, adipose tissue and brain cells that rarely, if ever, divide in the adult mammal. DNA mutation is more likely to be important in tissues in which there is cell division throughout life, such as skin, gut lining and some glands.

It has long been known that the rate of mutation of genes can be increased by exposing germ cells to various forms of ionizing radiation, high temperatures or a wide variety of chemicals. Exposure to these agents during meiosis is particularly effective in promoting mutation, but many cells so treated fail to complete division because of extensive damage to their chromosomes. It was suggested that similar agents underlie the normal process of ageing and account for the decline in frequency of successful cell division, because somatic mutations and other forms of damage to chromosomes would accumulate, and impair both gene function and cell division. It was indeed found that some experimental animals subjected to high doses of radiation died young. Such experiments gave rise to the notion that ageing in wild populations (including humans) was due mainly to an accumulation of somatic mutations arising from prolonged exposure to the low level of radiation that occurs naturally (from cosmic rays and radioactive rocks).

An obvious test of this theory is to look for moderate curtailment of the lifespan as a result of moderately increased levels of background radiation. Such an experiment is shown in Figure 4.15. You can see that the irradiated flies actually lived longer than the controls, possibly because the radiation helped to break down potentially poisonous metabolic products and/or pathogens. Similar results have also been obtained from laboratory rodents. These experiments strongly indicate that although high levels of radiation are harmful in a variety of ways, these effects, and most forms of somatic mutation, have little to do with the natural process of senescence.

Low levels of radiation, whether naturally occurring or artificially produced, cannot be blamed for ageing and death. The scientific evidence indicates that almost all the DNA damage that is relevant to normal ageing occurs and is repaired as a result of endogenous mechanisms. There is also no direct evidence that the slowing down and eventual failure of cell division, which almost invariably accompanies cellular ageing, can be attributed to the accumulation of unrepaired defects in the genetic material. It is more likely that a change in the factor(s) that prompt cells to begin division is the main cause of the lengthening of the interval between successive divisions.

The genetic material has for a long time been the focus of studies of ageing and cell damage, but recent research has demonstrated a role of cytoplasmic and general metabolic processes in ageing. A major cause of damage to proteins (Section 2.1.2) is their oxidation by free radicals, which are formed as by-

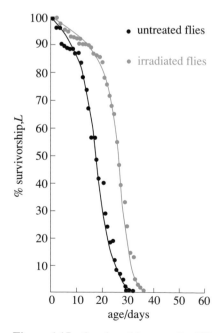

Figure 4.15   Survivorship curve for 119 untreated and 248 irradiated *Drosophila* reared at 25 °C.

products of various biochemical pathways. Several enzymes, of which the best known is **SOD (superoxide dismutase)**, catalyse the breakdown of superoxide radicals to oxygen and hydrogen peroxide, thereby protecting the cell fabric from such damage. Protection from superoxide radicals seems to be more efficient in longer-lived animals, and the lifespan of laboratory *Drosophila* can be extended by up to 10% by using genetic engineering techniques to increase their natural quota of SOD genes. Such extension is modest, and nowhere near sufficient to explain the enormous differences in longevity between species (Table 4.1). *Drosophila* also live longer if provided with genes that increase protein synthesis or lipid stores, or improve their protection from desiccation. It is not difficult to see how any of these 'improvements' to metabolism could result in a slightly longer lifespan.

Summary of Section 4.5

In tissues in which cell turnover is a part of their normal function, the rate of replacement slows as the whole organism becomes older. Serial transplantation of tissues into young animals and observations on cells in culture show that the progressive decline in capacity for division is an inherent property of the cell lineage. However, at least in the case of red blood cells, the longevity of a mature cell is unaffected by the age of the animal from which it comes or the age of its host. Both in culture and in intact organisms, tumour cells can continue dividing with undiminished vigour. Many tissues that contain only small quantities of collagen in young animals tend to accumulate the protein with age. In tissues rich in collagen, the protein becomes more extensively cross-linked in older animals; both these changes are clear indicators of the progress of senescence of the whole organism. Since fibrosis proceeds about thirty times faster in a mouse than in a human at the same temperature, it is unlikely to be a simple consequence of the gradual breaking down of the tertiary structure of the proteins. The genetic material in the nucleus is damaged by numerous naturally occurring agents, but most forms of damage can be repaired enzymically. DNA repair is more extensive in organisms that have longer life expectancies. Although somatic mutations can accumulate in long-lived organisms, attempts to accelerate senescence by experimentally increasing the dose of mutagens have yielded contradictory results. There is no direct evidence that the decline in cell division with age can be attributed to unrepaired damage to DNA. Proteins are damaged by glycosylation and by oxidation by free radicals. The latter are inactivated by SOD, which thus protects important proteins, but the lifespan of *Drosophila* is only slightly extended by artificially increasing the availability of SOD.

4.6 Death

After such a prolonged discussion of the changes in cells and in whole organisms that accompany advancing age, you are probably hoping for an explanation of what happens when organisms die. The short answer is that there is almost certainly no single mechanism of death, either at the cellular level or at the organism level. Although our understanding of the subject is advancing rapidly, some deaths are almost as difficult for us to explain in scientific terms as they seemed to our ancestors, who postulated witch's curses and other supernatural agents to account for instances, by no means rare even now, in which apparently healthy young adults suddenly died.

Perhaps partly as a result of 20th-century attitudes to death (which have been compared to 19th-century taboos about sex) people tend to think of it as a chaotic process, lacking the structural order and homeostatic regulation which are the hallmarks of 'proper' biological processes. Recent research shows that this view is often incorrect, particularly in the case of the death of cells: dying can be an orderly, genetically determined, functionally useful process.

4.6.1 Cell death

Cells die in two ways that differ fundamentally in both the cause and the course of dying. **Necrosis** is death by starvation, poisoning, injury or invasion by foreign bacteria or viruses, and thus might be compared to murder; in **apoptosis** or programmed cell death, apparently healthy cells in a normal environment die without obvious external cause, i.e. they 'commit suicide'.

Necrotic cells are easily recognized: within 30 min of injury or acute poisoning (e.g. inhibition of ATP formation), necrotic cells swell, blebs form on the surface and cellular proteins become disordered. Such cells are completely dead within 2–3 h. The immediate cause seems to be collapse of cytoskeleton and its detachment from cell membrane but lack of oxygen, acidification of the cell contents (due to formation of lactic acid) and accumulation of calcium and sodium ions (through failure of ATP-dependent ion pumps) also contribute. Dying cells often burst, spilling their contents into the extracellular space. The debris is cleared up by phagocytic cells of the immune system: their assembly from the blood capillaries and elsewhere in the tissue produces inflammation. For a few days, the affected area becomes warm, red and swollen.

Death by apoptosis is much less spectacular and usually quicker: indeed, the process is so inconspicuous that until recently it was hardly noticed. Cells dying in this way shrink, sometimes to as little as a quarter of their former volume, numerous large vesicles appear in the cytoplasm and the chromatin (i.e. chromosomal material in interphase of mitosis) condenses around the edges of the nucleus, forming darkly stained bulges (Figure 4.16a). Apoptotic cells break up rather than explode and their remains are quickly phagocytosed by their neighbours, assisted by any macrophages present (macrophages are phagocytes that live permanently in tissues other than the blood). There is no detectable inflammation and the whole process can be completed in less than an hour. The clearing up is so efficient that finding traces of cells that have died by apoptosis in histological sections is nearly as difficult as locating stem cells (Section 2.1.1).

Drugs that inhibit mRNA or protein synthesis suppress apoptosis in some kinds of cells in culture.

■   What can you conclude from this observation about the mechanism of apoptosis?

The process requires the synthesis of new proteins of a type not normally made by non-apoptotic cells. More recently, many examples of cells have been found, among them fibroblasts, certain lineages of neuron-forming cells (Figure 4.16) and cartilage-forming cells, that can be induced to die by apoptosis in the presence of high concentrations of such inhibitors, or even when their nuclei are absent.

■   What can you conclude from this observation about the mechanism of apoptosis?

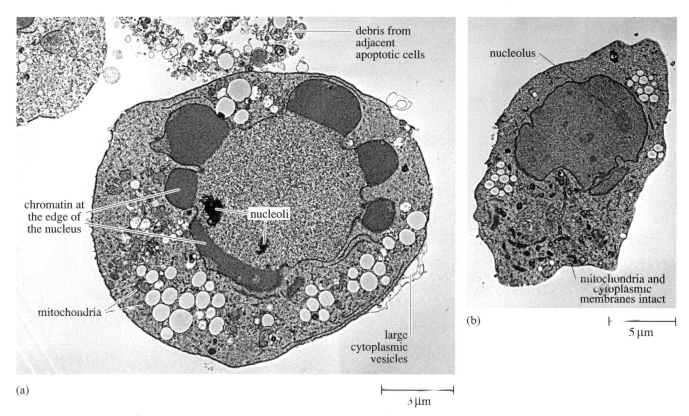

Figure 4.16   Electron micrographs of stem cells for oligodendrites (a kind of neuron) in culture. (a) A cell poisoned for 6 h with staurosporine, which inhibits the protein kinases that transmit messages within the cytoplasm. This cell is dying by apoptosis because it is unable to receive intercellular signals. (b) A similar healthy cell growing in the culture medium. Note differences in scales.

The necessary proteins are synthesized long before apoptosis begins and are stored in the cytoplasm in an inactive form. Studies of fetal development, where up to half of all cells die by apoptosis within hours of being formed, suggest that the necessary biochemical apparatus is produced each time the cell divides.

All cells die unless they continuously receive intercellular signals in the forms of mechanical contact and/or intercellular messenger molecules, growth factors or hormones secreted by other cells of the same tissue. The chemical identity of most such intercellular signals is not yet established, but IGFs (Section 1.4.1 and Chapter 2) are strongly implicated. The need for such signals explains why cells in culture often die if they are too dilute. Cells in such circumstances can be 'rescued' by the addition of medium taken from a higher-density culture of the same type of cells.

Apoptosis is an integral and essential part of growth and tissue maintenance at all stages of the life cycle and occurs extensively even under completely normal conditions. It is in no way comparable to senescence and death of whole organisms. Indeed, apoptosis seems to occur more frequently during fetal and juvenile growth than in adult and elderly animals: of the 1 090 somatic cells (the products of 10–11 generations of cell division) formed during the development of genetically normal *Caenorhabditis* (Sections 2.1.1 and 4.4), at least 131 (12%) die by apoptosis. In developing vertebrates, the proportion may be even higher: certain kinds of neurons in the developing optic rat nerve die at a rate of $10\,000\,day^{-1}$, every day for many weeks, and that rate is certainly not the maximum for a mammalian tissue.

Apoptosis is the fate of all cells that fail to attract contact with neighbours, those lacking receptors for the right chemical signals and those infected with foreign particles such as viruses. Some viruses are known to produce inhibitors of apoptosis.

■   Why would this property make the virus more dangerous?

Viruses can only replicate in living cells. Preventing apoptosis in the cells they have invaded for long enough to replicate is essential to their proliferation. Apoptosis is also triggered in cells in which the DNA is damaged beyond repair (Section 4.5.3). The process is mediated by a protein called *p53*, which attaches directly to chromatin, and modulates the activity of the genes that produce the proteins necessary for apoptosis.

Apoptosis is now seen as essential to all multicellular organisms. As stressed in Chapter 2, cell replacement and renewal are essential in all metazoans, especially large, long-lived animals, to repair wear and injuries, and to eliminate infected or defective cells, even if the organisms or tissues do not grow larger. But too rapid cell division, producing too many undifferentiated cells, is harmful because such cells use oxygen and nutrients but do not contribute efficiently to the well-being of the organism as a whole (i.e. by serving as dedicated liver, lung or kidney cells, etc.).

When localized as a large mass, such rogue cells become a tumour. Tumour cells remain small and do not differentiate to form any recognizable tissue. There is a constant balance between the risks of incomplete replacement and establishment of infection (i.e. insufficient production of new cells) and tumour formation (i.e. excess production of new cells). The solution seems to be continuous cell division, curbed by a large proportion of the daughter cells dying by apoptosis, unless stimulated to continue their differentiation into fully functional cells by appropriate signals and/or contact.

4.6.2 Death in organisms

The highly synchronized deaths of organisms such as *Drosophila* (Figure 4.7) and many annual plants and invertebrates suggest that some organisms may die by a process analogous to cellular apoptosis. However, although senescence in whole organisms (unicellular and multicellular) appears to follow a definite course, and to be at least partly under genetic control (Sections 4.2 and 4.3), death in larger, longer-lived organisms is almost always more similar to necrosis than to apoptosis. Some external agent, such as a predator, infection or excessive heat or cold, damages some vital metabolic process or organ, such as the oxygen transport mechanism, ATP formation, water and cation balance, the brain or the lungs. If senescence is already well advanced, homeostatic and regulatory mechanisms may not respond to environmental changes as promptly or efficiently as they did in their youth, tissue repair may be slower, and the capacity to improvise (e.g. by more anaerobic respiration when oxygen is short) weaker (see Figure 4.4).

■   Would there be more cell death by necrosis or apoptosis as the organism dies?

Cell deaths by necrosis would increase: shortages of oxygen and nutrients, and the accumulation of toxic metabolites would starve or poison many cells. Conversely, deaths by apoptosis may decline for lack of substrates to support the protein synthesis that is usually necessary before cells can die in this way.

Death is often due to the progressive failure of the functional interlocking between different anatomical and physiological systems in the organism as a whole. For example, the donkey whose jaws are shown in Figure 4.17 was 34 years old at the time of death, which is elderly even by the standards of 'donkey's years'. Although excellently cared for and offered plenty of nutritious food, it was severely emaciated, and starvation was clearly the immediate cause of death. As in horses and many other ungulates, the molar teeth normally function as a flat grinding surface, with wear from a diet of hard, abrasive grasses offset by slow, continuous eruption of the very long teeth. In this animal, some molar teeth had continued to grow even though those opposite, against which they would normally have ground, were worn down or decayed. Instead of forming a flat grinding surface, the teeth had become uneven and jagged, throwing the whole chewing mechanism badly out of kilter and causing injury to the surrounding tissues, which further impeded chewing and led eventually to starvation.

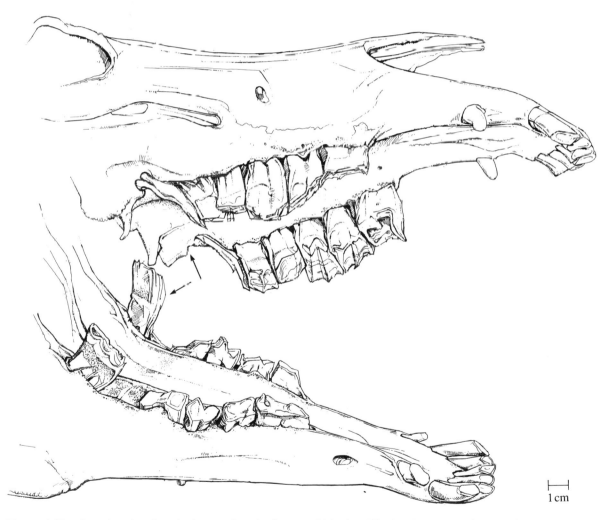

1 cm

Figure 4.17 Growth and ageing: the jaws and teeth of a very old donkey (tilted to show as much as possible of the teeth), illustrating the long-term consequences of mismatch between growth and wear. The last molar tooth of the left side of the upper jaw (arrowed) is missing, probably as a result of a tooth abscess. The lower tooth opposite it has failed to wear, although it has continued to erupt and has become much larger than others of its row, so the dentition has become uneven, impeding normal chewing. The other cheek teeth have also become uneven through breakages, abscesses and excessive wear. Note that the incisors are almost recumbent instead of vertical as in a young horse or donkey.

■ Could these problems be rectified by regeneration and tissue repair?

No. The adult set of teeth cannot be replaced and the jaw and other tissues of the chewing mechanism can be only slightly adjusted. Similar problems in modern people could be corrected by major surgery, but natural mechanisms cannot put them right. Thus, a relatively trivial disorder such as a tooth abscess has, over perhaps 20 years, brought about the death of this donkey because normal growth has continued in spite of the changed circumstances. Accident, disease or even senescent processes were not directly responsible for this death: minor damage to a single organ could not be made good, and the resulting mismatch between interlocking parts gradually brought about death.

Many biochemical and physiological systems fail in analogous ways. One of the most crucial is the matching of cell division to cell apoptosis: groups of cells that proliferate excessively or in an abnormal way form tumours which may further 'escape' from normal regulators of cell division, differentiation and senescence to produce malignant cancer. It would be impossible, as well as inappropriate, to try to describe here the numerous theories of the origin of cancer. The following brief comments are included to explain why scientists believe that the disease represents abnormal functioning of some of the basic mechanisms that control the integration of cell division, differentiation and ageing with the growth, maturation and senescence of the whole organism.

As mentioned in Section 4.5.1, cells derived from tumours are often exceptionally vigorous in culture and can be perpetuated through many more cell divisions than normal cells. Some lineages of tumour cells have outlived their original donor organism by tens of years. Most forms of cancer are very much more common in elderly people (Figure 4.18): in people aged 60–75 y, cancer is second only to disorders of the heart and circulation as the major cause of death.

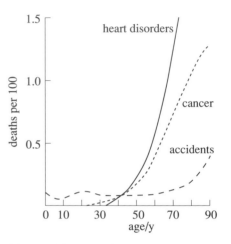

Figure 4.18 Death from various causes as a function of age. The data refer to people who died in the USA during 1968.

■ Why is it surprising to find that a disease that is characterized by excessive growth involving extensive cell division rather than cell enlargement is more prevalent in elderly people?

Because both in culture and *in vivo,* the cells of older organisms divide more slowly (Sections 2.2, 2.4 and 4.5.1) and cell enlargement is the predominant mechanism of growth. Somehow, tumour cells have 'taken on a new lease of life' in spite of having originated from an organism in which senescence was well advanced.

■ Can you suggest some senescent changes that may promote the appearance of such cell lineages in elderly people more often than in young people?

Rogue cell lineages may be able to prosper because slightly abnormal cells are less efficiently identified and exterminated in elderly bodies (Section 4.5.1), or because cells that should die by apoptosis fail to do so (Section 4.6.1).

One of cancer's least understood (and most feared) properties is the fact that its incidence can be related to experiences and events in the animal's life which took place a very long time before symptoms of the disease become obvious. The most likely mediators for these effects are **oncogenes**, genes which, by their altered expression or abnormal gene product, promote tumour formation in many different types of cells both *in vivo* and *in vitro*. More than fifty different oncogenes have been described (and that is certainly not all of them) from a wide variety of species and cell types. Many are derived from proto-oncogenes that are present in almost all kinds of cells and encode for growth factors or hormone receptors that are essential to the regulation of normal growth and repair. Such genes become oncogenes if they duplicate themselves so the genome contains too many copies which produce too much growth factor or too many receptors for signals that trigger division, so the cells divide even in the absence of the proper stimuli for division. The cell surface receptors may also be altered so the cells no longer respond normally to the intercellular signals that prevent or promote apoptosis (Section 4.6.1).

Oncogenes can also be introduced into normal cells by viruses, by artificial hybridization of cells in culture and by as yet unknown agents that move them from cell to cell within the same individual. The many endogenous and exogenous agents (i.e. prolonged exposure to tobacco smoke) known to promote tumour formation may act by mutation of oncogenes already present, or by making cells susceptible to invasion from foreign oncogenes.

Summary of Section 4.6

Cell necrosis is caused by damage or infection and results in inflammation. Apoptosis is an orderly, internally generated sequence of events that does not involve the immune system except in the removal of the debris of dead cells. Most cells die by apoptosis in the absence of appropriate stimuli to continue differentiation or division. Apoptosis is most extensive during development. The process occurs in all multicellular organisms and may be essential to cell replacement, tissue repair and the defence against infection. The immediate cause of death in multicellular organisms is usually either an external agent or progressive failure of coordination between anatomical and physiological systems. Tumours are lineages of cells in which regulation of proliferation and/or apoptosis is defective, so the cells divide excessively to form numerous small, undifferentiated cells. Such abnormal growth may be due to changes in oncogenes that code for receptors for the signals that promote division.

4.7 Conclusion

As in the case of growth (Chapter 1), one of the most striking features of senescence is the species differences in its rate and manifestations. Organisms that share many similarities in structure and metabolism, have the same body temperature and similar diets, nonetheless age at widely different rates. Slow processes (that cannot be artificially accelerated) are always unattractive as research projects, so until recently there were few detailed studies of natural ageing. But with more and more people living longer, it is now urgent to find out more about the physiological bases of ageing.

The study of ageing demonstrates that growth is a risky process for the organism as a whole: excessive proliferation of certain lineages of cells, and/or inefficient apoptosis can be harmful, even lethal. As in complex metabolic pathways, control is most effectively achieved by a cascade of numerous small steps and by having several control systems operating in parallel. Growth is too important, and potentially too dangerous, to be left to a single regulator (Section 1.4). The diversity and complexity of the control mechanisms frustrate disruption from mutant genes and pathogens such as viruses, as well as biologists who try to unravel or manipulate them.

the domestic pig) almost all the muscles are intimately associated with tendon and other connective tissues. Clearly, the properties of the individual tissues are best understood in terms of their roles in the musculo-skeletal system as a whole. Biologists and physicians are concerned with how the different tissues work together to generate movement, and how the activity of the entire system is controlled and coordinated by the nervous system.

5.1.1 Methods in the study of muscle tissue

Muscle is an exceptionally robust tissue which retains its elaborate histological structure and many of its metabolic capabilities for some time after it has been isolated from the animal. Many of the enzymes and structural proteins can withstand rigorous chemical separation procedures and the contractile components of muscle retain the ability to convert metabolic energy into movement, even after much of the rest of the cell structure has been removed by solvents, and after preservation for many months at $-20\,°C$. Such treatment would irrevocably damage most biochemical pathways in liver, intestinal or brain cells (although some individual enzymes may remain active after freezing and thawing). The robustness of muscle and skeletal tissues has made possible the demonstration of a huge range of properties, many of them involving grossly non-physiological conditions. Consequently, although a great deal of information about muscle and skeletal tissues is now available, it is not always clear which properties are relevant to their role in the living animal. It is therefore essential to combine studies on isolated molecules, organelles and cells with investigations into how living animals actually use their muscles and skeletal tissues during normal movement.

The situation is further complicated by long-established traditions of using only certain muscles for certain kinds of investigation. Frogs have been a favourite since the London-based physiologist Professor Archibald V. Hill began his classic studies in the 1920s: their long muscular hindlegs are adapted to both leaping and swimming so some muscles can contract very fast, while others are capable of producing powerful, sustained forces. Frogs are also a convenient size: their leg muscles are small enough for good diffusion of oxygen to be maintained for hours, and powerful enough to produce forces that can be easily measured (via the stout tendons attached to the muscle) using not too delicate apparatus. Finally, frogs are poikilothermic and the muscles of those native to the USA or northern Europe contract very well at room temperature and moderately well at $0\,°C$, a temperature that is relatively easy to hold constant. But frog muscle proteins are unstable in solution, so rabbit muscle, particularly the psoas in the back, which consists mainly of long parallel fibres, is preferred for biochemical and many biophysical studies. While it is true that the biochemical differences between the muscles of frogs and rabbits are quite minor, we cannot be sure that it is valid to match the details of mechanical studies on one species with those from chemical studies on the other.

Insects are very small, but they share with frogs the advantages for physiologists of being poikilothermic. Their flight muscles have a highly ordered structure and produce exceptionally powerful contractions that involve very little shortening. The mechanical properties and fine structure of the muscles of the giant water bug *Lethocerus* (several different species of adult body mass about 3 g occur in the humid tropics of South America, Africa and southeast Asia) and large dung beetles, such as those that feed on elephant dung, have been much studied. Although these large insects rarely fly in the wild when the temperature is below 30–35 °C, their flight muscles contract well at room temperature.

Another advantage of insects has recently been exploited for muscle research: they can grow to maturity and breed quite well with flight muscles that are grossly defective due to gene mutations that cause the absence or alteration of particular muscle proteins. So rare mutants of insects such as the fruit-fly *Drosophila* can be bred in the laboratory and many different aspects of their muscles examined (Section 5.2.2). Vertebrates with comparable defects in their skeletal muscles would probably be unable to walk or swim, or even to breathe normally, and hence would die long before they reached breeding age.

The specialized muscles of even more exotic animals lend themselves well to certain kinds of investigations: some giant barnacles native to the Pacific Ocean have exceptionally large muscle fibres, and those of molluscs such as clams and oysters have a unique mechanism that enables the animals to hold their shells tightly closed for hours using almost no energy. Clearly modern muscle biology is a rich mixture of many different investigative techniques applied to many different kinds of muscle from a huge range of species.

5.2 The structure of muscle

Figure 5.1 (*overleaf*) illustrates the basic organization of the contractile components of vertebrate striated muscles: a whole muscle is composed of from scores to thousands of **muscle fibres**, each 10–200 μm in diameter (in vertebrates, usually 50–100 μm) and from 1 mm to several centimetres long. In any one muscle, most fibres are about the same length but, as explained in Section 6.4, skeletal muscle may have several different arrangements of muscle fibres and tendons. In general, large animals have somewhat longer muscle fibres than related smaller species: for example, it is obvious that the muscle fibres of mice could never be longer than about a centimetre. Other structures shown are discussed later in this section.

Bundles of muscle fibres (Figure 5.1, ring 2) are bounded by tough collagenous tissue which merges with tendon, bone and other structures that attach muscle to the skeleton, and extends around and between the muscle fibres. This collagenous tissue, together with a layer of fine, amorphous collagen called the basal lamina, adheres closely to the plasmalemma of each muscle fibre (see Section 2.4 and Figures 2.13 and 5.6). These structures together form the **sarcolemma**, but in many texts this term is used more loosely to mean just the plasmalemma of the fibre. The plasmalemma of some muscle fibres, especially large vertebrate fibres, is electrically excitable and forms propagating action potentials. In vertebrates, a single motor neuron* forms one or more neuromuscular junctions on the plasmalemma, but invertebrate muscle fibres are usually innervated by several different motor neurons. Arterioles, venules and smaller nerves, together with blood vessels and, in many mammals, adipose tissue, are found between and around the muscle fibres.

---

* Often spelt motorneuron or motorneurone.

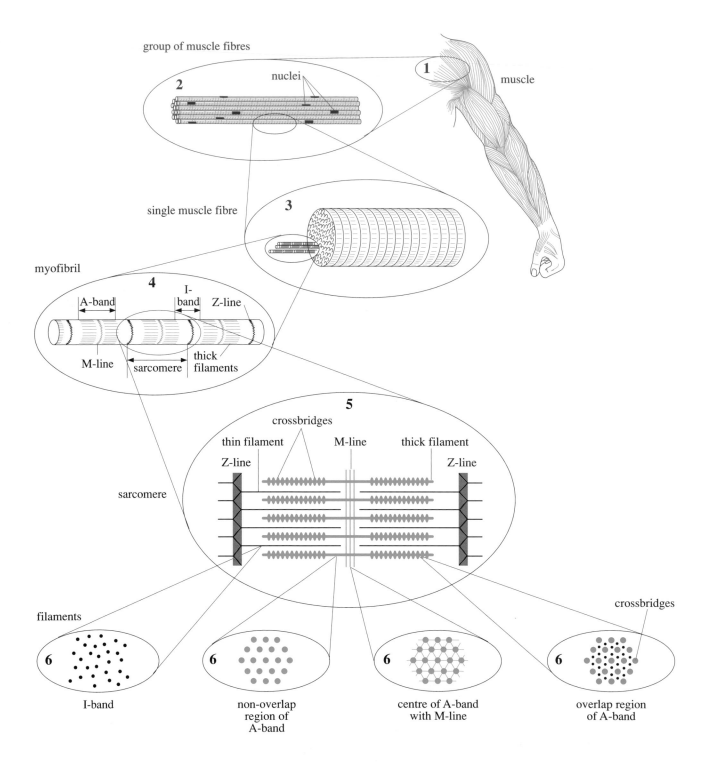

Figure 5.1   The basic organization of the contractile components of vertebrate striated muscles, drawn to show the relationships between the components, not to scale. The sarcoplasmic reticulum (SR) and other regulatory structures are omitted for simplicity. In ring 4, the thin filaments are omitted. The repeating unit along the myofibrils, the sarcomere, consists of several bands and zones identified by letters.

In vertebrates and larger invertebrates, each fibre contains thousands of **myofibrils**, which are usually polygonal in cross-section, and average about 0.5–2.0 µm in diameter. The structure is shown diagrammatically in Figure 5.1, ring 4. Several myofibrils are visible in longitudinal section in Figure 5.2. They are often arranged in groups of from half a dozen to a score or more, as shown in Figure 5.3 (*overleaf*). Between and around the groups of myofibrils there are from dozens to hundreds of relatively small nuclei (Section 2.4), mitochondria, several kinds of structural proteins and a system of internal membranes called the **sarcoplasmic reticulum** (SR) that has similarities with endoplasmic reticulum. The most important property of SR is its ability to take up calcium ions actively: in the relaxed state, the concentration of calcium ions around and within the myofibrils is only about 40 nmol l^{-1} (1 nmol l^{-1} ≡ 10^{-9} mol l^{-1}), lower than that of the cytoplasm of other cells such as liver and gut, because most of the calcium is sequestered inside the vesicles of the SR. Like many kinds of cell membranes, the plasmalemma actively extrudes calcium ions from the muscle fibres. Recent studies combining electron microscopy with labelling with fluorescent antibodies indicate that in a wide variety of cells as well as striated muscle, most calcium pumping takes place in minute depressions in the plasmalemma called caveolae.

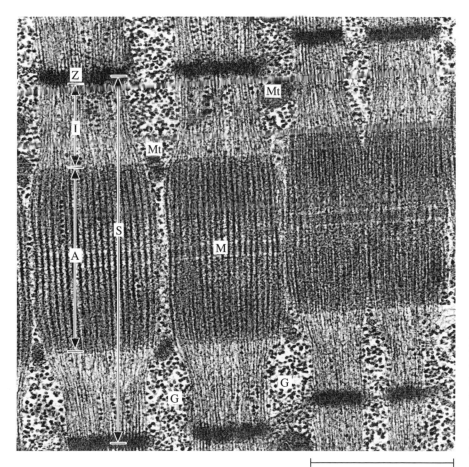

Figure 5.2   Electron micrograph of human striated muscle. The sample was taken by biopsy from the gastrocnemius muscle of the lower leg. A longitudinal section of several adjacent myofibrils, showing whole sarcomeres (S) with A-bands (A), I-bands (I), M-lines (M) and Z-lines (Z), plus mitochondria (Mt) and glycogen granules (G).

1 µm

In vertebrates, the SR abuts closely to, but is not continuous with, another set of membranes called **T-tubules** ('T' stands for 'transverse') that form as invaginations and branches of the plasmalemma and extend deep into the muscle fibres. (T-tubules are shown in Figure 5.5.) As their name implies, T-tubules are predominantly, but not exclusively, transverse to the plane of the contractile apparatus. They are about 40 nm in diameter and, of course, they enclose part of the extracellular space. This property can be demonstrated by soaking the muscle in a medium containing large, lipid-insoluble molecules: these markers appear inside deep T-tubules, but not inside the muscle fibre itself.

The contractile proteins are assembled into regular, repeating units about 2.0–2.5 μm long called **sarcomeres**, arranged end to end along the length of each myofibril (Figure 5.1, rings 4 and 5, and Figure 5.2). For reasons that are still not entirely clear, sarcomeres of adjacent myofibrils are usually arranged in register, creating the pattern of dark and light bands across the myofibrils. These 'striations' were first seen in the mid-19th century by microscopists equipped with high-power light microscopes and it is to them that we owe the term 'striated' muscle.

Electron microscopy combined with chemical procedures that selectively leach out or disassemble certain proteins has revealed much about the internal organization of sarcomeres. Early staining techniques for electron micrographs demonstrated two different arrays of interdigitating longitudinal filaments, called the thin and the thick filaments, and at right angles to them, the **Z-lines*** and M-lines. The region of the sarcomere occupied by the thick filaments is called the A-band. The two regions near the ends of a sarcomere where the thin filaments extend beyond the region of overlap with the thick filaments are called the I-bands, as shown in Figure 5.1, ring 4.

To understand the three-dimensional organization of sarcomeres, compare Figure 5.1 (rings 5 and 6) with Figures 5.2 and 5.3, which were prepared from tiny pieces of the gastrocnemius muscle (the 'calf' muscle of the lower leg) of a normal adult human, excised with a biopsy needle. Figure 5.2 shows four complete sarcomeres, each in a different but adjacent myofibril, in longitudinal section, as shown diagrammatically in Figure 5.1, ring 5. The thin filaments are regularly arranged around the thick filaments, so in transverse section such as Figure 5.3, they appear as a geometrical pattern of large and small dots with or without tiny protrusions, as shown diagrammatically in the sixth group of rings in Figure 5.1. It is, of course, impossible to cut absolutely straight through a muscle fibre (its internal structure is invisible until the completed section is viewed in the electron microscope), and the myofibrils are not exactly aligned, so Figure 5.3 is a slightly oblique section that passes through the overlap region of the A-bands of the myofibrils at the top, the I-bands in the centre and the Z-lines in the lower right.

The lengths of the thick and thin filaments, and the exact pattern in which they are arranged, differ between species and (in invertebrates) between types of muscle in the same species. In vertebrate striated muscle, thick filaments are about 42 nm apart, and the spacing between thick and adjacent thin filaments is 22–30 nm.

* Also called Z-discs in some texts.

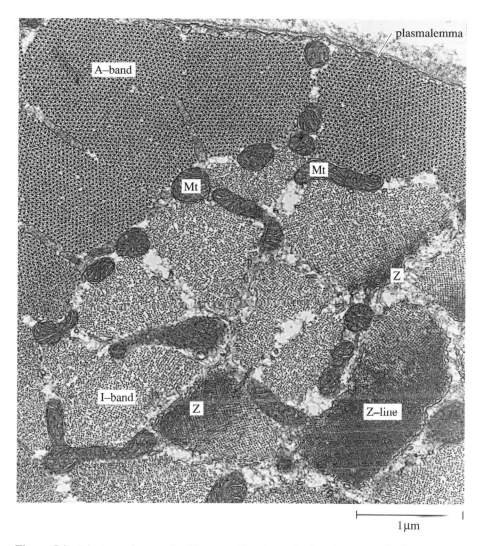

Figure 5.3   Electron micrograph of human striated muscle, showing parts of at least 16 myofibrils. The sample was taken by biopsy from the gastrocnemius muscle of the lower leg. The top third of the picture shows sections through A-bands; in the lower two-thirds the section passes mainly through I-bands and the regions marked 'Z' pass through Z-lines. The plasmalemma is visible at the top of the picture.

Insect flight is one of the most energetically demanding activities in the whole animal kingdom, and probably represents the highest mechanical power output of all poikilotherms. The wingbeat frequency of large tsetse flies is about 200 Hz which is audible as a low buzz; that of small flies such as mosquitoes and midges is up to 1 000 Hz, and sounds like a whine. As well as generating fast, powerful contractions, the flight muscles of such insects are exceptionally highly ordered, and hence produce beautiful electron micrographs such as Figure 5.4b (*overleaf*).

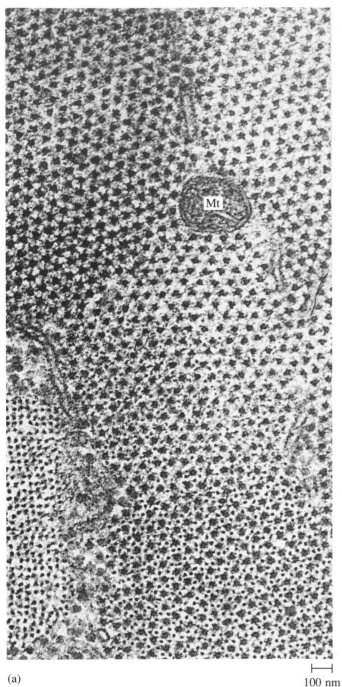

(a)

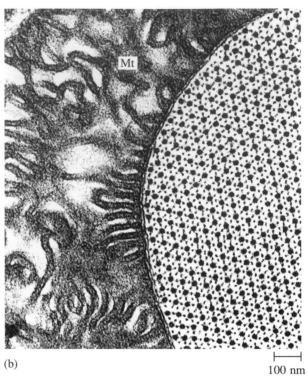

(b)

100 nm

Figure 5.4   Electron micrographs sectioned through the
A-band regions of sarcomeres of (a) the human gastrocnemius
muscle, and (b) the flight muscles of a tsetse fly.

100 nm

■   Calculate the average spacing of the thick filaments (by measuring a row of ten or more densely stained thick filaments) in Figures 5.4a and 5.4b. What can you conclude?

At the magnification used here, the thick filaments average 3.4 mm (the equivalent of about 68 nm) apart in Figure 5.4a but only 3.2 mm (roughly 56 nm) apart in Figure 5.4b, so there must therefore be proportionately more thick filaments in the vertebrate muscles. In fact, the ratio of thin to thick filaments is 2 : 1 in all vertebrate striated muscles, and 3 : 1 in insect flight muscle. The ratio is as high as 5 : 1 or 6 : 1 in some insect leg and body muscles, and the thin filaments are arranged in various different patterns around the thick filaments.

Crossbridges are regularly arranged protrusions of the thick filaments in the regions where they overlap with the thin filaments, as shown diagrammatically in Figure 5.1, rings 5 and 6. They are often difficult to demonstrate in electron micrographs of vertebrate muscle and are only faintly visible in Figure 5.2. Crossbridges are more clearly seen, and apparently more regularly arranged, in insect flight muscle than in any other kind of muscle, so much of the information about their role in muscle contraction comes from the study of this tissue.

The other important structures visible in Figure 5.2 are the Z-lines and M-lines. Both have an intricate internal structure that is visible with very high resolution electron microscopy, and they contain several unique proteins. For reasons explained in Section 5.2.1, both thick and thin filaments are polarized, i.e. their molecular components are asymmetrical and are assembled so that they are 'facing' one way or the other. The thick filaments in the two halves of the sarcomere, i.e. either side of the M-line, are of opposite polarity. Up to five bands perpendicular to the filaments are visible in the M-lines of certain muscles, but the functional implications of the structural differences (compare Figures 5.2 and 5.6 with Figure 5.10) found between taxa (e.g. insects, worms and vertebrates) and types of muscle are unknown. Thin filaments of opposite polarity from adjacent sarcomeres are joined at the Z-lines, which, in three dimensions, appear to form discs that cap each sarcomere of each myofibril, like the two ends of a tin can (Figures 5.2 and 5.3).

In some muscles, particularly those adapted to high power output and rapid onset and termination of contraction, the T-tubules and sarcoplasmic reticulum are arranged in a regular pattern of parallel tubes and vesicles between the myofibrils, often concentrated around the Z-lines and M-lines.

■   How would such T-tubules and sarcoplasmic reticulum appear in thin sections seen in the electron microscope?

In cross-section or longitudinal section, these membranes appear as rings or parallel bands, called triads, situated between the myofibrils (as shown in Figure 5.5). However, as with many aspects of muscle structure, the abundance of these membranes and of mitochondria, and their arrangements in relation to the sarcomeres are very variable: there are differences between taxa, between different muscles of the same individual, and ontogenetic changes within a single muscle. The functional implications of the many different patterns have not been investigated in detail.

It has probably occurred to you by now that this orderly arrangement of sarcomeres and membranes could be thrown out of alignment each time the muscle shortens. It is now becoming clear that Z-lines and M-lines have pivotal roles in the muscle cytoskeleton that connects the contractile proteins to the membranes and maintains their functional relationships. You can see the cytoskeletal attachments of the plasmalemma to the Z-lines in Figure 5.6a. When a muscle fibre shortens, its whole sarcolemma is deformed into deep folds (Figure 5.6b) and remains closely applied to the sarcomeres only at the Z-lines. The protein that forms the mechanical connection between these components of the sarcomeres and the outer membrane is called **desmin**.

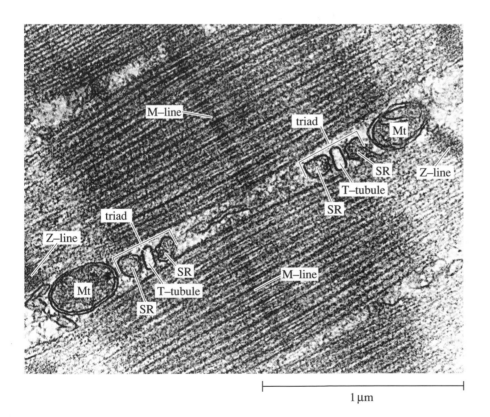

1 μm

Figure 5.5   Longitudinal section of the same human muscle shown in Figures 5.2, 5.3 and 5.4 to show two triads of sarcoplasmic reticulum (SR) and T-tubules (T). Mt, mitochondrion.

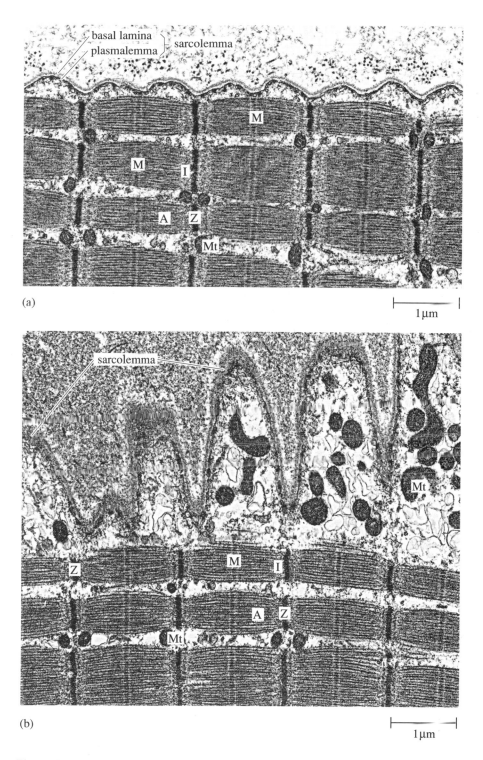

Figure 5.6   Electron micrographs of sections of sarcomeres and sarcolemma of a human gastrocnemius muscle when (a) moderately contracted, with I-bands substantial and clearly visible, and (b) strongly contracted, with I-bands almost occluded. Note that the sarcomeres are 10% shorter in (b) than they are in (a).

5.2.1 Muscle proteins

Because they are chemically robust and many occur in, for a biological system, a relatively pure and concentrated form, muscle proteins are easier than most to isolate and so have been intensively studied. Dozens of proteins have been isolated, characterized and named, which gives the impression that muscle contains a wide variety of proteins. In fact, compared to other kinds of cells such as liver or white blood cells, muscle contains relatively few kinds of protein. It is just that we know more about more of them. The following account refers mainly to mammalian striated muscle and describes only those proteins for which the localization and/or function are fairly well established.

The thin filaments are about 1.1 μm in length and 5–10 nm in diameter and consist mainly of polymerized chains of the globular protein, **actin**, with much smaller quantities of regulatory proteins called **troponin** and **tropomyosin**. Although approximately round in shape, actin monomers are asymmetrical and they always assemble 'nose to tail', which confers polarity on the entire thin filament. Actin seems to be chemically almost identical wherever it is found, although its abundance differs substantially in different kinds of muscle. In frog muscle, each thin filament contains about 380 actin molecules and about 22% of the total protein in whole muscle fibres is actin.

Troponin is a complex of three globular proteins which together are about twice the size of an actin monomer. Tropomyosin is a rod-shaped, helical protein and in the thin filament, one troponin complex is bound to a particular point on each tropomyosin molecule. Actin forms a double helical chain, like two strings of beads twisted together, and the tropomyosin molecules, each with a troponin complex, lie one on either side of the chain. Tropomyosin molecules are arranged end-to-end, and there is one molecule of tropomyosin for every seven actin monomers.

In vertebrate striated muscle, thick filaments are both wider and longer than thin filaments, about 1.6 μm in length, and are composed mostly of staggered bundles of **myosin** molecules, about 300 per filament. At 43–50% of the total protein, myosin is by far the most abundant kind of protein in muscle. It is a large protein of about M_r 520 000, that dissociates into two heavy chains of M_r about 220 000 each, and four light chains of M_r 20 000. Myosin occurs in several different **isoforms** that are produced by different genes. Although they differ only slightly in chemical structure and hardly at all in size, myosin isoforms are major factors in determining how fast a muscle can contract (Section 5.3.3).

The heavy chains form a long fibrous tail and two heads that act as enzymes and protrude from the thick filaments towards the adjacent thin filaments, forming the crossbridges with the light chains bound to them. The bundles of myosin molecules are assembled in a way that gives the thick filaments a clear polarity, with those of each half-sarcomere having opposite polarity. Some of the tails of the myosin molecules, the heads of which are forming crossbridges in the two regions of the sarcomere where the thick and thin filaments overlap, meet at the M-line (see Figures 5.2, 5.5, 5.6 and 5.7). Some of the unique proteins that form the M-line are probably involved in binding these myosin tails together. Others are enzymes, including creatine kinase, the enzyme that generates ATP from phosphocreatine.

The myosin heads, probably in conjunction with specialized sites on the thin filaments, are ATPases that convert chemical energy into mechanical force. Only two other known proteins have this remarkable property (the others being kinesin and dynein in neurons and in cilia and flagella) which is the essence of muscle contraction.

Attachment, detachment and/or changes in the angles of the crossbridges result, under appropriate mechanical conditions, in the thin and thick filaments sliding past each other. The many detailed studies of the mechanism of this process and its control are beyond the scope of this course. J. T. Finer and others working at Stanford University, California and London, have built some very ingenious apparatus that enables them to measure the forces generated by a single isolated myosin molecule interacting with actin. They find that for each ATP molecule hydrolysed, a myosin head (which forms the crossbridge, see Figure 5.1, ring 5) can move about 11 nm along an actin filament, and can produce about 3–4 pN (1 piconewton $\equiv 10^{-12}$ newtons) of force. The whole sarcomere shortens, almost entirely from a symmetrical reduction in the lengths of the I-bands. When all (or a large proportion) of the sarcomeres of a myofibril contract more or less simultaneously, these small events sum to produce substantial forces in the myofibril as a whole.

Recent improvement in techniques for cutting and staining material for the electron microscope has demonstrated super-thin filaments, less than 5 nm in diameter, in vertebrate muscles. These filaments consist of **titin**, which, with an M_r of 3×10^6 and length of up to 1 µm, is the largest single-chain protein so far described in any organism. As illustrated in Figure 5.7, titin molecules extend from the M-line to the Z-line along the thick filaments and into the I-band. Z-lines are the points of attachment of titin and actin filaments between adjacent sarcomeres. The amino acid sequence of titin, and hence the form of its folding is different in the A-band and the I-band. Vertebrate striated muscle is about 10% titin, and current research suggests that each thick filament contains six of these huge proteins and that they may contribute to the assembly and alignment of the myosin molecules, and hence to the pattern of crossbridges.

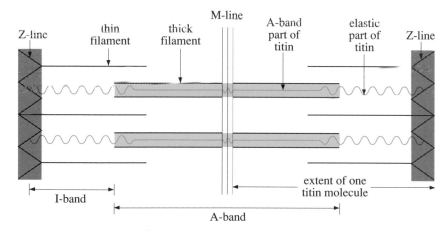

Figure 5.7   Diagram of the arrangement of the major proteins in a single sarcomere of vertebrate striated muscle.

Another recently discovered fibrous protein in muscle is **nebulin**, which spans the entire length of the thin filaments. At an M_r of around 8×10^5, nebulin is also a very large molecule, though only about a quarter of the size of titin, and it accounts of 5% of the total muscle protein. Nebulin may determine the length of the thin filaments, and hence of the sarcomere as a whole. But its exact arrangement in the thin filaments, and its role in maintaining the arrangement and relative abundance of actin, troponin and tropomyosin, are not yet known, so it is not shown in Figure 5.7.

The Z-lines that 'cap' each sarcomere consist mainly of actin from the ends of the thin filaments and α-**actinin** and, in insect flight muscle, another very large protein called kettin. Kettin and α-actinin seem to bind the thin filaments

S324 Book 3 Size and Action

together at the ends of each sarcomere (Figures 5.2, 5.3, 5.5 and 5.6). The Z-lines of adjacent myofibrils are connected by a filamentous network of desmin. These proteins form the internal cytoskeleton that binds the myofibrils together and maintains their highly ordered structure; they are probably essential to effective communication between the fibre membranes and the contractile proteins, which, as explained in Section 5.3.2, is crucial in controlling contraction.

Several more proteins have been isolated from muscle and identified, including some very minor constituents such as dystrophin (Section 5.4.3) which accounts for only 0.002% of the total muscle protein. Sophisticated electron microscopy combined with immunocytochemistry has revealed the normal location and probable physiological function for many of such minor constituents of muscle. As a result of such intensive study, striated muscle is now one of the best known of all vertebrate tissues from the chemical and micro-anatomical point of view: our 'map' of the structure and arrangement of liver cells or neurons is not nearly as complete.

5.2.2 Sarcomere assembly

The unique properties of muscle arise from the precise ordering of the many different proteins described above rather than from the chemical composition of any one of them. The two most abundant muscle proteins are by no means confined to muscle: actin is found in almost all eukaryotic cells (where, among other functions, it is a component of the mitotic spindle), and fibrous proteins with many features in common with myosin occur in many kinds of animal cells. But only in muscle are these proteins arranged in ways that enable them to contract rapidly and to generate high power. Crystallographers, biochemists, electron microscopists and more recently geneticists have studied what substances and conditions are essential to the formation of this all-important order.

Several lines of evidence indicate that sarcomeres can assemble themselves. Heart muscle of vertebrates differs from skeletal muscle in that it generates its own electrical signals that initiate contraction (so hearts continue to beat for several seconds after excision, extendable to many minutes of activity under appropriate conditions). Heart muscle myofibrils can be dissociated into their component filaments by incubating them with the proteolytic enzyme trypsin. If the enzyme is then removed, the filaments reassemble spontaneously in a few hours to form normal-looking sarcomeres, some of which start to contract. This process takes place even if drugs such as cycloheximide that inhibit protein synthesis are added to the incubation medium. However, the presence of Z-lines with at least some actin filaments attached to them seems to be essential to reassembly.

In *Drosophila*, the major proteins of the flight muscles are generated by different genes from those that produce the proteins for the muscles of the legs, mouthparts, etc. Thus flies carrying mutant genes for flight muscle proteins are viable except that they cannot fly: they feed, walk, mate and breed normally and do not appear to suffer any inconvenience. The study of such lineages of *Drosophila* has revealed more about what materials are essential to the formation of certain components of sarcomeres. Figure 5.8a shows the flight muscles of a mutant fly that cannot synthesize flight muscle actin, Figure 5.8b shows those of another lineage of flies in which the gene for flight muscle myosin is defective and Figure 5.8c is of flies bred to have both mutations.

■ What can you conclude from the electron micrograph appearance of such deficient muscles?

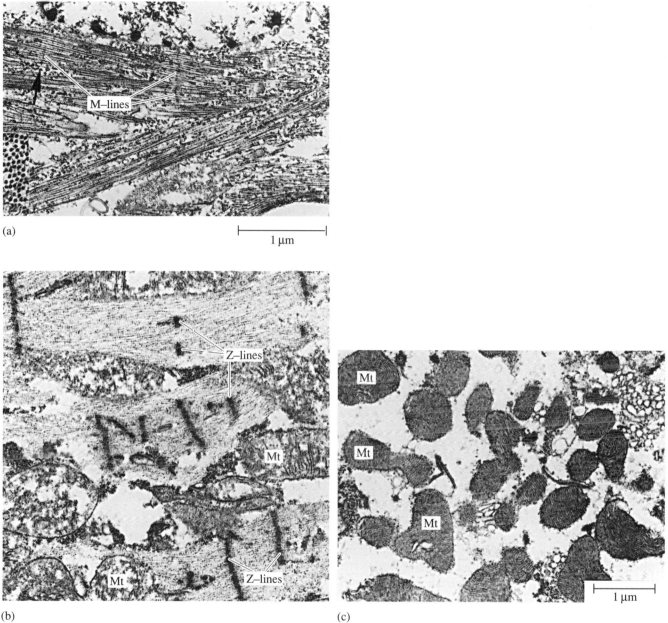

Figure 5.8   Flight muscles of mutant fruit-flies *Drosophila*. (a) A longitudinal section of muscle fibre that cannot synthesize flight muscle actin. Note the arrays of thick filaments and rudimentary M-lines. (b) Longitudinal section from a fruit-fly that does not synthesize flight muscle myosin. Note the Z-lines with thin filaments emerging from both sides. (c) The 'flight muscles' of a fruit-fly that has both mutations. The mitochondria and some membranes form normally, but there are no arrays of contractile proteins.

Thick filaments and M-lines can form in the absence of actin (Figure 5.8a) and thin filaments are viable without myosin, but both are necessary for the formation of regular, discrete sarcomeres. Furthermore, normal-looking Z-lines are clearly visible in Figure 5.8b, demonstrating that they can form in the absence of myosin. Flies that are heterozygous for both mutations have only one of the normal two genes for each protein, so although all necessary proteins are present, their relative abundance is abnormal. Electron micrographs of the muscles of such flies show filaments of widely different lengths and very few assemblages that could be called sarcomeres. Too much of certain proteins is as disruptive to the formation of normal sarcomeres as too little. In the mutant flies, the proteins are synthesized in the wrong proportions, and so very few filaments of exactly the right length for sarcomere formation assemble themselves.

Summary of Section 5.2

Muscles consist of bundles of fibres composed of myofibrils, several different kinds of membranes, nuclei and mitochondria. The contractile proteins are organized into sarcomeres, which consist of A- and I-bands, and M- and Z-lines, and are arranged end to end along the myofibril. Actin and smaller quantities of nebulin, tropomyosin and troponin form the thin filaments and myosin and titin form the thick filaments. The heads of the myosin molecules form crossbridges; part of the heads acts as an ATPase.

5.3 Muscle mechanics

The most spectacular, and most widely discussed, property of muscle is its ability to generate force actively using ATP. Muscle does not use chemical energy to become longer, but, like all elastic materials, it can store and later release some of the mechanical energy applied to it. The response of relaxed and semi-relaxed muscle to externally applied forces plays a major role in determining the form of all movements, because all actions require muscles to be moved as well as to produce forces that tend to cause movement. If you have ever had a minor injury in a muscle, you may have been surprised by the range of ordinary movements that seem to involve that muscle, even if you are trying hard not to 'use' it actively. As well as generating forces themselves, muscles are stretched and twisted by external forces and by the actions of other muscles as part of all normal activities. So before we address the active, ATP-using properties of muscle, it is appropriate to describe briefly the passive properties.

5.3.1 Passive properties of muscle

The passive mechanical properties of muscle are familiar to all cooks: although it is soft and pliable, muscle resists large deformations, and when twisted or pummelled, it tends to spring back to its original shape. These properties can be quantified accurately by stretching the muscle by a known fraction of its original length while measuring the tension (i.e. the force required to overcome resistance to extension).

Figure 5.9 shows the tension measured when various freshly excised muscles were stretched without being stimulated to perform active contraction; the muscles were not permanently damaged by the procedure because they were stretched only to lengths from which they would recoil elastically to their original length when released. You can see that the basic shape of all the curves is similar; there is an initial phase in which the muscle is extended by quite small forces, but for most of the range, tension is proportional to stretch. However, the bee flight muscle is very stiff and hardly stretches at all even when quite large forces are applied, while the muscles in the 'foot' of snails are readily extensible, and can be extended to 160% of their normal length in the body without injury. These passive properties are referred to collectively as the internal elastic components of the muscle.

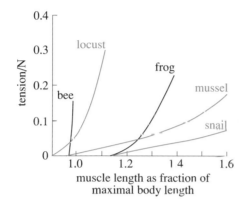

Figure 5.9 The tension measured in various muscles that are stretched beyond their resting lengths. Resting length in the intact animal = 1. When released from stretch, bee flight muscle is shorter than its maximal length *in situ*.

Some of these passive elastic properties can be demonstrated in muscle in which the connective, vascular and nervous tissues within and around myofibrils have been dissolved away.

■ What can you conclude from such observations about the physical basis of passive elastic properties of muscle?

Much of the internal elasticity of muscle must arise from properties of the sarcomeres themselves. Before the discovery of titin and nebulin (Section 5.2.1), the molecular basis of the passive strength and internal elasticity was not clear: the I-band seemed to be the weakest point, as it was hard to see how actin, being a globular protein, could have much mechanical strength. Current research indicates that titin is the main agent of mechanical continuity in relaxed muscle. The regions of the super-thin filaments in the I-bands are more extensible than those in the A-bands: they may crumple during active contraction, or stretch when the whole muscle is stretched, then recoil when the sarcomere relaxes or is released. The linear arrangement of these very long molecules suggests that the elasticity arises from folding and unfolding of portions of the protein rather than from molecules sliding past each other.

■ In view of this explanation, how would you expect the structure of sarcomeres in bee muscle to differ from those of snails?

Bee muscle has relatively very short I-bands. A comparison of the bee flight muscle in Figure 5.10 (*overleaf*) with the mammalian muscle in Figure 5.2 illustrates this difference very clearly: at a length of 2.4 μm, the sarcomeres of the flight muscles of insects such as bees are about the same length as those of vertebrates, but the insect A-bands are 2.2 μm long, compared to about 1.6 μm in almost all vertebrate muscles.

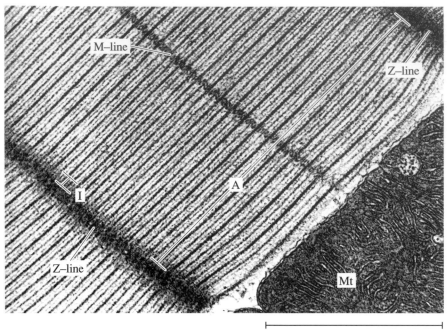

Figure 5.10   Longitudinal section of a single sarcomere in the flight muscle of a bumble bee *Bombus*. Notice that the structure of the M-line of this invertebrate muscle is different from that of human muscle in Figure 5.2. Mt, mitochondrion.

More extensible muscles have longer sarcomeres but the long I-bands make such sarcomeres mechanically weak, which seems to set the upper limit to their maximum possible length. Sarcomeres 10–15 μm long have been reported from crabs and other crustaceans, but those of vertebrate muscles are all between 2 and 3 μm long. Collagenous connective tissue also contributes to elasticity, and snail and mussel muscle have much more connective tissue between fibres than bee muscle.

The proteins that form the cytoskeleton and maintain the structure of the thick filaments seem to be different in invertebrate and vertebrate muscles. True titin is known only from vertebrate muscles, but many arthropods and nematodes have a protein that is chemically similar although smaller (M_r about 8×10^5) and that may have a similar role. The thick filaments of insect flight muscle and many molluscan muscles contain relatively large quantities of a protein unique to invertebrates called paramyosin.

The elastic properties of titin, combined with its role in maintaining the array of myosin molecules, may keep the A-band exactly in the centre of the sarcomere, thereby preventing it from becoming unstable by generating unequal forces in its two halves. If titin molecules are broken by exposing whole sarcomeres to radiation, the A-band deviates from the exactly central position that it invariably occupies in all natural muscles.

5.3.2 Muscle contraction

Initiation

In most striated muscles, the sequence of events leading to contraction begins when an action potential in its motor neuron reaches the neuromuscular junctions and depolarizes the plasmalemma. In many vertebrate muscles (and a few insect muscles), the plasmalemma and its extensions, the T-tubules, can produce regenerative action potentials in the same way as neurons can. Action potentials thus travel rapidly over and through the entire muscle. Action potentials do not propagate over the plasmalemmas of most invertebrate muscles, but their motor neurons branch to form many more neuromuscular junctions, which together depolarize the membrane. In either case, the electrical changes can be picked up by fine wires inserted into or near the muscles and amplified to produce a display that indicates which muscles are active.

■   If conduction velocity of action potentials over the plasmalemma is $5 \, m \, s^{-1}$, how long does an action potential take to travel over a 5 cm long muscle fibre in which the neuromuscular junction is at its centre?

The time taken for the action potential to travel the 25 mm from the centre to the ends of the fibre is 5 ms. Depolarization in the plasmalemma and T-tubules causes (by a mechanism not understood in detail) the SR to release its calcium ions, abruptly raising their concentration around the contractile proteins by over a hundredfold to about $10 \, \mu mol \, l^{-1}$. If ATP is present and various other chemical conditions are met, the influx of calcium initiates the mechanisms that lead to hydrolysis of ATP and the generation of active contraction.

Myosin by itself hydrolyses ATP only very slowly: both thin and thick filaments are necessary to produce the rate of ATPase activity observed in intact muscle. The major steps in this process can be investigated by studying various combinations and arrangements of the muscle protein *in vitro*, to which free calcium ions are added to induce 'contraction'. Such observations show that the calcium binds to the troponin complex in the thin filaments, which alters the arrangement of the tropomyosin lying against the actin in a way that exposes the active sites on the actin. With their inhibitory covering of tropomyosin temporarily removed, these sites interact with the ATPase on the crossbridges of the adjacent thick filaments to accelerate ATP breakdown and cause contraction.

The depolarization in the plasmalemma wanes after a few milliseconds unless it is maintained by a series of action potentials arriving in quick succession. With repolarization of the plasmalemma, the SR accumulates the calcium it released, quickly reducing the concentration of Ca^{2+} ions inside the fibre and terminating active force generation. The SR, like other ion-pumping membranes, uses ATP to take up the calcium ions against a concentration gradient.

Modern research techniques enable biologists to identify which components of the filaments are necessary for hydrolysing ATP and generating movement. When mixed with pure actin, pure myosin 'contracts' by wriggling along the actin filament. At a maximum velocity of about $9 \, \mu m \, s^{-1}$, the movement is not fast compared to that of intact muscle, but it can readily be measured under the light microscope, and is widely used as an assay of motility. Thus assessed, the motility of myosin isolated without the light chains around its enzymic heads is less than one-tenth that of myosin from the same source (chicken breast muscle) with its light chains in place, but the rates of ATP breakdown are similar in both cases.

■   What can you conclude from these observations about the structure of the crossbridges?

The light chains are not essential for ATPase activity but they are necessary for the generation of movement: in other words, the two processes take place in different parts of the crossbridge region of the myosin molecule. Other kinds of experiments indicate that, under certain mechanical conditions, the crossbridges can detach and re-attach without using more ATP, which also points to a separation between enzymic activity and movement generation.

The stimulus regime

The mechanical contraction itself lasts much longer than the chemical events that initiated it. The muscle plasmalemma, like the membrane of neurons, is capable of supporting another action potential only a few milliseconds after the first has passed. Unlike action potentials, mechanical contractions can summate, so the timing of a sequence of electrical stimuli to muscle is a major determinant of the maximum force generated and the duration of a contraction.

How natural trains of action potentials generated by the nervous system determine muscle activity *in vivo* is described in Section 6.5; for analysing the relationship between stimulus regime and mechanical response, it is usually more convenient to apply artificial pulses to an isolated muscle. The data in Figure 5.11 were obtained from an intact freshly excised muscle that was fixed firmly at one end and attached at the other end to apparatus that measured the tension produced with minimum compliance (i.e. the apparatus was so stiff that the muscle could hardly shorten at all).

To most people the word 'contraction' means shrinkage or shortening, usually as a result of internally generated forces. Muscle physiologists use the term to refer to the active state of the muscle which, if the mechanical constraints allow it, result in the muscle becoming shorter; in many cases, the contracting muscle exerts tension on the tendon or bone to which it is attached, but, as we shall see in Chapters 6 and 8, it may not undergo any net shortening at all. It is also important to remember that muscles contract at constant volume: they get thicker as they get shorter, and do not in any way shrink or shrivel, nor do they inflate on relaxation.

Dissecting out the motor neurons with the muscle is difficult, so for studying isolated muscles in the laboratory, it is convenient to simulate natural action potentials by applying brief depolarizing pulses directly to the plasmalemma. The mechanical response of a typical limb muscle to a single such artificial stimulus is called a **twitch** and is shown in Figure 5.11a. The stimulus, and the depolarization that it elicited in the plasmalemma and T-tubules lasts less than 5 ms, but the mechanical events continue for at least 40 ms.* Maximum tension is reached after about 30 ms, but the relaxation phase takes longer than the contraction phase, so the curve is asymmetrical.

■   For the conditions mentioned above, what fraction of the total rise time of the twitch does the time for conduction of action potentials over the plasmalemma represent? How could this delay be reduced?

*The flight muscles of insects with very high wingbeat frequency such as tsetse flies (Section 5.2) are specialized. Their contraction time is much shorter, often as little as 3 ms.

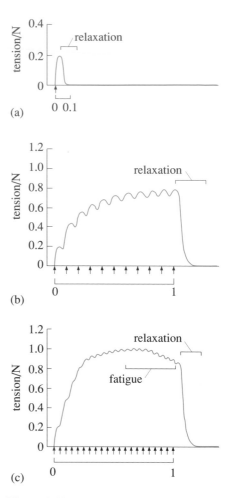

Figure 5.11   The mechanical responses of a typical mammalian muscle to stimuli (arrowed) at various frequencies (the lines shown below the graphs). The scale bars on the *x*-axes are in seconds. (a) A single twitch contraction. (b) A tetanus produced by stimuli at 10 Hz. (c) A tetanus produced by stimuli at 20 Hz. The force produced by the muscle starts to decline after 0.8 s of stimulation because of muscle fatigue. Note that the tension measurements in (a) are shown on a different scale from (b) and (c).

The conduction time is about 17% ((5/30) × 100) of the rise time of the twitch. It would be shorter if the neuromuscular junctions were closer together, muscle fibres were shorter or action potentials travelled faster across the plasmalemma. These features are found in muscles adapted to very fast, powerful movement for which close synchrony between all the sarcomeres of all the myofibrils is essential. In many postural muscles, electrical stimuli lasting only a few ms may produce mechanical responses that last hundreds or ms or even seconds.

Contractions elicited by several successive stimuli can summate, giving rise to **tetanus**, in which the maximum force generated is four times larger than that of a single twitch. In the tetanic contraction shown in Figure 5.11b, the muscle is stimulated with brief pulses at 10 Hz. At this frequency, about two-thirds of the first twitch is already completed before the next stimulus starts active contraction again, so the time course of force production is not linear and the contraction takes almost a second to reach its maximum. Force generation continues for as long as the stimuli are applied and then declines with a similar time course to the twitch in Figure 5.11a, although it takes longer because the maximum contraction is greater. If the muscle is stimulated at 20 Hz (Figure 5.11c), the force from the first twitch has only just begun to wane before the second stimulus arrives, so the twitches fuse to produce a steeply rising, almost smooth contraction of much greater maximum force than the single twitch and the lower-frequency tetanus.

Twitches fuse to form tetani because, as explained at the beginning of Section 5.3, all muscles are to some degree extensible when relaxed; much of the active contraction performed during the initial phase of a twitch is dissipated in stretching the internal elastic components of the muscle itself, and is therefore not available to do work on external loads. However, if, as happens during tetanus, a second stimulus arrives before the active contraction of the first one has decayed, a greater proportion of the contraction it initiates is available to perform work on an external load, because the internal elastic components have been stretched by the first contraction.

■   Would you expect (a) the maximum twitch tension, (b) the total rise time of the twitch, (c) the ratio of maximum tetanus tension to maximum twitch tension, to be greater or smaller in short muscle fibres with numerous neuromuscular junctions and high conduction velocity of action potentials than in longer, more slowly conducting fibres with fewer neuromuscular junctions?

A greater density of neuromuscular junctions and high conduction velocity promote near-synchronous activation of all the sarcomeres so the internal elastic components would quickly be fully stretched by the active contraction, producing higher maximum twitch tension and a shorter time to peak tension. However, because the mechanical conditions of the twitch in such muscle fibres are more similar to those of a tetanic contraction, the ratio of maximum tetanus tension to maximum twitch tension would be lower in fibres adapted to very fast, powerful movement than in those that contract more slowly.

Looking closely at Figures 5.11b and 5.11c, you can see that the total force produced in response to the second stimulus does indeed appear to be greater than that elicited by the first stimulus. In the high-frequency tetanus (Figure 5.11c), the force produced by the muscle gradually wanes after about 0.6 s, although the stimulation frequency is unchanged. This effect, called **muscle**

fatigue, almost certainly involves several different mechanisms: transmission failure at the neuromuscular junction, depletion of the energy supply, and changes in the mechanisms that control contraction are among the processes implicated in this phenomenon, which is familiar to everyone who performs strenuous or repetitive actions.

Like the rates of most chemical reactions, the rates of increase in force production and the relaxation of muscles proceed much more slowly at lower temperatures. Certain muscles of homeothermic animals can produce steeply rising contractions like those shown in Figure 5.11, but the contractions of the muscles of poikilothermic slugs or sea anemones may take several seconds to reach peak force.

■   How would you expect the minimum frequency at which trains of twitches fuse to form tetani to change with temperature?

Twitch contractions would fuse to form tetani at a lower frequency in cooler muscles because each twitch lasts longer at lower temperatures.

The maximum speed of contraction, and the form and duration of the response to standard stimuli differ enormously between different muscles. Differences in sarcomere dimensions affect contraction velocity in the way expected from the crossbridge theory of muscle contraction. Muscles with longer A-bands have longer thick filaments with more crossbridges and so can contract faster. Those with longer I-bands (but not longer A-bands) can function at a greater range of lengths but the maximum shortening velocity is lower because a smaller proportion of the whole length of the muscle is overlap region (see Figure 5.1, rings 5 and 6).

5.3.3 Fibre types

In Section 5.3.2, we described how the work performed and time course of the contraction of a whole muscle depend upon external factors such as mechanical constraints, frequency of stimulation, state of fatigue of the muscle and temperature. However, there are also intrinsic differences in the structure and metabolism of individual muscle fibres within a whole muscle. The most important of these intrinsic differences are the maximum rate at which the contractile apparatus is capable of generating tension, the metabolic fuel used, and the way in which the motor nerves and plasmalemma initiate contraction. Most physiologists recognize four main types of fibres in mammalian skeletal muscles; similar categories of fibres can be distinguished on slightly different criteria in birds, reptiles, amphibians and fishes.

Tonic fibres (sometimes called 'slow' fibres) contract very slowly, and it is usually impossible to identify a twitch response to a single stimulus (see Figure 5.11a). They require very little energy to develop and maintain tension and their deep red colour shows that they are rich in myoglobin, the oxygen-binding pigment that takes up oxygen from the haemoglobin in the blood. Their economical metabolism and plentiful reserves of oxygen mean that they can sustain prolonged activity because they fatigue very slowly. Tonic fibres are rare in the muscles of most mammals.

Muscle fibres that can produce a twitch contraction in response to a single stimulus are called phasic fibres, although the time course of the twitch may be quite different from that shown in Figure 5.11a. There are three main types of phasic fibres that differ in the rates at which they fatigue and in the sources of their metabolic energy. The energy supply of **slow phasic fibres** comes from both oxidative phosphorylation and glycolysis. They usually contain many mitochondria and are rich in myoglobin. They can therefore contract repeatedly or continuously for long periods without significant fatigue.

The two main types of fast phasic fibres are distinguished mainly by the metabolic pathways by which ATP is synthesized. **Fast oxidative fibres** also derive most of their energy from oxidative phosphorylation, and therefore contain numerous mitochondria; as long as the blood supply is maintained, they are resistant to fatigue during prolonged exercise. Fast oxidative fibres are usually rich in myoglobin and so are red. The other group, the **fast glycolytic fibres**, generate ATP from glycolysis and hence have very few mitochondria; they contain very little myoglobin and so are pale pink or white. The maximum rate of ATP breakdown in fast glycolytic fibres is several times greater than that in slow phasic fibres. Glycolytic fibres contract at about the same speed as fast oxidative fibres but their small store of high-energy phosphate compounds is quickly exhausted and they fatigue very rapidly, sometimes within a second or two, when stimulated repeatedly.

Synchronous, powerful activation of all the fibres of a muscle can generate forces large enough to break the bones to which they are attached. Simultaneous stimulation may be achieved artificially (e.g. by an electric shock), but it occurs very rarely, probably never, as part of natural movements, and indeed there seem to be neural control mechanisms that prevent it from happening (Section 6.5.1). During many activities, including steady walking, most of the fast glycolytic fibres are moved passively by the forces produced by the other fibres; the movements of high velocity and high power produced by the glycolytic fibres are important only for brief bursts of strenuous activity, such as escape swimming, take-off in flight, and running very fast.

The different types of fibres can be distinguished using histochemical techniques: small pieces of muscle are frozen within a few minutes of the animal's death and the thin sections cut from it are treated in ways that reveal differences in fibre biochemistry. Sometimes stains that combine selectively with particular enzymes are used. For example, the section in Figure 5.12a has been stained to show the distribution within the muscle of succinate dehydrogenase, a key enzyme of the tricarboxylic acid (TCA) cycle which takes place in the mitochondria. Fibres in which oxidative phosphorylation is an important source of ATP appear darker, but glycolytic fibres, which have few mitochondria, take up very little stain. Histochemists also take advantage of the as yet unexplained fact that the myosin ATPase (Section 5.2) of fast fibres is unaltered even by quite strong alkalis, whereas that of slow fibres retains its affinity for the stain only in acid solution.

■ To what category does the fibre indicated by the small arrows in Figure 5.12 belong?

It is a slow phasic fibre; it appears much paler than its neighbours in Figure 5.12b, but it takes up large quantities of the stains used in Figures 5.12a and

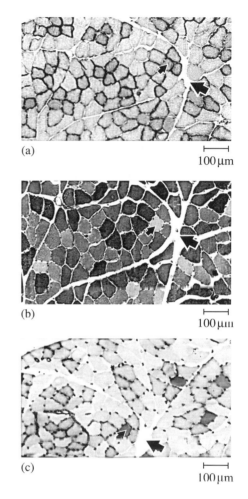

(a)   ⊢——⊣ 100 μm

(b)   ⊢——⊣ 100 μm

(c)   ⊢——⊣ 100 μm

Figure 5.12 Serial sections of the biceps femoris muscle in the thigh of an adult guinea-pig, stained in three different ways, and reproduced to the same scale. The collagenous material around and between the fibres is invisible because it does not take up the stain, but its distinctive shapes (large arrows) enable you to identify the same fibres in all three sections. (a) When stained for the mitochondrial enzyme succinate dehydrogenase, the darker fibres are those for which oxidative phosphorylation is the major pathway for ATP production, i.e. slow and fast oxidative fibres. (b) At pH 9.5, the myosin ATPase of both kinds of fast fibre stain darkly but the slow phasic fibres remain pale. (c) At pH 4.6 (acidic), the myosin ATPase of the slow fibres are more densely stained than the more abundant fast fibres; the black dots are nuclei, which take up stain in acid solution. Note the much smaller scale of these light micrographs compared to the electron micrographs.

5.12c, so it and the other oxidative fibres here appear darkly stained. These and other histochemical methods can be combined to identify the major types of fibre in vertebrate muscles.

It may seem strange that the fastest contractile machinery of mammalian muscles should have the fewest mitochondria and a very low reserve of oxygen. Fast glycolytic fibres consume energy very rapidly and there is not sufficient space between the myofibrils for as many mitochondria as would be necessary to sustain the supply of aerobically generated ATP. These fibres are able to produce fast, powerful contractions because they consist mostly of myofibril; only a small fraction of their volume is occupied by mitochondria and other supply apparatus.

■   Would you expect fast glycolytic fibres to be able to use fatty acids as an energy source as readily as they use glucose?

No. Most vertebrate tissues can metabolize fatty acids only by aerobic pathways, so these fast fibres use glucose almost exclusively. Free glucose in the muscle and surrounding blood is exhausted after only a few seconds of exercise; more glucose is quickly produced by breakdown of glycogen in the muscle fibres, but these energy stores are enough for only for a few hundred contractions, or about five minutes of strenuous exercise in humans.

The other types of fibre utilize both fats and carbohydrates. The provision of lipids to fuel muscular activity during exercise may be the main reason why intermuscular adipose tissue, which is always only a small fraction of the total adipose tissue in the body, occurs in close association with skeletal muscle. It has several physiological properties consistent with a role as a local fuel supply for adjacent muscle fibres. Intermuscular adipose tissue is relatively abundant in most meat animals and humans compared with small mammals such as rats, but it is also abundant in certain muscles of some wild mammals, such as fin whales, where it is intimately associated with the bundles of muscle fibres (Figure 5.13).

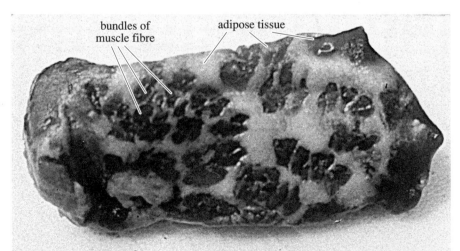

Figure 5.13   Muscle and adipose tissue in the muscles of the floor of the mouth of a fin whale, *Balaenoptera physalus*. Ruler scale in mm.

High-resolution electron microscopy and immunohistochemistry (the use of antibodies linked to pigments or fluorescent molecules to identify and locate particular proteins) have demonstrated differences between fibre types in the structure and protein content of the M-lines and Z-lines and in the isoforms of myosin light and heavy chains (Section 5.2.1). Isoforms are slightly different forms of proteins usually distinguished by the capacity of antibodies raised against a protein extracted from one source to bind to another. Tonic fibres with 'slow' myosin isoforms occur in narrower fibres that contain proportionately more nuclei (and less cytoplasm) than those in which 'fast' myosin predominates.

Fast fibres tend to have fewer visible bands in the M-line and narrower Z-lines than slow fibres, and 'slow' and 'fast' myosin appear to be distinct proteins that form slightly different thick filaments, but all these features have not been consistently found in all the fibres identified on histochemical criteria to belong to one or other category. The picture that emerges from these complicated and fast-moving studies is of continuous variation in structure and composition of muscle fibres rather than discrete categories: even in large muscles such as the flight muscles of the chicken breast (pectoralis), very few fibres have been found to be identical in every detail. Different isoforms of the subunits of myosin are now known to be important determinants of contraction velocity, but since we do not know which of the other features compared determine energy utilization, the functional implications of this wide range of structures and compositions are unclear.

Although it is technically possible to study single fibres dissected from a whole muscle, physiologists usually find it quicker and more convenient to make use of those few specialized muscles in which most of the fibres are of only one type. In most mammals, certain postural muscles around the spinal column and the soleus muscle in the calf region of the lower leg, which steadies the ankle joint during standing, consist of about 85% slow phasic fibres. The sartorius muscle of the thigh and the muscles that flex and extend the fingers and toes (known as flexor digitorum longus (FDL) and extensor digitorum longus (EDL), see Figure 2.14) usually consist mainly of fast phasic fibres. It is important to emphasize, however, that the terms 'fast' and 'slow' refer to the *relative* rates of contraction; as with most other aspects of metabolism (Section 3.3), the *absolute* rate at which chemical energy is converted into mechanical work depends upon body size. Thus the fast fibres of a horse probably have a lower maximum intrinsic speed of shortening than the slow fibres of a mouse.

The criteria upon which fibres are distinguished and the neural control of invertebrate muscles differ in several important ways from that of vertebrates, but similar physiological principles apply: muscle is a very active tissue that needs a copious supply of ATP to sustain contraction. Notice the large mitochondrion lying close beside the contractile proteins in bumble bee flight muscle (Figure 5.10) and the numerous mitochondria almost filling the spaces between the myofibrils in Figure 5.4b, as they do in the human muscle shown in Figure 5.3.

5.3.4 The determinants of the fibre-type composition of muscles

Most mammalian muscles resemble the biceps femoris muscle of the guinea-pig (Figure 5.12) in consisting of a mixture of several types of fibre; different combinations of fibres are stimulated to contract according to the speed and form of the movement. The principal leg muscles of people leading an ordinary life consist of about equal numbers of slow phasic and fast phasic fibres. However, the fibre-type composition of the homologous muscles of trained athletes can be very different. Up to 76% of the fibres in the leg muscles of sprinters, who specialize in running very fast for 0.5–3.0 min, are of the fast glycolytic type, as are 88% of the muscle fibres of thoroughbred horses trained for short-distance flat racing; the limb muscles of greyhounds are said to be 97% fast phasic fibres, most of them deriving energy from anaerobic glycolysis.

Champion marathon runners can cover 42.2 km (more than 26 miles) in a little over 2 h, although 3–4 h might be more typical for an amateur athlete. As few as 21% of the fibres in the large leg muscles of such athletes are of the fast glycolytic type, the rest being mostly fast oxidative fibres that use mainly fatty acids as an energy source during prolonged, strenuous exercise. However, all muscle fibres have to use a certain amount of glucose as well as fatty acids, which, after the first few seconds, is obtained from the breakdown of glycogen stored in the muscles themselves or in the liver.

■   What simple measurement would indicate when the muscles of an animal or person who is exercising vigorously starts to use substantial quantities of lipid?

The respiratory exchange ratio (RER) is 1 when carbohydrate is the only fuel, but decreases when fat is being oxidized. In vigorous exercise, the striated muscles become the largest consumers of energy and oxygen, so the RER measured for the whole body reflects the metabolism of the locomotory muscles fairly accurately. The thigh muscles of a resting, well-fed person contain about $0.1 \, \text{mmol} \, \text{g}^{-1}$ glycogen but this carbohydrate reserve is halved after 20 min of fast running, and exhausted after 80–90 min, long before the much larger stores of lipid in adipose tissue are significantly depleted. Switching to lipids as the main fuel source for muscles early in the bout of exercise and using mostly oxidative fibres helps to spare the precious glycogen, and thereby enables athletes to keep going longer, but glycogen depletion is always the main cause of severe exhaustion after prolonged, strenuous exercise.

The leg muscles of saddle horses bred and trained to carry heavy riders over long distances consist of about 67% fast fibres. Many of the differences between individuals in fibre-type composition seem to be genetically determined; in this sense, champion athletes and racehorses are born, not made. But there is also some evidence that physical training can cause certain fast glycolytic fibres to acquire the biochemical machinery that enables them to derive energy from the aerobic metabolism of fatty acids; so even people who are not endowed with the appropriate physique can improve their athletic performance by practice.

In newborn mammals, all muscle fibres are relatively small and more or less similar in structure and biochemical properties, depending mainly upon oxidative metabolism. All muscle fibres grow rapidly during infancy and childhood (Section 2.4) and, by weaning, most of the larger fibres have become fast glycolytic whereas the smaller ones remain oxidative. Several lines of evidence indicate that the neural input to the muscle influences this maturation, and is certainly essential to the transformation of fibres from one type to another in fully formed muscle.

Investigators have interchanged the innervation of the soleus muscle (85% slow phasic fibres) and the adjacent EDL muscle (mainly fast phasic fibres; Section 5.3.3) in the hindlimb, allowed the motor neurons to establish sound contacts with their new fibres, then studied their mechanics of contraction and their composition. Relatively large mammals such as cats or rabbits have to be used for such experiments because rat motor neurons are too small to be handled, but the subjects are able, indeed encouraged, to exercise freely. A year after the operation, the total duration of a single twitch (see Figure 5.11a) of soleus muscles that had received the EDL innervation was only 25 ms, compared with 87 ms in similarly treated animals in which the innervation was unaltered. There were also differences in the properties of the light and heavy chains of myosin and in the activities of oxidative and glycolytic enzymes. Similar experiments have shown that fast fibres could be made slower, and slow fibres faster by cutting their motor neurons and allowing them to be re-innervated by different nerves.

Advances in microelectronics have enabled muscle physiologists to determine experimentally whether these effects arose from the pattern or frequency of action potentials or from some chemical factor. Small stimulator capsules were placed in the abdomen and connected by fine wires to certain muscles in one hindlimb with the homologous muscle on the other side serving as a control. The muscles could be thus stimulated continuously for up to 20 weeks, enabling investigators to simulate or oppose the effects of removal of the muscles' own motor neurons and their reinnervation by different ones. The duration of a single twitch, the isoform of myosin and various aspects of energy metabolism were found to have changed in muscles thus stimulated for as little as 12 weeks. None of these features changed in cross-innervated muscles that were stimulated for a similar period in the mode characteristic of their original innervation.

■   How do these experiments confirm the suggestion that the pattern of electrical activity in the plasmalemma rather than trophic effects determines the chemical composition and mechanical properties of muscle fibres?

Changes in electrical activity without cross-innervation alter the type of fibres in the muscle, but cross-innervation without changes in electrical activity do not.

The changes occurred much faster under artificial stimulation than ever happens naturally (in less than a quarter of the time) because the stimuli were applied continuously; normally the muscle would not be used all the time, and hence would receive the action potentials in the characteristic pattern only intermittently. Over a period of weeks or months, the pattern of electrical activity in the plasmalemma somehow activates the genes for certain kinds of myosin, troponin and M-line proteins which form fast or slow fibres, and activates changes in metabolism and fuel utilization.

The fibre-type composition of muscle can also alter under selective breeding and indeed evolutionary changes in the relative masses of muscles, and in the proportions of different fibres, are some of the most important changes that equip related species for different habits and habitats. The breast muscles of ducks and pigeons are dark red and consist mainly of oxidative fibres, which are active during steady, prolonged flight. Interspersed between them are some fast glycolytic fibres which may be used to provide additional power for short periods during take-off.

■   From your own experience, what would you expect the fibre composition of the flight (i.e. breast) muscles in domestic hens and turkeys to be?

The flight muscles of these birds are pale because almost all the fibres are of the fast glycolytic type and blood perfusion is very low. Wild turkeys and poultry live in dense forests and they fly mainly in brief but strenuous bursts, often from feeding sites on the ground to the safety of nearby trees; they do not migrate and rarely fly above the forest canopy. Farm turkeys and hens kept in small cages do not fly at all. Artificial selective breeding has produced birds with relatively massive breast muscles that are nearly white, indicating that their blood supply is even more sparse than that of their wild ancestors.

■   Could selective breeding ever produce breast muscle that was pure white?

No. Even if the muscles do not need oxygen and other blood-borne nutrients for contraction, such supplies are certainly necessary for growth and maintenance. Like most modern domestic livestock (Section 1.3.2), poultry are selected to grow unnaturally fast so their muscles must receive a certain amount of blood. However, the difference in colour between a chicken breast muscle, and those of wild duck, grouse or pigeon gives you an idea of how much more blood perfusion is required to sustain vigorous exercise than to support even rapid growth.

Flight muscles are used only for flight, but the leg muscles are essential for both standing and running. These activities involve different kinds of fibre, so some compromise has to be reached in animals that do a great deal of standing and running. Ratites (emus, ostriches, rheas and cassowaries) do not fly but they can run very fast over long distances to escape from predators. If undisturbed, these exceptionally large birds spend most of the day standing or walking slowly while eating, and lie down only to sleep or incubate their eggs. Australian biologists have recently studied the gross anatomy and fibre-type composition of the leg muscles of their native ratite, the emu (*Dromaius novaehollandiae*). The largest muscle of the lower leg, the gastrocnemius, was found to consist almost entirely of fast fibres, 55–72% fast glycolytic and 28–25% fast oxidative. Only the much smaller digital flexor muscles resembled the situation in the homologous muscle of most other birds in containing a mixture of approximately equal numbers of slow, fast glycolytic and fast oxidative fibres.

■   What can you conclude from these observations about the roles of these muscles in standing, walking and running?

The gastrocnemius must be used almost exclusively for fast running: it is not equipped to contribute to standing or slow walking. These actions must be powered and maintained by the digital flexor muscles, and the gastrocnemius is probably relaxed and electrically silent in undisturbed birds.

This arrangement, in which muscles of different metabolic capacities have similar anatomical connections and are used for contrasting functions, is also common in fishes. As in fishes, most of the work most of the time is performed by quite small muscles, and the largest, most conspicuous muscles are inactive except during brief periods of vigorous exercise, such as chasing prey or escaping from predators.

Summary of Section 5.3

Muscle contraction is started by depolarization of the plasmalemma, normally following the arrival of an action potential at the fibre's neuromuscular junction. The depolarization spreads through the T-tubules and causes the release of calcium ions from the sarcoplasmic reticulum, and thereby causes ATP breakdown and contraction. Studies of isolated muscle protein suggest that the myosin light chain is essential for generating movement but not for ATPase activity. *In vitro* studies of isolated muscles show that a single stimulus produces a twitch, and a train of stimuli, a tetanus. Production of force wanes during prolonged tetanic contractions because the muscle fatigues. The four main types of muscle fibres differ in their maximum rate of contraction and their energy metabolism and in the kind of myosin they contain. The large differences between muscles in different species, and between different muscles in the same individual, in the intrinsic rate of shortening and hence in the form and duration of the twitch and tetanus contractions can be explained in part by the types of fibres of which they are composed. Muscles with similar anatomical connections but composed of different types of fibres may have very different functions. Fibres change in 'type' during ontogeny; changes in fibre type can also be induced by cross-innervation or by artificially stimulating the muscle fibre for days or weeks.

5.4 Muscle in whole-body metabolism

Most textbooks leave the story here, but since the main theme of this course is the physiology of the animal as a whole, it is appropriate to mention some other ways in which muscles contribute to whole-body metabolism. Movement might be the most important function of muscle, and is certainly the most widely studied, but it is not its only role. Like bone, liver, adipose tissue and indeed most other tissues, muscle is capable of many different metabolic pathways and contributes to several physiological functions.

Muscle is the most massive tissue in the body (except in very obese or atrophied individuals) and thus is by far the largest repository of proteins, and a major participant in protein turnover (Section 2.1.2). The previous sections have concentrated on the structure and properties of the 80% of the volume of muscle fibres occupied by myofibrils and the 10% or so that is membranes and mitochondria. The remaining 10% of muscle volume performs several biochemical processes not directly related to contractility. Although these processes represent only a small fraction of the muscles' own energy expenditure, they make an essential contribution to the metabolism of other body tissues.

5.4.1 Properties of muscle other than contractility

Muscle is the major site of disposal of glucose that enters the blood following a meal rich in carbohydrates and thus is central to glucose homeostasis of the body as a whole. The muscle plasmalemma contains many insulin receptors and its capacity to take up glucose is stimulated rapidly and effectively by insulin secreted into the blood in response to a rise in blood glucose. Once inside the muscle, some of the glucose may be oxidized at once, but most of it is converted into glycogen and stored as such granules in and around the fibres, as shown in Figure 5.14.

The turnover of glycogen in muscle is fairly rapid. Abrupt increases in glycogen can cause the skeletal muscles to swell noticeably, enough to make tight clothes feel tighter over the hips and thighs, within about half an hour of eating a large carbohydrate-rich meal after many hours of fasting.

■   Why does uptake of glycogen cause muscles to swell?

Glycogen granules always have about three times their own mass of water associated with them, so the muscle takes up more water from the extracellular space as well as the glucose.

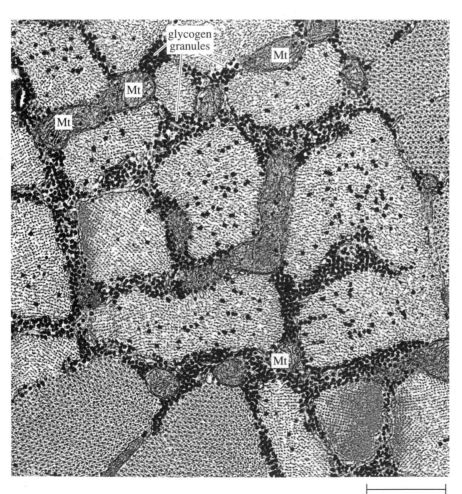

Figure 5.14 Electron micrograph of a transverse section of a human gastrocnemius (calf) muscle. Note the ranges of sizes and shapes of the myofibrils, and the many glycogen granules (stained dense black) and mitochondria (Mt) packed around them. The majority of the glycogen granules are seen between rather than within the myofibrils.

1 μm

Recent experiments have also demonstrated that skeletal muscle is the major source of the amino acid glutamine. Although constituting only 3% of most proteins (including muscle proteins), glutamine accounts for 35% of the free amino acids in the muscle cytosol, reaching concentrations as high as $20\,\text{mmol}\,\text{l}^{-1}$ in some human muscles, compared to about $0.5\,\text{mmol}\,\text{l}^{-1}$ for other amino acids.

■   Can you suggest a role for these free amino acids?

They may arise from the breakdown of muscle proteins and could be the raw material for the synthesis of more such proteins (Section 2.1.2). However, this role cannot account for the very high concentration of glutamine in the cytosol compared to its abundance in muscle proteins. An alternative interpretation is suggested by the observation that lymphocytes and some other cells of the immune system have a high capacity to utilize glutamine, both as a fuel and as a raw material for synthesis. Sepsis (i.e. the presence of foreign bacteria) stimulates the immune system and accelerates the rate of lymphocyte proliferation, thereby greatly increasing the system's need for fuel and substrates, including glutamine. Experiments using rats show that under such conditions, the skeletal muscles of the hindleg (and probably those elsewhere in the body as well) release more glutamine into the blood, suggesting that a major function of muscle's ability to synthesize and accumulate glutamine is to supply the metabolite to the immune system when required. What role, if any, the contractile components of muscle play in these metabolic pathways, and whether strenuous mechanical activity affects their efficiency, are currently under investigation.

■   How would an animal's ability to combat infection be affected by major damage to muscle (e.g. from a gunshot wound, or being crushed by a motor vehicle)?

Such injuries could impair the muscle's ability to supply the immune system with glutamine. Although for a long time the study of wound healing concentrated on local processes in particular tissues (see Chapter 2), it is now becoming clear that all major injuries (surgical or accidental) have many effects on the body's metabolism as a whole, among them glutamine metabolism.

5.4.2 Protein turnover in muscle

As described in Section 2.1.2, the constituents of tissues are continuously replaced, and such turnover is an integral part of the mechanisms of their growth and their capacity to adapt to new activities and to repair injury. Being near the surface of the body and around the limbs, and sustaining high strain forces, muscle is very susceptible to mechanical damage — bruises, sprains and worse. It is also continually adapting to changes in habits and activities: physical training both increases muscle mass and improves the efficiency of muscle metabolism, but we quickly lose 'fitness' after a few weeks of relative inactivity. Both processes are due in part to changes in the relative rates of degradation and synthesis of contractile proteins and internal membranes, and hence in the addition or loss of myofibrils from muscle fibres.

In striated muscle, calpain (Section 2.1.2) is the major agent of breakdown of myofibrillar proteins. Perhaps surprisingly, the enzyme does not cleave myosin and actin, but vigorously attacks desmin, nebulin, and parts of titin, Z-lines and the troponin complex.

■ Which aspects of myofibril structure would break down first?

Nebulin and troponin are parts of the thin filament and desmin connects the Z-lines in adjacent myofibrils (Section 5.2.1), so the I-bands and the Z-lines would be the first features of the muscle to be disrupted.

■ How could the activity of such an enzyme be increased by running and other strenuous physical activity?

Calpain is a calcium-activated enzyme (Section 2.1.2). One form, m-calpain, is active at calcium concentrations of around $1 \, mmol \, l^{-1}$, and the other, μ-calpain, is active at micromolar calcium concentrations ($3–50 \, \mu mol \, l^{-1} \, Ca^{2+}$). The calcium concentration in the cytosol of resting muscle is low (Section 5.3.2), lower than that of almost all other types of cells, and too low for either form of calpain to become active. The agent of the coupling between excitation of the plasmalemma by its motor neuron and contraction of the sarcomeres is the release of calcium ions from the SR into areas around the contractile proteins (Section 5.3.2). More contraction means that relatively high concentrations of calcium prevail for a larger proportion of the time, increasing the chance of calpain being activated.

As explained in Section 2.4.1, more mechanical activity also stimulates growth and regeneration of fibres, so normally the net effect of more frequent or more prolonged periods of higher intracellular calcium is a slightly higher rate of turnover of the muscle fabric, which may improve the muscle's strength and its ability to take up and use oxygen and fuels efficiently. These effects contribute to physical training that improves muscle performance and endurance.

5.4.3 Muscular dystrophy

Human diseases of the contractile mechanism itself are rare, possibly because fetuses with severely defective contractility would not survive gestation. But several disorders of the muscle membranes and the neural control of movement are both devastating and moderately common. One of the best known is Duchenne muscular dystrophy, named after the French neurologist and physician, Guillaume Duchenne, who, in the 1840s and 1850s, made the first thorough study of the disease and the first serious (though unsuccessful) attempts to treat it. The disease affects boys from early childhood and is due to a defective gene carried on the X chromosome. It involves progressive weakening and atrophy of skeletal and heart muscle, usually leading to death from cardiac or respiratory insufficiency before the age of 25. During the last ten years, many different kinds of investigations, from molecular biology and ultrastructure to comparative medicine and studies of muscle mechanics and growth, have combined to elucidate several major features of the disease, and to indicate some possible therapies. The following brief account illustrates how these diverse approaches come together, and is not intended to be comprehensive or conclusive.

In the early stages of the disease (around the age of 2–4 years), affected boys are not disabled and indeed some of their muscles, notably the gastrocnemius, are often larger than normal, but biochemical examination of blood samples reveal exceptionally high levels of enzymes derived from muscle fibres, such as creatine kinase (CK).

■ How could you explain the presence of such enzymes in blood serum?

They must have diffused out of muscle fibres in which the sarcolemma was torn or had become leaky.

By the age of 5–7, the muscles are noticeably wasted and strength is diminished. Electron micrographs (Figure 5.15) of small samples of muscle from such boys showed clearly that the immediate cause of these symptoms is disordered, incomplete sarcomeres and damaged myofibrils. Figure 5.15a shows two stages of breakdown of the muscle fibres. The lower fibre is necrotic: the muscle proteins have been reduced to a homogenous mass, and almost no ordered

Figure 5.15 (a) Adjacent muscle fibres showing two stages of breakdown in Duchenne muscular dystrophy. (b) Fragments of myofibrils broken up by calpain. The cell in the centre is a polymorphonuclear leucocyte with a large, irregularly shaped nucleus, and that on the lower right is a part of a macrophage.

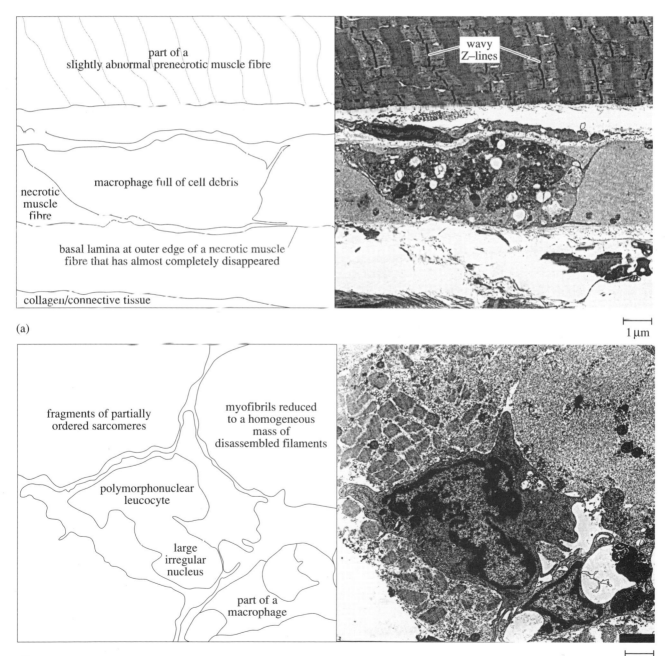

structure is visible. The other (upper) is only slightly abnormal, with wavy Z-lines and abnormally large T-tubules. The large macrophage in the centre is full of cell debris. On the upper left of Figure 5.15b, the myofibrils are reduced to a mass of A-bands (consisting mostly of thick filaments), the Z-lines having been broken up by calpain. Cells of the immune system, including a macrophage (Figure 5.15a) and a polymorphonuclear leucocyte (Figure 5.15b), have moved into the dying muscle fibre. By the time these defects are well advanced, the abnormally high levels of CK in the serum decrease and continue to decline as the children become older. Cells of connective tissue and adipose tissue may accumulate outside the dying muscle fibres.

After an intensive search for laboratory animals in which to investigate the disease, scientists eventually found several mutant strains of mice, and certain cats and dogs that develop many, but not all, of the symptoms of muscular dystrophy observed in humans. Much of the detailed information about the initial stages and progress of the disease comes from the comparative study of these animal models.

In 1987, scientists investigating the disease identified a gene apparently associated with muscular dystrophy (in boys as well as mice), and named its product **dystrophin**, but it was not until several years later that the protein produced by this gene was successfully isolated and characterized. Dystrophin is a large protein, M_r 427 000, with structural resemblances to α-actinin and other cytoskeletal proteins, but it is present in only very small quantities, constituting only 0.002% of the total muscle protein (2% of membrane-associated muscle proteins). It occurs on the inside of the plasmalemma of all normal striated muscles, and in many other tissues including non-striated muscle, certain neurons and the retina and cornea of the eye, but is greatly reduced or absent from dystrophic muscles.

The protein can be located in electron micrographs of muscle using specific antibodies to which particles of gold are attached, so each dystrophin molecule is marked by an electron-dense blob (Figure 5.16). As you can see from Figure 5.16, in normal muscle dystrophin is scattered thinly but fairly evenly across the plasmalemma. This labelling procedure never reveals any dystrophin in biopsies from boys with Duchenne muscular dystrophy, but the protein may be present in people suffering from other kinds of muscular dystrophy.

By studying the form of contractions of muscles isolated from certain strains of mice that develop muscular dystrophy, biologists showed that single twitches of dystrophic muscles developed less maximum force and lasted longer than those of the homologous muscles of normal mice.

■   What can you conclude from these facts about (a) the athletic ability of a dystrophic mouse or child, and (b) the underlying mechanisms?

The actions would be weaker and slower than those of a normal child or mouse. But the differences might be smaller than expected, because additional fibres may be recruited (Section 6.5) which together would partially compensate for the weakness of each fibre. The reduced peak force is to be expected if dystrophic muscle contains fewer functional sarcomeres. But this defect alone could not cause the twitch to last longer: the duration of contraction depends upon the SR releasing and taking up calcium ions. Measurements of Ca^{2+} ion concentration showed that although the maximum levels were similar in dystrophic and normal muscle fibres, the concentration did not return as quickly or as completely to the very low calcium level typical of normal relaxed muscle.

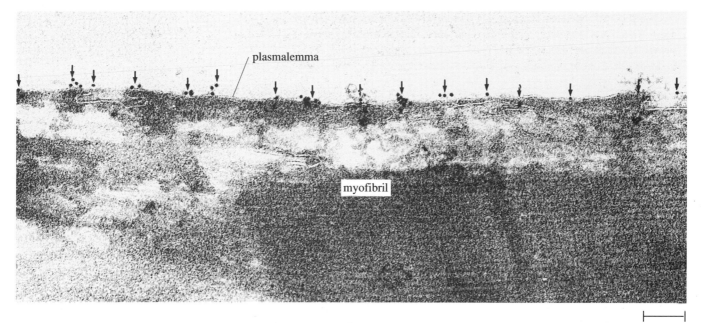

plasmalemma

myofibril

100 nm

Figure 5.16   An example of immunogold labelling of dystrophin in a normal human gastrocnemius muscle. The primary antibody was raised against one end of the dystrophin protein and conjugated to tiny particles of gold. The gold appears in this electron micrograph as dense spots, concentrated close to the plasmalemma, as indicated by arrows.

■   How could slightly more calcium around the sarcomeres for slightly longer at each contraction cause them to atrophy?

More calcium could activate calpain, and accelerate the breakdown of sarcomeres. The Z-lines are the first to be degraded (Section 5.4.2) by the enzyme and can be badly disrupted without visible damage to the rest of the sarcomere.

■   How would the muscle respond to an increased rate of muscle breakdown?

The mechanisms of regeneration and repair (Section 2.4) would be activated and would form new myofibrils, or even whole new muscle fibres, that replaced the disintegrating ones. Almost complete repair is, in principle, possible because in muscular dystrophy, the collagenous components of the sarcolemma remain intact, providing a cytoskeletal framework upon which new contractile material can reassemble. If regeneration mechanisms were operating efficiently, all defective myofibrils would heal and muscle function should be unimpaired. In young boys who are not yet obviously disabled by the disease, there is much evidence of regeneration: electron micrographs of biopsy samples reveal satellite cells (Section 2.4, Figure 2.13) dividing and new myofibrils forming in damaged fibres. But these regeneration processes wane in older boys and become barely detectable in the advanced stages of the disease.

■   Why does connective tissue develop in place of the degenerated muscle of older boys?

As pointed out in Section 2.4.2, in any damaged tissue that is slow to repair itself, fibroblasts proliferate and form scar tissue before regeneration is complete, often preventing further growth of the 'proper' tissue. This process happens extensively in human muscular dystrophy.

During the late 1980s, the absence of dystrophin was noted in certain dogs, cats and strains of mice, of which the best known is called the *mdx*-mouse. The defects appeared spontaneously and genetic studies of the lineages in which they were observed showed that most were X-linked, although the structure and position on the chromosome of the genes involved were different in each species. Both biochemical and electron microscope studies of muscle (see Figure 5.16) showed conclusively that dystrophin was absent from the membranes of their skeletal muscles. The interesting point is that although the the primary defects are almost identical, and the genetics impressively similar, the courses of the diseases are remarkably different from that of human muscular dystrophy.

After a brief period at 2–3 weeks old in which blood creatine kinase is abnormally high and fibre necrosis can be detected in the muscles, *mdx*-mice recover, the creatine kinase in the blood declines and many become larger and stronger than normal mice. The *mdx*-mice breed successfully and many live as long as genetically normal mice. Dystrophin deficiency in cats was only noticed because the affected animals appeared stiff, not because they were weak or atrophied. Far from being wasted, many such cats have hypertrophied muscles. However, in dogs that lack dystrophin, symptoms similar to human muscular dystrophy are evident early in life: all affected puppies are small and wasted, and some die from muscular weakness during their first year. As in boys, the sarcomeres are disordered and connective tissue replaces the atrophied muscles. However, the dogs that survive their first year improve and live many more years, some developing massive muscles similar to those of 'dystrophic' cats.

■   How do these observations on cats, dogs and *mdx*-mice help to explain the course of human muscular dystrophy?

They show that the debilitating symptoms of human muscular dystrophy that lead to early death are *not* an inevitable consequence of the absence of dystrophin: cats and *mdx*-mice thrive, although their dystrophin genes are mutated and so produce a defective protein. Far from becoming wasted, their muscles grow massive and strong.

■   What treatment for human muscular dystrophy does this conclusion suggest?

Symptoms could be cured if genetically normal myoblasts (Section 2.4) could become established and grow to replace the dystrophin-deficient muscle fibres. Physicians are trying such therapy, but there are always immunological problems associated with introducing foreign tissues into the body and the introduced myoblasts do not migrate far into the muscle.

The observations on *mdx*-mice show that the decrease with age of the serum CK (also observed in boys) is not due simply to fewer muscle fibres being left to leak enzymes into the blood: there is actually more muscle in the mice, so their sarcolemmas must have become less leaky. Although, in the early stages of the disease, high serum creatine kinase, necrotic muscle fibres, etc., occur in very young *mdx*-mice, their muscles respond by growing so much that they become hypertrophied, and there is no space within them for connective tissue to grow. The sarcolemma seems to strengthen with advancing age, so it becomes less permeable or less susceptible to mechanical damage.

■   What normal ageing process could explain this change?

The collagen content of muscles increases steadily from early in the juvenile period onwards (Section 4.5.2). Most collagen is extracellular, accumulating in and around the sarcolemma.

The problem of muscular dystrophy now becomes one of growth, tissue regeneration and ageing rather than of muscle physiology *per se*, and that is where we must leave this story. Although the emphasis has now shifted, it is clear that mechanical studies, our understanding of the organization of the cytoskeleton, membranes and contractile apparatus, and of interactions between muscle and adjacent tissues, and a knowledge of genes for muscle proteins were all essential to reaching this conclusion. Without such detailed knowledge, the mechanism of this disease would not have been elucidated.

The story of muscular dystrophy illustrates the intricacy of the biochemical mechanisms that regulate turnover and contractility of muscle: the absence of one rare protein can lead, over many years, to self-destruction of the whole muscle mass. Perhaps we should be more impressed by how well the system normally retains its intricate structure and continues to function efficiently for so long in the face of over-exertion, bruising, oxygen deficiency and temporary nutrient shortages.

Summary of Section 5.4

In addition to its major roles in maintaining posture and producing movement, muscle is a major short-term repository of glucose and takes up and releases glutamine which is an essential fuel for the immune system. A primary defect of Duchenne muscular dystrophy is the lack of dystrophin, a protein associated with the plasmalemma. Its absence probably weakens the sarcolemma, making it more susceptible to mechanical damage which prevents the muscle fibres from maintaining their normal low internal calcium concentration. Raised concentrations of calcium stimulate fibre breakdown, which in small species such as mice may be balanced by fibre growth, leading to normal or hypertrophied muscles, but in humans produces gradual atrophy of muscles. Affected humans become progressively disabled as regeneration and repair fail to keep pace with destruction of muscle fibres.

Objectives for Chapter 5

When you have completed this chapter, you should be able to:

5.1   Define and use, or recognize definitions and applications of each of the **bold** terms.

5.2   Describe the gross anatomy, fine structure and chemical composition of a typical vertebrate muscle.

5.3   Outline some differences in the composition and structure of muscles from different kinds of animals and explain their functional implications.

5.4   Describe some passive mechanical properties of living muscle and explain why a knowledge of these properties is essential to our understanding of the role of the muscles in the intact animal.

5.5   Outline the main events leading to contraction of muscles *in situ* and describe the mechanical response of muscle to one or several artificial stimuli *in vitro*.

5.6   Describe the main types of muscle fibre in mammals and explain why their properties are believed to represent intrinsic differences in the energy transduction system of the muscle.

5.7   Describe the contribution of muscle to the carbohydrate, lipid and protein metabolism of the whole body.

5.8   Outline our current understanding of the root cause and progression of Duchenne muscular dystrophy and explain briefly what kinds of laboratory studies contributed to the theories.

Questions for Chapter 5

(*Answers to questions are at the end of the book.*)

Question 5.1 (Objective 5.2)

Arrange the following components of muscle in order of increasing size: crossbridge, muscle fibre, myofibril, myoglobin, myosin, nebulin, sarcolemma, sarcomere, T-tubule, titin, Z-line.

Question 5.2 (Objectives 5.2 and 5.3)

Identify the features of muscle listed below as constant (i.e. universal to all striated muscle, although they may differ in abundance) or variable (i.e. present in only certain muscles or substantially different in chemical composition or arrangement between species or between different muscles of the same species):

Actin, ATPase, I-bands, myosin, M-lines, sarcolemma, sarcomeres, sarcoplasmic reticulum, sliding filaments, titin, troponin, T-tubules.

Question 5.3 (Objective 5.3)

Describe the fine structure and composition of (a) an insect muscle adapted to high-frequency, powerful contractions over short distances; (b) a vertebrate muscle adapted to generate force at a wide range of lengths.

Question 5.4 (Objective 5.4)

Why is it essential for muscles to be extensible? What would happen if all muscles were inextensible?

Question 5.5 (Objective 5.5)

Which of the following reasons (a)–(e) explaining why the total force during a twitch is less than that during tetanus are correct?

(a)   Contraction can take place only while the sarcolemma is depolarized by the motor neurons; because the electrical events on the sarcolemma last only a short time in a twitch, the contraction is terminated prematurely.

(b)   For a muscle *in vitro*, only a small minority of the muscle fibres are stimulated to contract during a twitch.

(c)   During a twitch, some of the force produced by the sarcomeres is dissipated in stretching the internal elastic components of the muscle.

(d)   During a tetanus, all the different types of muscle fibre contract at the same speed, thus producing greater total force.

(e)   When the stimulus frequency is low enough for the mechanical force to rise in 'steps', the external force generated by the mechanical response to the second stimulus is usually greater than that to the first, but smaller than that to the last stimulus of a prolonged tetanus.

Question 5.6 (Objective 5.6)

Describe the major differences in the structure, composition and normal function of oxidative and glycolytic muscle fibres in mammals and birds.

Question 5.7 (Objective 5.7)

(a)   List three biochemical mechanisms essential to the role of muscle in removing glucose from the circulation.

(b)   List three observations that suggest that glutamine is more important as a fuel for other tissues than as a constituent of muscle proteins.

Question 5.8 (Objective 5.8)

How has the study of laboratory and domestic animals with gene defects similar to those of boys suffering from Duchenne muscle dystrophy helped scientists to understand the biochemical mechanisms behind the disease?

CHAPTER 6   MUSCLE PERFORMANCE AND ITS NEURAL CONTROL

6.1 Introduction

This chapter is about muscle performance and how it is controlled by the nervous system. As already mentioned, contracting muscle is among the most metabolically active of all tissues. In all but the most sedentary animals, it is also a very abundant tissue, so clearly it has the potential for consuming a large share of the body's total energy budget. The study of muscle performance has revealed that the mechanical and thermal conditions under which the muscles are operating determine the speed of contraction, the maximum power produced and the rate of energy consumption. The performance and energetic cost of actions depend greatly upon how the muscles are deployed.

As already pointed out (Section 5.3.1), muscles have characteristic passive mechanical responses to external forces applied to them, as well as generating forces themselves. To formulate neural commands that produce precisely the 'intended' posture or movements, the nervous system needs information about the exact position of muscles and whole limbs, and about any such external forces acting on them. The many kinds of sense organs that measure such information are called **proprioreceptors** (from *proprio*, of one's own self) and, although we are rarely aware of them, their functions are indispensable to all movements.

The first part of this chapter is about muscle performance and refers mainly to the study of isolated, living muscles. The second part is about how the nervous system finds out about where limbs are in relation to each other and the trunk, how long each muscle is, what external forces are being applied to them, and how it uses such information to formulate and adjust the neural commands sent to the muscles to achieve the 'desired' actions in the most energetically efficient way.

6.2 The mechanics of contraction

In Figure 5.11, the force produced by the muscle was measured as tension development, but some shortening was also taking place. In an attempt to understand the mechanism of contractility from analysis of its mechanical performance, physiologists have devised apparatus in which most of the force produced by the muscle appears as either movement or tension development. The work performed by any mechanical system is defined as (force generated) × (distance moved); if the muscle shortens (and thereby moves or stretches tissues to which it is attached), it is said to have done **positive work**. A contraction that does not result in some shortening theoretically does not produce any external positive work at all; however, such a muscle is doing internal work in stretching its own passive elastic components (Section 5.3.1).

The ability of a muscle to produce tension without significant shortening can be studied separately by clamping it between two firm supports, thereby preventing it from shortening by more than a minute distance. In such apparatus, nearly all the external forces produced by the muscle appear as tension, and the muscle is said to be contracting isometrically (**isometric** = of the same length).* The maximum isometric tension (P_{max}) that vertebrate muscle can produce when contracting at its optimum temperature is about 100–400 kN m^{-2} (= 10–40 kPa) of muscle fibres; P_{max} differs little between muscles of different chemical composition (Section 5.3.3) or anatomical arrangement (Section 6.4.2).

Muscle shortening can be studied by attaching the muscles to a very light lever. The idealized state in which the muscle is not exerting any tension on a load is called an **isotonic** (= of the same force) contraction. As in the case of perfectly isometric contractions, completely isotonic contractions involve no work, but in practice, of course, the muscle is exerting a small force in accelerating its own mass. In contrast to maximum isometric tension, the maximum rate of isotonic shortening differs between different muscles by more than a thousandfold, from about 0.1 to 100 mm s^{-1}. As mentioned in Section 5.3.2, the rate at which muscles can shorten is probably their most widely ranging property and is important to their role in posture and locomotion (Chapter 8). It is important to emphasize that these concepts were developed to analyse the performance of excised muscles *in vitro*: in real life, most contractions involve both shortening and tension development (albeit in widely different proportions), and are thus neither perfectly isometric, nor perfectly isotonic.

During the 1920s and early 1930s, Archibald V. Hill and Walace Fenn performed detailed *in vitro* studies of the relationship between mechanical constraints on contraction and the total power output of excised muscles, particularly the leg muscles of the frog at 0 °C. They studied muscles stimulated at their natural resting length and contracting under a range of mechanical conditions from perfectly isometric to perfectly isotonic. They summarized their findings in the following equation ('Hill's equation'), which relates the maximum velocity of shortening (v_{max}) of any particular contraction to the tension that the muscle generates (P).

$$(P + a)v_{max} = b(P_{max} - P) \qquad \text{(Hill's equation)}$$

The constants a and b are specific for the particular muscle under investigation, and, as already mentioned, P_{max} is the maximum isometric tension. Hill's measurements are shown graphically in Figure 6.1. You can see that muscles shorten fastest when they have no external load. When P is equal to P_{max}, the right-hand side of the equation becomes zero and there is no shortening, i.e. the velocity is zero (Figure 6.1a) and the contraction is isotonic. The total power output (= force × velocity) of the muscle contracting under any particular conditions is given by $P \times v_{max}$ and is shown in Figure 6.1b.

■   Why are there two points on the curve in Figure 6.1b that indicate zero power output?

No power is produced when there is no shortening, as in an isometric contraction (i.e. the velocity is zero), and when no tension is produced, as in a

* Note that this meaning of 'isometric' is different from that used in connection with allometry (Section 3.1.2).

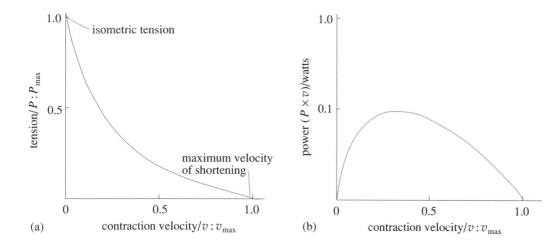

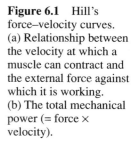

Figure 6.1 Hill's force–velocity curves. (a) Relationship between the velocity at which a muscle can contract and the external force against which it is working. (b) The total mechanical power (= force × velocity).

perfectly isotonic contraction. Note that the power output is maximal when the muscle is contracting relatively slowly, at only about one-third of its maximum possible speed of shortening (v_{max}).

■ On the basis of Figure 6.1, would you expect power output to be higher in nearly isometric or nearly isotonic contractions?

Power output would be higher in almost isometric than almost isotonic contractions because the peak of the curve of Figure 6.1b is nearer to zero contraction velocity than to v_{max} but the highest power output of all would occur in contractions that were neither isometric nor isotonic, but involved a small amount of shortening and much tension production. The maximum possible power output of mammalian muscle is about 0.5–1.0 watts (W) g^{-1} wet weight, sustainable for at most a few seconds, but the maximum power output sustainable for more than a second or two is only about 0.2–0.3 W g^{-1}.

A third mode of contraction involves arranging the external load so that it actively extends the muscle while the contraction is in progress. The muscle may thus be longer at the end of the contraction than it was at the start, all its energy having been used to exert tension on the load. Such contractions are said to produce **negative work**, because, as explained earlier in this section, some shortening is necessary for the muscle to be said to perform positive work, according to the strict definition.

In concluding this section, it is important to stress that all the physiological data described come from studies of isolated muscles working under artificial conditions. Professor Hill was an engineer by training and sought to produce a synthetic theory of muscle properties, as one might for a new kind of steel or plastic. The mechanical conditions and stimulus regimes were chosen for their convenience in quantifying the results and developing such a theory, not for their similarity to the conditions and neural commands under which the muscles operate in intact animals. Such measurements can at best indicate how muscles *might* operate in living animals and set limits on the maximum possible performance; information about how they *do* work involves measuring the magnitude and time course of forces produced by muscles in intact animals.

Recent advances in the technology for such measurements have shown that some of the concepts derived from the study of isolated muscle are of limited relevance to the function of the musculo-skeletal system as a whole in living animals (this topic is discussed in Chapter 8).

6.2.1 Length and tension

Hill's equation applies only to muscle at its natural resting length. However, muscle is often required to exert forces when longer or shorter than this length: muscles shorten as they contract isotonically, and they are also stretched passively by external forces and by the contraction of antagonistic muscles. How does the length of a muscle fibre affect the mechanical forces it can generate and its total power output?

The structural basis for the relationship of the length of the sarcomeres to the tension their contractile proteins could develop was demonstrated by the now famous measurements and observations conducted by Professor Andrew Huxley and his colleagues at University College, London, in 1967. To study single fast twitch fibres (Section 5.3.3) dissected from the leg muscles of frogs, they developed a most ingenious apparatus in which the length of an area in the centre of the fibre (where all the sarcomeres are of identical length in resting muscle) was held constant, thus enabling them to measure the isometric tension produced by that region of the fibre at precisely determined sarcomere lengths. The muscle fibre was bathed in a solution that maintained the integrity of the membranes and supplied oxygen, etc., and was stimulated to contract with artificial electrical pulses. A powerful phase-contrast microscope enabled the experimenters to measure the lengths of the A- and I-bands in the stimulated region of the fibre without the need for chemical fixation or stains.

■   What would have been the advantages of using (a) frogs, and (b) single fibres?

As mentioned in Section 5.1.1, muscles from poikilothermic animals such as frogs contract well at room temperature. Frogs are jumping animals so (for the reasons described in greater detail in Chapter 8), their muscles are adapted for fast shortening over a significant distance. As explained in Sections 5.2.1, 5.3 and 5.4, whole muscles always contain connective tissue as well as blood vessels, nerves, adipose tissue, etc., which have mechanical properties similar to the passive elastic properties of muscle. For accurate studies of the relationship between sarcomere structure and force production, these non-contractile components of muscle are best eliminated by dissecting out single fibres.

The results of these experiments are shown in Figure 6.2. Figure 6.2a resembles Figures 5.1, ring 5, and 5.7 and shows the 'standard' lengths of the regions of a sarcomere in frog muscle. Figure 6.2c shows sarcomeres at various lengths, numbered 1–6, that represent critical situations in the overlap between thick and thin filaments at different sarcomere lengths. Figure 6.2b shows the corresponding tension developed by the sarcomeres at these lengths.

In situation 1, the muscle fibre has been stretched far beyond its natural range of lengths, and the sarcomeres are stretched to 3.65 μm long, so there is almost no

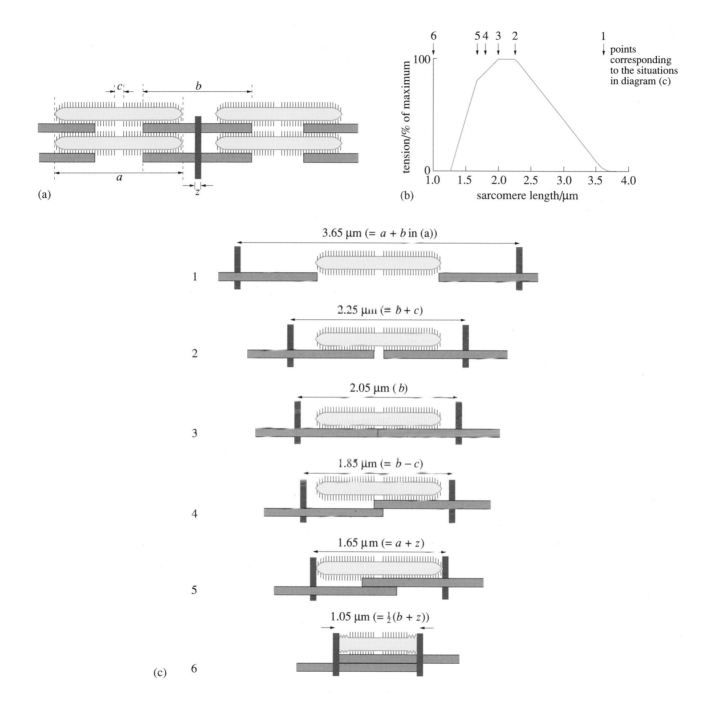

Figure 6.2   (a) Diagram of the major sarcomere components in frog muscle, not drawn to scale. The protrusions from the thick filaments represent the crossbridges. a, 1.6 μm; b, 2.05 μm; c, 0.2 μm; z, 0.05 μm. (b) The tension generated at different lengths by part of a single muscle fibre. The numbered arrows along the top show the situations of overlap that are portrayed in (c). (c) Critical situations in the overlap between thick and thin filaments at different sarcomere lengths.

overlap between thick and thin filaments, and, as shown on the extreme right of Figure 6.2b, no tension. Between situations 1 and 2, the number of crossbridges that are overlapping with thin filaments increases linearly with the decrease in the length of the sarcomere; the tension produced also increases, as shown in Figure 6.2b as you go from right to left. At point 2 (sarcomere length 2.25 μm), the ends of the thin filaments enter the zone around the M-line that is without crossbridges and a further decrease in sarcomere length to situation 3 does not cause a further increase in the number of crossbridges that are overlapped; the tension that the muscle fibre produced stays constant between situations 2 and 3, as shown in Figure 6.2b. At point 3 (sarcomere length 2.05 μm), the ends of the thin filaments butt against each other, and from 4 onwards the thin filaments overlap each other. The tension produced declines with further decrease of the sarcomere length and the rate of fall-off of tension increases at a sarcomere length of 1.65 μm, in which state the thick myosin filaments butt against the Z-line (point 5). The tension is zero at sarcomere lengths below 1.27 μm, when the filaments become crumpled as shown in situation 6 of Figure 6.2c.

■   What does this experiment show about the mechanism of force generation?

The highest force is produced at situations 2 and 3, when the portions of the thick filaments that bear crossbridges overlap to the greatest extent with the thin filaments. Less force is produced when the muscle is overstretched (situation 1) and when it is stimulated to shorten unnaturally far so that first the thin filaments (4), then the thick filaments and Z-lines (5) interfere with each other. We do not know exactly what this 'interference' comprises: the portions of thin filaments in the reverse half of the sarcomere might push 'backwards', producing negative amounts of tension because of their directional properties (remember that the filaments are polar structures, Section 5.2) or the thick filaments might crumple, which could decrease the number of crossbridges 'in touch' with actin in adjacent thin filaments.

■   Would the values shown on Figure 6.2b apply equally to all striated muscles?

No. Muscles with long sarcomeres are more extensible (Section 5.3.1) and can contract efficiently over a wide range of initial lengths, so the curve would have a longer, flatter top. Conversely, muscles such as bee flight muscle (Figure 5.10) would reach situation 5 if they shortened by more than a few per cent.

As explained in Section 6.4, the musculo-skeletal system is organized so that situations 1, 4, 5 and 6 never happen in normal muscle. However, in muscular dystrophy (Section 5.4.3), damaged myofibrils are chronically exposed to high concentrations of calcium, which causes excessive activation of the contractile mechanism that may lead to supercontraction, producing sarcomeres in a state that resembles situations 5 and 6 of Figure 6.2c. Such supercontracted sarcomeres are easily seen in electron micrographs, and their presence is a diagnostic feature of muscular dystrophy.

This experiment represents some of the best evidence for the theory that the contractile force is generated by interactions between the crossbridges and the thin filaments and that shortening involves the filaments sliding past each other. From a functional point of view, it explains why the initial length of muscle is so important to the maximum power that it can generate and, as explained in Section 6.3, to the quantity of ATP used per unit of mechanical work produced.

6.2.2 The effects of temperature

Several aspects of muscle physiology, including the maximum rate of shortening (v_{max}), maximum force production (P_{max}) and the rate of relaxation from a twitch (see Figure 5.11a) are among the processes most affected by body temperature. Table 6.1 shows the maximum rate of shortening, in muscle lengths per second, of various muscles measured *in vitro*. In general, muscles contract more slowly and produce less maximum force at lower temperatures. The leg muscles of the desert iguana (*Dipsosaurus dorsalis*) can contract seven times faster and produce ten times more force at the maximum temperature at which they were studied compared with the minimum. The rate of relaxation after single twitches and tetani (Section 5.3.2) is also much affected by temperature, that of the frog sartorius muscle decreasing by a factor of 2.2 for a 10 °C rise in temperature.

■ Why is an effect of temperature on relaxation more surprising than an effect on force or shortening (Table 6.1)?

The contractile proteins use ATP for shortening and force production but not during relaxation. However, relaxation involves other kinds of interactions between sarcomere proteins that are affected by temperature, and small amounts of ATP are used to fuel the calcium pumps in the sarcoplasmic reticulum (Sections 5.2, 5.3.2 and 5.4.3).

■ Do all striated muscles have similar properties at the same temperature?

No. There is a tenfold difference in velocity and a threefold difference in maximum power output between different muscles contracting at the same temperature. Notice also that, as in the case of fish (Book 2, Chapter 3, Section 5.5.2), the muscles of some species, particularly those of insects and

Table 6.1 Intrinsic maximum rate of shortening and maximum power output of different muscles measured *in vitro* at various temperatures.

Animal	Muscle	Velocity of shortening/lengths s^{-1}	Maximum power output/W kg^{-1}	Temperature/°C
Mouse	toe extensor muscle	22		37
	soleus (in the lower leg)	11	133	37
Rat	toe extensor muscle	17		37
	soleus	7	323	37
Chicken	slow phasic back muscle	18		35
	tonic back muscle	2		35
Tortoise	rectus femoris in thigh	1.5	7.1	20
Lizard	iliofibularis of hindleg	3.0	52	15
(desert iguana)		8.4	167	25
		14.6	325	35
		20.1	505	44
Locust	flight muscle	9	163	35
Scallop	shell-closing muscle	3		20

poikilothermic vertebrates such as the desert iguana, contract well enough to measure these parameters at a wide range of temperatures, while those of homeotherms work only at or close to their normal body temperature. Even if they are unable to contract efficiently at low temperature, most muscles are not permanently damaged by cooling (unless it is very prolonged) provided they do not freeze. Thus, the muscles of hibernators and species that become torpid function normally as soon as they are warm enough.

Summary of Section 6.2

Both mechanical conditions of contraction and the original length of the muscle determine how much power it can produce. For analysing the velocity of shortening, force production and energetics of isolated muscles, it is convenient to distinguish between isometric contractions, in which muscle length is held constant, and isotonic contractions, in which the muscle is free to shorten and does not produce external tension. If the muscle is stretched by an external force, while 'trying' to contract, it is said to produce negative work. Maximum force production is diminished if the sarcomeres are stretched so much that the region of overlap of the thick and thin filaments is reduced, or if the sarcomeres are supercontracted so that the thin filaments overlap or the thick filaments reach the Z-lines. Maximum velocity and maximum force production are lower and relaxation time longer at lower temperatures, but muscles differ greatly in how their properties change with temperature.

6.3 The energetics of contraction

Now we turn to a crucial aspect of muscle physiology: the relationship between the work that a muscle can do and the energy, in the form of ATP, that it consumes. Even at rest, striated muscle uses the largest share of the body's total energy expenditure, accounting for about 22% of BMR in adult men (Section 3.3.1). During strenuous exercise, the muscles may use three-quarters of the body's total energy and oxygen supply, so clearly any factors that alter the relationship between their energy utilization and work production would have a major effect on the energy economy of the body as a whole.

6.3.1 Heat production

Even when resting, the skeletal muscles make a significant contribution to the heat production of the mammalian body (Book 2), and during strenuous exercise so much heat is released as a by-product of muscle activity that special physiological mechanisms that dissipate it are brought into operation (Book 2, Chapter 8). In theory, measurements of the heat produced during contraction should yield valuable information about how and when the chemical energy is converted into mechanical work. However, the rates of the chemical reactions in muscle cannot be measured with the same accuracy and on as short a time-scale as heat production. The most convenient way of slowing down the chemical reactions that underlie muscle contraction is to lower the temperature (Book 2); consequently, most of our detailed information about the relationship between total mechanical power output and heat production comes not from mammalian muscles, but from frog muscles, which contract well at 0 °C. Two clear-cut and essential points emerge from studies of heat production. About 75% of the total energy consumed by isolated muscles contracting under controlled conditions is converted into heat. However, the rate at which heat is released is not constant throughout the contraction cycle: it is greatest during the early stages of an isometric contraction, when the muscle is doing work against its own internal elastic components (Section 5.3.1). The period of greatest heat production lasts only about 250 ms, even in muscles working at 0 °C. If the muscle is allowed to undergo net shortening, as it is in an isotonic contraction, more heat is released than in an isometric contraction of the same total mechanical power output. The extra heat, which seems to be a by-product of movement taking place within the sarcomeres, is often called the **heat of shortening**.

■   Would the muscles of your upper arm produce more heat during (a) sawing a log using a hand-saw, or (b) screwing or unscrewing a tight screw?

Sawing involves moving the elbow and shoulder through a wide angle; the biceps and triceps muscles in the upper arm shorten alternately through a considerable distance. The heat generated in these muscles soon makes the upper arm uncomfortably hot. When turning a stiff screw, both these muscles are working almost isometrically; although the muscles develop considerable tension, there is very little movement. One may become breathless from the exertion, and the muscles may feel noticeably tired afterwards, but overheating of the arm is not normally a problem. Thus heat production seems to be closely associated with doing mechanical work, particularly if there is substantial net shortening of the muscle.

Such heat not only wastes energy, it can be positively harmful, and valuable metabolites such as water may have to be used to dissipate it (Book 2). We are thus forced to the conclusion that, although the capacity for shortening is the most spectacular and remarkable property of muscle, it is not actually what it does most efficiently, or even most often. As we shall see in Chapters 7 and 8, tendons and skeletons are arranged in such a way that most of the muscles attached to them do not in fact normally shorten very much at all. The anatomical arrangement and neural control of most muscles ensure that they contract almost isometrically and, as often as not, muscles are actually becoming longer (by being stretched) while they are contracting, i.e. exerting a force that resists stretch.

Some heat continues to be produced for several minutes after all mechanical activity has ended. This recovery heat, first described by A.V. Hill, can be eliminated experimentally by keeping the muscle in an oxygen-free environment and by inhibiting lactic acid formation by adding iodoacetate to the bathing medium.

■   What conclusions could you draw from such an experiment?

Recovery heat is the result of active metabolic processes, which can be supported by both aerobic and anaerobic metabolism. The biochemistry of many of the chemical reactions taking place in muscle is sufficiently well understood for them to be studied *in vitro*. The energy released by all known reactions adds up to less than the total output of heat and mechanical work of living, intact muscle during active contraction, which suggests that there are unknown but important energy-releasing processes in muscle. Some such active metabolic processes take place when the muscle is relaxed, suggesting that some of the energy that powers muscle contraction is potential energy, i.e. the muscle needs to be in an energy-storing state before active contraction can begin.

A man generates power at a maximum rate of about 5.6 kW, and a woman about 3.4 kW, which is why minimization of heat production, and dissipation of excess heat are so important in prolonged exercise (Book 2, Chapter 8). People produce about 20% of this power, mostly as heat, just sitting quietly in a warm room, so it is hardly surprising that places like theatres or sports halls either have to be uncomfortably cold when you first arrive or have to have air conditioning to prevent actors and audiences from fainting with the heat before the end of the performance.

■ What kind of muscle activity is *adapted* to heat production?

Shivering (Book 2, Section 3.2.2) involves brief, fast contractions of many or all of the skeletal muscles and produces enough shortening to cause noticeable vibration of the limbs. Shivering thus maximizes heat production at the beginning of each of the numerous contractions and utilizes the heat of shortening effect.

6.3.2 Energy utilization

For most animals, the energetic cost of locomotion is a major item of the total energy budget. Therefore, measurements of the way in which chemical energy is utilized by the muscles are essential if we are to understand the functional significance of different kinds of locomotory apparatus and behaviour. The efficiency of a system that converts energy from one form into another, whether it is a steam engine converting coal into mechanical movement, or an electric motor, or a whole animal or a isolated muscle, is the ratio of the energy used to work performed.

The efficiency of any process in which chemical energy is converted into mechanical work is defined as:

$$\text{efficiency} = \frac{\text{mechanical energy output}}{\text{chemical energy input}}$$

The efficiency of conversion of chemical energy into mechanical work by a whole organism can be estimated by measuring the oxygen uptake (Book 1, Section 1.3). In one such experiment, a 70 kg man was found to consume oxygen at a rate of 25 cm^3 s^{-1} while walking up a 20% gradient to the horizontal at a speed of 0.8 m s^{-1}. The same man used oxygen at a rate of 4 cm^3 s^{-1} when resting.

■ Can you calculate this man's efficiency of energy conversion, given that aerobic metabolism using 1 cm^3 O$_2$ (g body mass)$^{-1}$ h^{-1} produces power at a rate of 5.6 W kg^{-1}?

The man consumed oxygen at a rate of 25 cm^3 s^{-1} while walking uphill, which is the equivalent of:

$$(25 \times 60 \times 60)/70\,000 = 1.286 \text{ cm}^3 \text{ g}^{-1} \text{ h}^{-1}$$

Of this oxygen consumption, $4\,cm^3\,s^{-1}$ ($= 0.206\,cm^3\,g^{-1}\,h^{-1}$) was used for the numerous metabolic processes that continue during locomotion as well as during 'rest'. Therefore $1.286 - 0.206 = 1.08\,cm^3\,g^{-1}\,h^{-1}$ can be attributed to the increase in metabolism during the movement of the muscles and the tissues, such as the cardiovascular and respiratory systems, that service them. If $1\,cm^3\,O_2\,g^{-1}\,h^{-1}$ is equivalent to $5.6\,W\,kg^{-1}$, $1.08\,cm^3\,O_2\,g^{-1}\,h^{-1}$ produces $6.05\,W\,kg^{-1}$. This 70 kg man therefore used $6.05 \times 70 = 424\,W$ ($1\,W \equiv 1\,J\,s^{-1}$) for walking up the 20% gradient, which would raise his mass through $0.8 \times 0.2 = 0.16\,m$ in each second. The man's weight is $70 \times 9.8 = 686\,N$ (assuming that the acceleration under gravity is $9.8\,m\,s^{-2}$). Therefore the total work done against gravity is $686 \times 0.16 = 110\,W$. The overall efficiency of energy conversion is $(110/424) \times 100 = 26\%$.

Similar measurements on other animals indicate that energy conversion of most muscles is about 20–30% efficient, but the efficiency of a few kinds of very slow muscles, notably the leg muscles of tortoises, is apparently very much higher. The remaining 70–80% of the chemical energy consumed is released as heat, about the same proportion as in machines such as the motor car. However, as pointed out in Section 6.3.1, the efficiency of energy conversion of isolated limb muscles is also about 25%, so either such muscles are used more efficiently in the intact animal than they are in the artificial conditions contrived by physiologists, or the 'service' tissues such as the lungs and the heart account for only a small fraction of the total energy consumed. It is therefore important to understand how mechanical conditions of contraction, fibre-type composition and the other variables affect the way in which the muscles convert chemical energy into mechanical work.

■ What are main energy-consuming processes in muscle?

The breakdown of ATP by the myosin ATPase (Section 5.2.1) and the ATP-dependent calcium pump of the sarcoplasmic reticulum.

If a muscle is stretched to become like situation 1 of Figure 6.2c, then stimulated maximally, it breaks down about 25% as much ATP as when it is stimulated at its normal resting length.

■ What does this observation tell you about the energy consumption of the contractile and membrane components of muscle?

Stretching to beyond overlap of the thick and thin filaments would prevent activation of the myosin ATPase, so, assuming that the sarcoplasmic reticulum is unaffected by stretch, its energy-using activities such as pumping Ca^{2+} ions must account for about 25% of the total ATP utilization, with 75% being used by the contractile proteins themselves.

It should be possible to measure the rate of release of inorganic phosphate in isolated muscles but, in most vertebrate muscles, the ADP generated by hydrolysis of ATP is immediately rephosphorylated. Therefore, in experimental situations, the principal enzymes involved in this rephosphorylation must be inhibited by a potent synthetic poison called fluoro-2,4-dinitrobenzene (FDNB, sometimes called DNFB).

Table 6.2 shows some data from studies of ATP metabolism in intact but isolated muscles during contractions of various durations. The muscles were kept in an atmosphere of nitrogen to preclude aerobic respiration, and anaerobic respiration

Table 6.2 The means and standard errors of the expenditure and economy of developing and maintaining isometric tension by isolated hamster biceps brachii (fast) and soleus (slow) muscles contracting *in vitro*.

		Duration of contraction		
		1.2 s	30 s	60 s
Expenditure/µmol high-energy fast	fast	1.5 ± 0.06	2.2 ± 0.05	2.5 ± 0.05
phosphate (g muscle)$^{-1}$	slow	1.1 ± 0.03	1.5 ± 0.02	1.8 ± 0.01
Economy/work done per µmol	fast	99 ± 7	$2\,483 \pm 110$	$3\,635 \pm 180$
high-energy phosphate consumed	slow	143 ± 8	$6\,377 \pm 250$	$9\,012 \pm 230$

was prevented by the addition of iodoacetate. You can see that for both brief and prolonged contractions, the breakdown of ATP was less rapid in muscles composed of slow fibres than in those consisting of fast fibres (Section 5.3.3). But the most striking contrast is the effect of the duration of the contractions on the energy economy of the muscles, i.e. the work done per unit of chemical energy consumed. Slow muscle fibres are from 1.5 to 2.5 times more economical than the muscle containing mostly fast fibres, and these fibres produce more than 60 times ($(9\,012/143) = 63$) as much work in a contraction lasting 1 min than in a contraction lasting one-fiftieth of that time. These data imply that slow, continuous movements require very much less energy than those in which fast muscle fibres perform brief, repetitive contractions.

The maximum rate of energy utilization of a particular muscle seems to be determined by the properties of its contractile proteins (Section 5.3.4). The relative volume of mitochondria increases a little when a sedentary person undergoes physical training, but there is no evidence that the supply of oxygen or the rate at which the mitochondria can produce ATP is limiting for a person or animal that exercises regularly.

The mechanical constraints imposed on the muscle while the contraction is in progress also affect the rate at which it uses ATP and its efficiency of conversion of metabolic energy into mechanical work. Figure 6.3 shows the rate at which ATP is broken down by a frog muscle poisoned with FDNB, while it is contracting under carefully controlled mechanical conditions. The sartorius muscle in the thigh was chosen because it is strap-like (Section 6.4) and thin and flat, so externally applied substances quickly diffuse into all the fibres. In the shaded area of the Figure, the muscle is being allowed to shorten almost isotonically. In the unshaded area, the muscle is being stretched by the apparatus in which it is mounted so it is contracting in the negative work mode. The rate of ATP breakdown while the muscle is being stretched at about 0.1 length s^{-1} is only about a quarter of that measured during isometric contraction (centre of Figure). In other words, slightly stretching the muscle while it is actively contracting *increases* the mechanical power produced per molecule of ATP consumed. In general, muscles use ATP at a higher rate when they are allowed to shorten (shaded part of curve), than when they are being stretched, but the rate of shortening greatly affects the rate of ATP utilization. The implications of these rather surprising findings for the functioning of the musculo-skeletal system as a whole are discussed in Chapter 8.

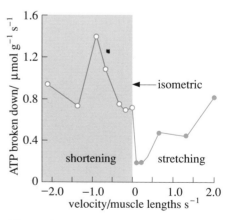

Figure 6.3 The mean rates of ATP breakdown in FDNB-poisoned frog thigh muscle contracting under various mechanical constraints.

According to the crossbridge theory of contractility (Section 5.2.1), contractions that involve active shortening use more ATP than isometric ones because the cycle of crossbridge attachment, detachment and reattachment, which uses a fixed, small number of ATP molecules (probably one) per cycle per crossbridge, proceeds faster under these conditions. Calculations based upon measurements from frog leg muscles at 0 °C indicate that the crossbridge cycle lasts about 0.5 s in isometric contractions, but at maximum velocity of shortening (the equivalent of between 1.5 and 2.5 μm s^{-1} half sarcomere^{-1}), it lasts only 0.02 s.

Summary of Section 6.3

Only 20–30% of the energy consumed during contraction is converted into mechanical work; the rest is released as heat. Heat production is greatest at the beginning of contraction and while the muscle is undergoing shortening. Much less ATP is broken down during slow contractions than during fast contractions, and energy consumption is lower when the muscle is stretched while the contraction is in progress (negative work) than when it is shortening or is working isometrically. Most energy is used at the beginning of the contraction so the mechanical work done per ATP molecule broken down is much greater during slow, sustained contractions than during a series of brief, fast contractions. The maximum rate of energy utilization is normally limited by the contractile proteins themselves, not by the supply of oxygen or ATP.

6.4 Relationships between muscles and tendons

As well as the biochemical differences between muscle fibres described in Sections 6.3 and 5.3.3, the organization of sarcomeres and their anatomical relationship to other tissues also contribute towards determining the form and time course of the forces that can be applied to the skeleton. The structure and properties of tendons and bone are described in greater detail in Chapter 7, but in this section we consider the anatomical relationships between muscle and these skeletal materials, and their implications for the structure and properties of muscle.

The maximum stress that a muscle can support without tearing is about 500 times less than that of tendon. Consequently, spindle-shaped muscles that consist of bundles of more or less parallel fibres can safely be connected to the skeleton via much thinner tendons. Muscle and the numerous fine blood vessels that perfuse it are readily damaged by pinching or squeezing but tendons can easily be attached to levers and force transducers, so spindle shaped muscles with relatively long tendons are very convenient for mechanical and energetic studies. It is often implied in textbooks that most muscles are spindle-shaped, but in fact, this arrangement is true only of the tiny minority of muscles that have been made famous by physiologists. Many other more elaborate (but from the physiologists' point of view, less convenient) arrangements of muscles and tendons are much more abundant.

Strap-like muscles, such as the teres minor muscle in Figure 6.4a, consist of bundles of parallel fibres, each containing many sarcomeres; they can shorten relatively fast because each sarcomere need contract only through a short distance for significant shortening of the whole muscle to be achieved. Strap-like muscles are usually joined to the skeleton by means of very short, broad tendons.

The other muscles shown in Figures 6.4a are **pennate*** in structure, so called because the fibres are attached at an angle to central tendons, which penetrate deep into the belly of the muscle, forming a featherlike pattern. The fibres in pennate muscles are shorter but more numerous than in strap-like muscles of the same total volume; the force exerted per fibre is also slightly less, because the long axes of the fibres are no longer parallel to that of the whole muscle. But, in spite of these effects, the maximum isometric tension produced by pennate muscles is still higher than in strap-like muscles of the same volume, because the total cross-sectional area of the sarcomeres is much greater. However, because each fibre is shorter than in a strap-like muscle of similar size, the maximum speed of shortening is always lower in pennate muscles than in strap-like muscles. Muscles that consist of several pennate segments are called multipennate (Figure 6.4b).

■ Referring again to Figure 6.4, can you suggest the role of (a) the teres minor, and (b) the subscapularis?

The teres minor is strap-like in structure and so can shorten rapidly and through a considerable distance. It can pull the arm briskly from an extended or raised position to its normal resting posture at the side of the body. The multipennate subscapularis holds the head of the humerus firmly against the joint socket in the shoulder blade; it can exert powerful forces which resist extension (e.g. when swinging from the arms), but its contraction produces only small movements. Its chief role is to hold the shoulder in position during lifting and other powerful movements of the arm.

■ What sort of muscles would enable a poikilothermic vertebrate to move fast even when the body temperature is low?

Very long, strap-like muscles; a good example is the head retractor muscles of turtles and terrapins. As you can see from Figure 6.5, these muscles extend from the base of the skull to the pelvic girdle, more than two-thirds of the total length of the body. They enable terrapins to retract the head into the shell at impressive speed, even when the body is cool. However, the total force produced is quite low, because the cross-sectional area of myofibrils is small: the withdrawal of a terrapin's head can easily be prevented if one can insert one's fingers behind its skull quickly enough, which, even with the advantage of being homeothermic, most people are unable to do.

Biochemists, physiologists and cooks usually choose muscles in which tendinous material is exceptionally sparse, because isolation of cell fragments, analysis of mechanical behaviour and palatability are all improved if the quantity of tough, insoluble tendinous material is minimized. Selection has to be particularly rigorous for the meat of large terrestrial animals such as cattle, sheep and pigs which always contains proportionately more of such undesirable

* Also spelt 'pinnate' in some texts.

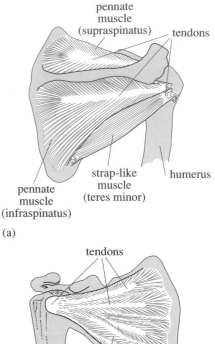

(a)

(b)

Figure 6.4 Some of the muscles of the human shoulder viewed from (a) the posterior, and (b) the anterior surface of the shoulder blade (scapula).

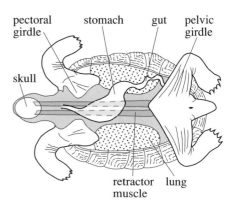

Figure 6.5 Ventral view of the retractor muscles of the neck of an American wood turtle, *Clemmys insculpta*. The ventral part of the shell and some of the viscera have been removed.

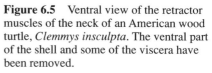

material than the muscles of poultry, rabbits or fish. A particular favourite with all three groups of people is the filet steak muscle, known to scientists as the psoas, which is a strap-like muscle that consists of exceptionally long, parallel fibres and very short tendons. The psoas runs underneath the lumbar region of the vertebral column, connecting the pelvic girdle to the thoracic vertebrae. It is particularly well developed in leaping and galloping animals such as rabbits, most hoofed animals and primates.

Contrary to the impression created by many texts, many mammalian trunk and limb muscles are pennate in form. Joints of meat consisting mostly of pennate muscles are usually cheaper, because they contain relatively large quantities of chewy and indigestible tendon and other collagenous material. The role of pennate muscles in locomotion is discussed in Chapter 8.

6.4.1 The myotendinous junction

The junctions between the muscle fibres and their tendons (myotendinous junctions) are clearly essential to the transmission of forces generated or sustained by the muscle. Myotendinous junctions consist of collagen fibres that interdigitate with the sarcolemma at the ends of the myofibrils as shown in the electron micrograph (Figure 6.6). Long processes of muscle fibre (marked with arrows on Figure 6.6) that attenuate to become mainly actin filaments plus several cytoskeletal proteins attached to the inner surface of the sarcolemma extend into the collagen of the myotendinous junction. As well as providing the passive strength and ordered structure of the contractile and membranous components of muscles (Section 5.2.1), cytoskeletal proteins are also central to the strength of myotendinous junctions.

If freshly excised vertebrate muscles and their tendons are strained to breaking point, they tear near one end of the muscle, leaving a ragged stump of muscle fibres attached to the tendon. When the thigh muscles of freshly killed frogs with their tendons attached were soaked for 3–24 h in solutions that removed divalent cations (i.e. Ca^{2+} and Mg^{2+}) before being pulled, they tore much closer to the myotendinous junction. Electron micrographs of muscles thus treated show that the specialized regions of the ends of the muscle fibres near the myotendinous junctions are disrupted.

■ What can you conclude from these experiments about the biochemical mechanisms that attach the muscle fibres to their tendons?

The integrity of the proteins that transmit the stress depends upon the appropriate concentration of Ca^{2+} and Mg^{2+}.

Dystrophin (Section 5.4.3) is more concentrated near the myotendinous junction than in the mid-fibre sarcolemma. The study of the development of the early symptoms of muscular dystrophy in *mdx*-mice and their 'recovery' as they become adult helps to elucidate the exact role of dystrophin. Electron micrographs of the myotendinous junctions of suckling *mdx*-mice (i.e. in the early stages of fibre degeneration) reveal many defects compatible with the mechanical weakness of the muscles, among them the fact that the actin filaments are less regularly associated with the sarcolemma than in genetically normal mice. Most of the defects disappear in older mice and the myotendinous

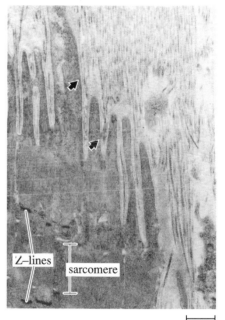

Figure 6.6 Electron micrograph of the junction between a muscle fibre and its tendon from the hindlimb muscles of a 6-week-old mouse. Arrows point to processes of muscle fibre into tendinous material.

junctions recover their strength but the attachment of the actin filaments to the sarcolemma never becomes normal, suggesting that dystrophin may be essential to this structural link.

The fine structure of the contacts between muscle fibres and tendon strands is abnormal in mutant *Drosophila* that lack α-actinin (Section 5.2.2). These comparisons suggest that cytoskeletal proteins, including dystrophin and α-actinin, play an important, though not indispensable, role in maintaining the structural integrity of the myotendinous junction and hence its mechanical strength.

6.4.2 The arrangement of muscles in the body

In apparatus designed to apply large forces about a joint or fulcrum, such as traditional mechanical scales, the weight pans are arranged approximately at right angles to the axle. Similarly, guy-ropes around a mast or a tent, or the strings on a string-operated puppet, work better if they are fastened as far apart as possible, because such arrangements apply forces at a favourable mechanical advantage. By analogous reasoning, we would expect muscles to be attached to the skeleton at angles of about 90°, but they are not arranged like that: muscles and their tendons are applied closely to the skeleton, so whole limbs look more like compact cylinders or cones (see Figure 5.1) than string-operated puppets. This very familiar, but mechanically rather surprising, arrangement can be explained in terms of the mechanics and energetics of muscle contraction described in the previous sections.

■   With reference to Section 6.2.1, how would the force produced by a muscle fibre change as it shortens?

Sarcomeres can generate maximum tension over only a narrow range of lengths (Figure 6.2). If the muscle is much extended before contraction begins and shortens a lot as the contraction proceeds, its maximum power output starts low, passes through a maximum, then declines. Clearly, such a scheme could be very inefficient if the muscle was accelerating a limb or biting into food. On the other hand, as pointed out in Section 6.3.2, a small stretch to a muscle within its range of optimum lengths applied while contraction is in progress actually increases the external work performed per unit of chemical energy consumed.

■   Are there any other disadvantages to an arrangement in which most muscle contractions involve substantial shortening?

Yes. More heat is generated by isotonic than by isometric contractions (Section 6.3.1) because chemical energy is converted into mechanical work less efficiently when contracting muscles shorten further. Having the insertions of muscles close to the joints that they flex may give them lower mechanical advantage, but it does reduce the shortening that muscle undergoes.

In the top row (a) of Figure 6.7, a fairly long muscle, such as the biceps muscle in the front side of the upper arm, is inserted close to the joint (i.e. high up on the forearm), so, as it folds the elbow, its length changes by only 25% between its maximally extended (a1 left) and maximally contracted (a3 right) positions.

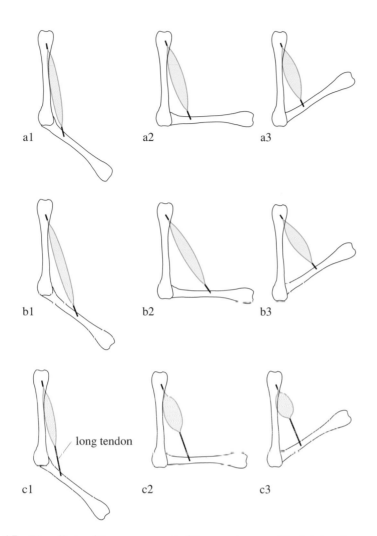

a1   a2   a3

b1   b2   b3

long tendon

c1   c2   c3

Figure 6.7   The effects of the arrangement of the muscle around the joint on the range of movements that its contraction can produce.

If the muscle were inserted further down the forearm, as in row (b), the same peak tension would pull harder on the arm, so the initial acceleration of the forearm would be greater, but the muscle would also have to shorten through a greater distance (40%) to achieve the same flexion of the elbow. If the muscle were long enough not to be damaged when the arm was fully extended in position b1, it might be able to exert very little tension when the elbow was fully flexed in position b3. The need to avoid too much muscle shortening also rules out the arrangement in row (c) for joints that have a wide excursion (i.e. that can bend through a wide angle). In row (c), the tendons are attached at the same positions on the forearm as in row (a); the total length of the muscle–tendon system is the same as in row (a) but the muscle is shorter and the tendon is longer. Since the tendon cannot shorten actively, the muscle must do so a lot to achieve flexion of the elbow (c3), and that could bring the sarcomeres into lengths at which they cannot exert much tension (see Figure 6.2c). Not surprisingly, the arrangement shown in row (a) is by far the most common.

■   Which kind of muscles would you expect to insert near to joints?

Pennate muscles, because they cannot shorten very far. The majority of mammalian muscles are pennate, with short, stout tendons.

The limits on the excursion of joints and the arrangement of muscles in antagonistic groups prevent a muscle from shortening so much that it could reach situations 4 or 5 of Figure 6.2c. As it approaches these situations, the force it can exert starts to decline, and the passive (and, if necessary, active) resistance of the reciprocal muscles oppose its further shortening.

No arrangement of muscle and skeleton can generate maximum power or maximum velocity at a wide range of joint angles (i.e. muscle lengths). As plumbers and carpenters know, there is an optimum position of the shoulder and elbow at which one's arm muscles can apply the greatest isometric forces to recalcitrant pipes and screws.

■   Could the muscle itself be specialized to produce even larger forces at this optimum length?

Yes. Some muscles such as insect flight muscles are specialized to operate at only a narrow range of lengths. The bee's muscles shown in Figure 5.10 are used only for flight and cannot shorten by more than 5% (normally only 1 or 2%) of the resting length. A carpenter with such muscles in his arm could tighten screws more tightly for less effort, but his arm would be useless for sawing planks (Section 6.3.1), and would be unable to produce enough movement in the almost fully flexed position to lift a drink to his mouth when the job was done.

As will be described in Chapter 8, the limb muscles of some animals, such as deer and horses, are specialized for fast running and when thus deployed produce much larger forces more efficiently and so with less production of excess heat than human muscles. Human limbs are 'jacks of all trades': we use our arm muscles for throwing balls (almost isotonic contraction), carrying heavy bags (almost isometric) and as shock absorbers to avoid injury when we fall over (negative work). With such a variety of uses, it is not surprising that they are not adapted for maximum efficiency in any of these modes, and many tasks make people hot or tired, or both.

Skill in many sports, particularly wrestling, weight-lifting and javelin-throwing, depends not only upon having muscle fibres with the right physiological properties (Section 5.3.3) but also upon adjusting posture and limb position so that they are deployed most efficiently. As we all know, such skills can only be acquired by much practice: the nervous system has to learn to initiate contraction when the muscle is at exactly the right length and to sustain it only for as long as it produces high power at high efficiency. Some of the neural mechanisms that contribute to the fine control of muscle length are described in Section 6.5.

■   What kind of muscle would be suitable for activities such as digging a burrow?

High force would be required because soil is dense, but digging and shovelling also involve significant shortening, so burrowers need strap-like muscles that are both long and thick. Large animals such as anteaters can have long muscles on long legs but such requirements are not easily accommodated in small digging animals such as dung beetles, digger wasps and moles, and may entail major modifications of the skeleton to which the muscles are attached.

Figure 6.8 shows some homologous bones from the limbs of two common mammals of approximately the same size (adult body mass 0.10–0.15 kg) but very different habits. In the stoat (Figure 6.8b), the scapula (shoulder blade) has the typical polygonal shape, and the humerus and the ulna of the forelimb and the femur and tibia of the hindleg are relatively long and slender with proportionately small areas for muscle attachment. In contrast, all the muscle attachment sites on the mole's shoulder and forelimb (Figure 6.8a), particularly the humerus, are expanded into flanges that accommodate the massively thick muscles and enable them to be as long and thick as possible on the short limbs. The humerus is almost square in outline, with long projections and deep cavities. The long bones of the hindlimbs are similar in the two species, but the pelvic girdle is clearly longer and more massive in moles.

The limbs of the stoat are adapted for fast galloping and the ability to pounce on prey: speed depends more upon the length than the thickness of the muscle so the limb bones are relatively long and slender and end in firm, narrow paws. Moles have broad, strong spade-like 'hands' and use their powerful forelimbs almost exclusively for digging in dense soil. Moles cannot run and do not even walk

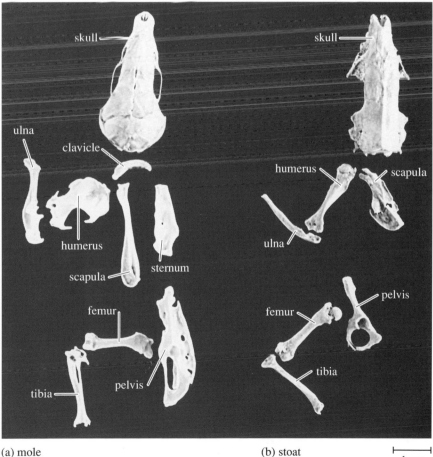

(a) mole   (b) stoat

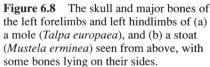

1 cm

Figure 6.8 The skull and major bones of the left forelimbs and left hindlimbs of (a) a mole (*Talpa europaea*), and (b) a stoat (*Mustela erminea*) seen from above, with some bones lying on their sides.

efficiently. They rarely emerge onto the surface but when stranded (e.g. by floods), they shuffle awkwardly on their bellies, propelling themselves with paddling movements of the limbs. Under such conditions, they are very vulnerable to predation, not least from stoats.

The sternum, to which the ends of the ribs are attached at the centre of the thorax, is large and stout in moles and its ventral surface is flared into a 'keel' on the midline. The sickle-shaped clavicle is also relatively large and stout. It acts as a 'pin' that holds the anterior end of the scapula to the sternum. The homologous bones in stoats are negligibly small and do not appear in Figure 6.8b.

■   In which other animals has comparable expansion of the sternum evolved?

All flying birds have a massive sternum that is expanded ventrally into the 'keel' or 'breast' bone. Its function is similar to the sternum in moles: it forms the insertion of the thick, powerful muscles that overlie the ribs and pull the humerus downwards and forwards in flight. Similar movements are essential to digging in moles.

Stoats (and other mammals that rely upon speed and agility) thus resemble high-jumpers and sprinters in having long, slender legs with almost straight bones and fast muscles, but moles have massive, muscular shoulders and forelimbs like those of weight-lifters or blacksmiths. Their flared bones support massive muscles that can generate powerful, sustained forces. The physique of most of us is a compromise between these extremes: we can run, jump, dig and lift to a modest extent but cannot outcompete those who, by heredity or by appropriate physical training, have the muscle and bone structure specifically adapted to one or other activity.

Summary of Section 6.4

Strap-like muscles, in which the fibres are long and parallel and the tendons are relatively short and do not extend into the contractile part of the muscle, can undergo rapid and extensive changes in length. Pennation is an adaptation to generating large isometric forces, but pennate muscles cannot shorten rapidly or over long distances. The physiological properties of muscles and their anatomical arrangement in the body are usually a compromise between maximum force production at the ideal length and the need to be able to generate a moderate amount of tension at a range of lengths. There is almost always an optimum length at which the muscle can produce maximum isometric force most efficiently. Muscles specialized to particular actions, such as insect flight muscles and the forelimbs of moles, may be almost useless for other activities. Part of the skill of physically demanding work and sports is adjusting the positions of limbs so that the muscles can be deployed most appropriately. In general, muscles that are normally used for a single activity such as chewing or walking are arranged so that most contractions are nearly isometric, thus minimizing the additional heat production associated with shortening.

6.5 The neural control of muscle

People know where their limbs are without looking at them, and what is meant by 'heavy', and many have experienced the sense of weightlessness when immersed in water or descending fast in a lift or roller coaster. These sensations arise from proprioreceptors, sense organs embedded in the muscles, tendons and joints that measure the length of the muscle, external forces acting on the muscle or tendon (e.g. gravity) and aspects of their rates of change in movement. This information is integrated with the neural commands sent from the nervous system to muscles and is essential to the maintenance of posture, counteracting external forces applied to the body (e.g. strong wind) and to the fine control of movement. Muscle spindles are the proprioreceptors in muscle that measure its length, velocity of shortening and rate of change of velocity.

6.5.1 Muscle spindles

Muscle spindles are unique to vertebrates and, for obvious reasons, are much more elaborate in terrestrial groups (mammals, birds, reptiles) than in fish. Mammalian muscles contain several very different types of spindle, only one of which is described here. Organs of very different structure but similar function have evolved, apparently independently, in insects and crustaceans.

The mammalian **muscle spindle** is a modified muscle fibre embedded among many much larger 'working' fibres, the motor neurons (Section 5.3.2) which are called α-motor neurons (Figure 6.9). The two ends contain sarcomeres that contract in response to impulses in the γ-motor neuron that arise from the spinal

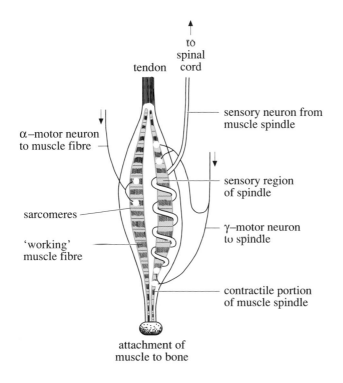

tendon

to spinal cord

sensory neuron from muscle spindle

α–motor neuron to muscle fibre

sarcomeres

sensory region of spindle

'working' muscle fibre

γ–motor neuron to spindle

contractile portion of muscle spindle

attachment of muscle to bone

Figure 6.9 An idealized diagram of a mammalian muscle spindle lying in parallel with a single 'working' muscle fibre.

cord. Being so small, the muscle spindle can do little work against an external load, but if the surrounding muscle fibres are shortening, such contraction shortens the muscle spindle. Like the rest of the muscle (see Figure 5.9), spindles can also be stretched passively.

The axon of a sensory neuron is wrapped around the sensory portion of the muscle spindle, and any length changes it undergoes, whether following its own shortening, or as a result of externally applied stretch, generate action potentials in the sensory neuron. The fibres in the muscle spindles contract when the 'working' muscle fibres around them shorten, thus maximizing sensitivity of the sensory system over the full range of muscle lengths. The sensory potentials generated in the muscle spindles travel to the spinal cord where they are integrated (via complex mechanisms that need not concern us here) with motor 'commands' from the brain to determine the exact form of the signals conveyed in the α-motor neurons to main muscle fibres.

This neural pathway also acts as a reflex that maintains muscles at constant length: any small change in muscle length, whether caused by the action of external forces, a change of posture or muscles elsewhere in the body becoming fatigued (Sections 5.3.2 and 5.3.3) generates signals in the sensory neuron. This sensory feedback modifies the neural activity in the α-motor neurons, thereby adjusting the force generated by the contractile fibres of the same muscle, and if necessary recruiting more fibres of the same muscle or those of other muscles to contract in parallel and/or inhibiting antagonistic muscles. Muscle spindles of slightly different internal structure respond to position (i.e. their signals provide a continuous report of the length of the muscle), movement (i.e. the rate and direction of change of position) and acceleration. Muscle sense organs in reptiles and birds are also somewhat different in structure from those of mammals.

The proprioreceptors embedded in tendons, called the Golgi* tendon organs, are similar in general structure to muscle spindles. They consist of a sensory nerve ending wrapped around small bundles of collagen fibres, and are concentrated near the myotendinous junction (described in Section 6.4.1 and shown in Figure 6.6). Like muscle spindles, they respond to strain, sending information to the spinal cord that is integrated with that from other proprioreceptors. Some tendon organs are as sensitive as muscle spindles, responding to tiny changes in the length of the tendon, although of course they cannot adjust their sensitivity by actively shortening as muscle spindles can. Other tendon organs produce action potentials only when subjected to large strains. Their feedback to the nervous system inhibits the α-motor neurons to the muscle fibres to which they are attached and they are believed to act as safety mechanisms that protect the musculo-skeletal system from excessive forces by preventing simultaneous activation of too many muscle fibres (Section 5.3.3).

■   Why do people sway slightly even when trying to stand absolutely still, especially if they are exposed to a high wind or wearing high-heels or skates?

Standing still means keeping the dozens of muscles involved in maintaining the posture of the ankle, hip, back, etc. at an exactly constant length. Any slight excess or reduction in force produced would result in a small movement, which

* The Italian anatomist Golgi also described an important intracellular organelle that is named after him.

would activate muscle spindle reflexes and stretch other muscles, thereby stimulating their muscle spindles. Such reflexes maintain a steady posture by activating other fibres to replace those that become fatigued and so produce less force. The movements involved in such fine control of muscle length appear as swaying or trembling. Many postures cannot be maintained for more than a few seconds before swaying movements become more frequent and of greater amplitude, as more muscle fibres become fatigued and joints become compressed and painful. Even in 'comfortable' postures, people start to fidget after a few minutes. Many animals, particularly ambushing predators such as herons, chameleons, cats, polar bears, praying mantises and many kinds of snakes are much better at keeping completely still than we are.

The maintenance of steady postures and smooth, graceful movements requires a succession of minor adjustments to the signals to dozens of muscles. The fine control of muscle activity differs slightly in different people, producing characteristic styles of movement by which we can often recognize familiar individuals from distances much greater than those from which we can see faces. Activities such as gymnastics, dancing and skating depend more upon the fine control and coordination of the force generated by thousands of different muscle fibres than upon their power production. They thus require much practice to perfect, and much concentration to perform.

■ What kinds of activities do not involve proprioreceptors?

Abrupt, powerful movements in response to pain or danger are too fast to incorporate signals from sense organs in muscles and tendons. Integration of sensory information from the proprioreceptors with commands from the brain takes time (between about 10 and 100 ms, depending upon the size of the animal and the number of muscles and spindles involved). In an emergency, such delays are bypassed, with the result that alarm or escape movements are often poorly controlled and may be more powerful and of greater amplitude than we intend. Muscles specialized for very fast contraction over a short range of lengths, such as insect flight muscle (Figure 5.10) also do not have much sensory control.

The role of sensory feedback in controlling movement is also reduced while performing fast, stereotyped movements such as running down a flight of smooth, evenly spaced steps. We are all familiar with falling when one of a flight of steps turns out to be missing or defective, when we could easily have kept our balance if we had 'known' that the steps were irregular. With practice, sensory control of muscle activity is transferred from vision, acting via the brain, to local proprioreceptors, enabling us to learn to touch-type, and to do tasks ranging from tying a shoelace to playing the piano without seeing where our fingers are.

■ Prolonged exposure to cold or compression temporarily inhibits the transmission of nerve impulses. How does numbness of limbs, for example the sensations experienced when they 'go to sleep', affect our ability to walk and to perform delicate manual tasks?

The muscles themselves work almost normally: powerful, if clumsy, movements are still possible, but the neural control is deficient. Even such minor impairment of the sensory components of muscle makes commonplace movements such as walking almost impossible. Everyone who has experienced numbness and limbs 'going to sleep' must be impressed by how debilitating the effects are. Although we are normally unaware of it, the many continuous sensory messages from muscles are essential for all controlled movements. Anomalous sensations in the form of tingling may be uncomfortable for some time until all the small nerves have fully recovered, but the effects of limbs 'going to sleep' are completely reversible. Certain kinds of nerve damage interfere with the formation, transmission or integration of signals from muscle spindles and their spinal reflexes, causing movements to become jerky, exaggerated or trembling, and greatly impairing walking and all forms of manual dexterity.

Recording muscle activity

As mentioned at the beginning of Section 5.2, one of the simplest and least intrusive ways of finding out which muscles are active while a particular action, such as walking or eating, is in progress, is to record the pattern of potentials on the plasmalemma. Such signals are generated by patterns of action potentials in the α-motor neurons, which in turn arise from a mixture of 'commands' from the brain and spinal reflexes involving the muscle spindles.

■   How accurately would such recordings indicate the total force produced by the muscles?

Not very accurately at all. The same pattern of signals in the α-motor neurons can lead to very different tensions and changes of length because the force generated depends upon the initial length of the muscle (Figure 6.2) and how much it is allowed to shorten by the mechanical conditions under which it is operating (Figure 6.1), about which almost no information can be obtained from electrical recordings. Electrical recordings can only indicate which fibres are active, and the approximate strength of the commands that the nervous system is sending to the muscles. Except in very simple situations, such as insect flight, they say little about what movements are actually performed.

6.6 Conclusion

Muscle is a very diverse and adaptable tissue. Although the basic organization of sarcomeres and probably the basic mechanism of contraction are similar in all striated muscle, different muscles are specialized to a wide range of functional requirements. As sophisticated methods such as electron microscopy, genetic analysis and the use of antibodies to distinguish between closely similar proteins are applied to a wider range of animals (e.g. worms, insects, exotic fish) more and more such specializations become known. Even fairly minor differences in a muscle's chemical composition or physiological properties as studied *in vitro* can have important implications for the performance of the animal as a whole. Indeed, how muscles are controlled, the range of velocities and initial lengths over which they can work effectively and their energetic efficiency determine many of crucial differences in what animals can do, where they can live and how they avoid predators.

As well as being adaptable, most muscles are readily controllable: muscle spindles and tendon organs adjust the neural stimuli to the muscle, keeping constant its length, or its rate of change of length (i.e. keeping still, or moving steadily). Different kinds of muscle fibres are used selectively for different tasks, and fresh muscle fibres can be activated to replace those that fatigue.

Muscle is also a very robust tissue. Unlike the brain or the lungs, it remains viable even under far from optimum conditions: slow and fast oxidative fibres continue to contract under anoxic conditions (at least until their considerable capacity to generate ATP is exhausted), some force is generated even when the muscle is too short or too long (Figure 6.2), too hot or too cold (Table 6.1) or inappropriately loaded (Figure 6.1) and the tissue has great powers of healing (Section 2.4).

Objectives for Chapter 6

When you have completed this chapter, you should be able to:

6.1   Define and use, or recognize definitions and applications of each of the **bold** terms.

6.2   Describe three mechanical conditions under which the contraction of freshly excised muscle has been studied, and describe Hill's equation for the relationship between power output and shortening.

6.3   Explain the effects of the initial length of the muscle on the tension it can generate in terms of sarcomere structure and the sliding filament theory of muscle contraction.

6.4   Outline why muscle contraction generates heat and describe how the stimulation pattern, mechanical conditions and inherent properties of a muscle affect the energetic efficiency of contraction.

6.5   Explain the functional significance of the anatomical relationships between muscles and tendons.

6.6   Account for some general features of the arrangement of vertebrate muscles on the skeleton in terms of the mechanics and energetics of muscle contraction.

6.7   Outline the structure and principles of operation of mammalian muscle spindles.

Questions for Chapter 6

(Answers to questions are at the end of the book.)

Question 6.1 (Objective 6.2)

Which of the following (a–f) are correct statements referring to metabolic changes that accompany stretching the muscle while it is contracting?

(a)   ATP ceases to be broken down.

(b)   The muscle is able to shorten.

(c)   More heat is produced than during isometric contractions.

(d)   Electrical activity in the plasmalemma ceases to regulate the form or timing of the contraction.

(e)   The total force generated per unit of ATP broken down is greater.

(f)   The muscle is prevented from fatiguing.

Explain in a few sentences how the observations in Figure 6.2 show that the force of muscle contraction arises from interactions between certain regions of the thick and thin filaments.

Question 6.3 (Objective 6.4)

Explain why (a) contractions in which the muscle shortens rapidly are energetically less efficient than those in which the muscle length does not change; (b) actions involving many frequently repeated contractions use more metabolic energy for the same power output than those that consist of steady sustained activity.

Question 6.4 (Objective 6.5)

Which of the following statements (a–f) are true of pennate muscles as compared with strap-like muscles?

(a)   A greater proportion of their volume is occupied by tendinous tissue.

(b)   The fibres are shorter.

(c)   There are more fibres per gram of muscle tissue.

(d)   The maximum isometric stress per gram of muscle tissue is greater.

(e)   The maximum velocity of contraction per gram of muscle tissue is greater.

(f)   Pennation is a specialized property of a small minority of mammalian muscles.

Question 6.5 (Objective 6.6)

Answer the following questions in up to three sentences:

(a)   What factors limit the maximum rate at which a muscle can shorten?

(b)   What factors limit the maximum distance through which a muscle can shorten?

(c)   What factors limit the initial length of the muscle at which shortening can begin?

Question 6.6 (Objective 6.7)

Answer the following questions in one to three sentences:

(a)   Why is sensory control of muscle activity essential for locomotion over rough ground on land?

(b)   How does contractility of muscle spindles improve their efficiency as sense organs?

(c)   Why is sensory information for muscle spindles not incorporated into alarm responses to pain or fear?

CHAPTER 7 TENDONS, BONES AND JOINTS

7.1 Introduction

In older texts, locomotion and other movements are presented as arising almost entirely from the active shortening of muscles, with skeletons and tendons acting merely as passive struts and ropes. During the last twenty years, accurate measurements of the mechanical properties and anatomical arrangement of the skeleton and tendons combined with theoretical studies have revolutionized our understanding of the exact role of muscle contraction, and the contribution of non-muscle tissues to movement, particularly cyclical, stereotyped activities such as locomotion. It is now clear that skeletal tissues make an essential contribution to the form and energy economy of movement and that the mechanical properties of muscles cannot be interpreted properly without reference to those of the tendons and skeleton to which they are attached. So this chapter describes the structure and properties of tendons, ligaments, joints and hard skeletal tissues and how their properties integrate with those of muscle (Chapters 5 and 6). Chapter 8 draws on these detailed studies of the components of the musculo-skeletal system to explain the mechanics and physiology of locomotion.

Tendon and bone are robust tissues which retain their elaborate histological structure and many of their mechanical properties for some time after they have been isolated from the animal. So, as with muscle, physicists, chemists and engineers studing isolated tissues, as well as biologists, have made major contributions to our knowledge of the properties of skeletal tissues and how they are arranged in the body.

7.2 Collagenous tissues

Collagen is found in small quantities in many kinds of invertebrates and is by far the most abundant structural protein in vertebrates, occurring at least in small quantities in almost all tissues except the brain and the blood. It is almost always in a fibrous form, but the fibres may be quite small and randomly orientated in a felt-like structure, as in skin, loose connective tissue and cartilage. Collagen occurs in a very pure form and is assembled into bundles of parallel fibres in **tendons**, which link muscles to the skeleton, and **ligaments**, which join parts of the skeleton together. Sheets of collagen fibres spread over or between the muscle fibres are called **aponeuroses.*** Collagenous material linking muscles to adjacent tissues such as adipose tissue and skin is called **fascia.** The extracellular portion of tendons consists of long parallel fibres of collagen, which, as you can see from the electron micrograph in Figure 7.1 (*overleaf*), are crimped along their length. If stretched beyond the point at which the crimp is straightened, these fibres resist deformation under tension, but are compliant to compression, bending and twisting.

* Singular 'aponeurosis'. The term 'aponeurosis' is derived from the Greek word 'neuron', which means 'sinew'. The early anatomists did not distinguish between nerves and tendons, both of which appear white and fibrous in dead mammals. So it is the terms for the skeletal tissues, not those for the nervous system, that are etymologically correct.

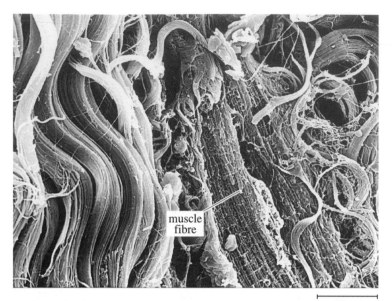

muscle fibre

10 µm

Figure 7.1   Scanning electron micrograph of muscle fibres and associated collagenous material in the interosseus muscle of a lamb's leg. The collagen on the left is wavy and crimped. Sarcomeres are visible in the muscle fibres (right).

In its functional state, collagen is nearly always extracellular, so collagenous tissues typically consist of a high proportion of extracellular matrix, and relatively few cells. In tendons, ligaments and aponeuroses, collagen is synthesized by cells called fibroblasts and secreted into the extracellular space. The fibroblasts mature into fibrocytes, which are small, spindle-shaped cells about 10 µm long. Fibrocytes are enmeshed between the collagen fibres throughout the tendon, sometimes in a fairly regular pattern, but they occupy only a small proportion of its volume.

■   Would the metabolic rate of tendons be high or low compared to muscle or liver?

The metabolic rate of the mature tissue is very low because cells are sparse and those present are not involved in contraction or secretion or any other energetically demanding biochemical process. Consequently, the blood supply to healthy tendon is very low. In fact, one of the most important features of tendons is also the most obvious: they are very pale in colour, even in living animals, because they contain little blood and no myoglobin or similar pigment.

■   What are the consequences of this situation for tissue repair?

Tendon healing is slow. The blood supply increases following major injury, but even so, tendons heal very slowly compared to skin, bone or muscle (Section 2.4). Tendons also do not readily 'become fit' with regular, strenuous exercise, i.e. their mechanical properties are little changed by repeated strain.

Although the myotendinous junction (Section 6.4.1) may be fragile compared to pure tendon or muscle, tendons make very strong attachments to bones because strands of collagen arising from the tendon penetrate into the bone, meshing with the bone collagen and weaving around and between the mineral and cellular components of the bone. If limbs are subjected to exceptionally large forces (e.g. from a fall or while skiing), a tendon or muscle may tear, or a bone may break, but the tendon–bone junctions very rarely fail.

7.2.1 Molecular structure of collagen

In mature connective tissue, collagen molecules consist of polypeptides assembled in a formation resembling a three-stranded rope. Except for short sequences at the ends of the molecules, every third amino acid residue of each polypeptide is glycine. About 30% of the rest consists of the imino acids, proline and hydroxyproline. Imino acids differ from amino acids in that the nitrogen atom is linked to two carbons, forming a ring. Their presence limits the usual rotation of one residue onto another so the resulting polypeptide is rather inflexible and does not form an α-helix as readily as other proteins. Because proline and hydroxyproline are quite rare in enzymes and in most other structural proteins, measurement of their abundance provides a sensitive assay for collagen (Section 3.2.4).

Each of the polypeptide strands is a helix with almost three residues per turn and the three such strands can coil round each other, with glycine, the smallest of the amino acids, occupying the central core of the three-stranded rope. The three strands form a right-handed superhelix with a pitch of approximately 8.7 nm. The whole molecule is about 260–300 nm in length, and 1.3 nm in diameter; a triple helix is the basic structure along all but the final 12 nm at each end of the molecule, which are rich in lysine and hydroxylysine.

In living tendons, collagen molecules are assembled into fibrils of diameter 20–500 nm which show the characteristic banding pattern, repeated every 68 nm, illustrated in Figure 7.2. The banding pattern is believed to arise from the staggered arrangement of parallel collagen molecules, as shown in Figure 7.3. The electron micrograph stain accumulates where the head of one molecule lies beside the tail-end of another, forming a dark band; the light bands represent the spaces between the molecules in the same row. Light and dark bands therefore appear every 68 nm, although the true unit of structure involves five molecules and so repeats every 340 nm. The collagen molecules assemble themselves into this pattern, and the structure may be stabilized by covalent cross-links which form between oxidized lysine and hydroxylysine residues in the non-helical ends of adjacent collagen molecules; this structure makes the tendon strong in tension, but weak in torsion and in compression.

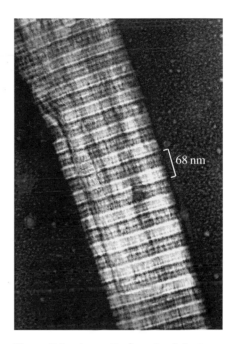

Figure 7.2 A negatively stained electron micrograph of a single fibril of a tendon in a rat's tail, showing alternating light and dark regions.

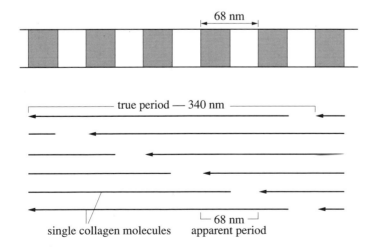

Figure 7.3 Diagram showing the most probable arrangement of collagen molecules that produces the banding pattern shown in the electron micrograph in Figure 7.2.

As in most proteins, hydrogen bonds play a central role in maintaining the tertiary and quaternary structure of collagen molecules. Bacon slices shrink and curl as they are heated, and pig skin becomes pork crackling, because the hydrogen bonds in the collagen of the skin, adipose tissue and muscle become unstable at high temperatures, causing the elaborate internal architecture of the collagen molecules to collapse; the energy so released causes irreversible shrinkage and stiffening of the tissues. Collagen from any source can be broken down into its constituent polypeptides by prolonged immersion in boiling water. The result is an amorphous, jelly-like substance, called glue* when concentrated, or soup stock when dilute; the polypeptide chains have unwound from each other, and the triple helical structure has been destroyed. Although helical collagen molecules can be disassembled and reassembled into fibrils artificially, the triple helical structure cannot be recreated once the three polypeptide strands have been completely dissociated from each other.

Once assembled, collagen is among the most chemically inert proteins in the body, because most proteolytic enzymes do not attack the imino acids proline and hydroxyproline. In mammals, certain cells in the uterus and cervix, and those involved in healing and remodelling of bone (Section 2.3), secrete a specific collagenase and can thereby remodel the shape or alter the mechanical properties of the reproductive tract and skeleton. The anaerobic bacterium *Clostridium histolyticum* is one of the few other organisms to produce enzymes that attack collagen directly. *C. histolyticum* is common in soil, where it plays an essential role in completing the breakdown of dead vertebrates. However, it sometimes strays into the inadequately cleansed wounds of living vertebrates, where it destroys aponeuroses around muscles, tendons and all other collagen-containing tissues, particularly if poor blood supply or tight bandaging promote anaerobic conditions. *C. histolyticum* and other *Clostridium* species cause gangrene, a common and often fatal complication of lacerations and puncture wounds in wild animals and, until modern antibiotics became available, in humans.

7.2.2 Mechanical properties of tendons

Tissues rich in collagen are extensible, resilient and flexible: that is, they are tough enough to be able to absorb energy without tearing or snapping, they recoil when released after a stretch, and they can transmit forces around and across joints. Tendons, which are almost pure collagen, are the most thoroughly studied of such tissues, because of their convenient size and shape and their functionally important association with muscle.

Tendons are almost always loaded in tension, so the most biologically meaningful measurements are those of tensile strength (i.e. the force required to pull the tendon apart) and tensile stiffness (i.e. the mechanical response to stretch). Stiffness can be measured by mounting a sample of tendon firmly in a movable clamp. The force required to stretch it through a measured distance is recorded. The tendons in the tail of the rat, and the Achilles tendon† of sheep or pigs (see also Section 3.2.2, Figure

---

* 'Collagen' means 'glue-producing' and the name derives from the fact that, until the 20th century, most commercial glues were made by boiling the skins, tendons and bones of slaughtered animals.

† The Achilles tendon links the gastrocnemius muscle in the lower leg to the ankle bone. Its name refers to the mythological Greek warrior, Achilles, who was killed by an injury to this tendon at the heel.

3.7), are most frequently studied because they are readily obtainable and, being relatively long and thin, are convenient for the apparatus. However, it is important to remember that much of the collagenous material associated with muscle is in the form of strands of tendon and aponeuroses that extend deep into and through muscles (Section 6.4).

Some typical results for a limb tendon are shown in Figure 7.4; the y-axis is the stress (s), the force per unit area, measured in $N\,m^{-2}$ or pascals (Pa) (see Section 3.2.2), and the x-axis is strain (e), the length of extension expressed as a percentage of the unstretched length. In the 'toe' region of the curve, only small stresses are needed to stretch the tendon. However, once the strain exceeds about 0.6%, larger forces are needed to achieve further stretching. When these mechanical changes are correlated with changes in the ultrastructure of the collagen fibrils, it is found that the 'toe' region of the graph corresponds to stretching out the crimp of the collagen fibres (see Figure 7.1). The linear part of the curve corresponds to stretching the bonds within and between collagen fibrils; stretching in this region is completely reversible and does not permanently alter the structure of the tendon. However, if the tendon is stretched by more than about 8–10%, its internal structure starts to break down and it is permanently deformed, i.e. it does not recoil to its original length when released from stretch. At points called **critical tensile stress** and **critical tensile strain**, as well as failing to recoil, the tendon becomes weak and is easily torn apart by small additional stretch.

When comparing the mechanical properties of one tissue with those of another or with a synthetic material, it is useful to have a simple modulus that summarizes the material's behaviour. **Young's modulus,*** E, is the slope of the linear region of stress/strain curves like the one in Figure 7.4.

$$E = s/e$$

Table 7.1 (*overleaf*) shows Young's modulus, the critical tensile stress (s_t) and the critical tensile strain (e_t) for tendons and various other natural materials.

■   During fast running, the Achilles tendon of a 70 kg man is subjected to a stress of 5 kN (about 0.5 tonne force, or seven times the man's own weight). From the data in Table 7.1, can you calculate the minimum cross-sectional area that the Achilles tendon must have in order to withstand this stress?

Stress is defined as force per unit area; the maximum stress that the tendon can withstand is 80 MPa (see Table 7.1) = $8 \times 10^7\,N\,m^{-2}$, therefore the area of tendon needed = $(5\,000\,N)/(8 \times 10^7\,N\,m^{-2}) = 6.25 \times 10^{-5}\,m^2 = 0.625\,cm^2$.

■   The Achilles tendon of most men is about $0.7\,cm^2$ in area. What is the safety factor (see Section 3.2.2) under which the tendon is operating during fast running?

The safety factor is only 0.7/0.625 = 1.12, a very low value for the normal usage of a biological material. Human athletes apparently stress their Achilles tendons almost to breaking point during fast running. Rupture of this tendon is a common sports injury.

* First formulated and measured by Thomas Young (1773–1829), a physician, biologist, physicist and Egyptologist who was born in Somerset and spent most of his working life in London.

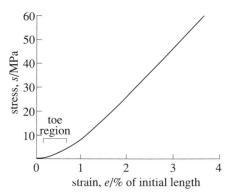

Figure 7.4   The relationship between load (stress) and extension (strain) for the plantaris tendon in the hindleg of a sheep.

Table 7.1   Some properties of biological materials that are normally loaded in tension. s_t is the critical tensile stress and e_t is the critical tensile strain at which the material begins to suffer irreversible damage. $1\,\text{GPa} \equiv 10^9\,\text{Pa} \equiv 10^3\,\text{MPa}$.

Material	Young's modulus E/GPa	s_t/MPa	e_t/%
Mammalian tendon	1–2	80	8
Wool fibre	3–4	60	2
Silk	4	800	>20
Insect cuticle	20	500	3
Mammalian long bone	20	140	0.5
Humerus in king penguin flipper	22	290	n.d.
Mammalian tooth enamel	84	n.d.	n.d.
Molluscan shell	50	50	0.3
Wood	25–40	20–120	2

n.d., not determined

In adult humans, the average length of the Achilles tendon, including the aponeuroses extending into the gastrocnemius muscle, is about 30 cm.

■   By how much can the Achilles tendon safely be extended?

From Table 7.1, the maximum strain (e_t) is 8% of 30 = 2.4 cm. If the safety factor calculated above also applies to stretching of the tendon, its normal maximum extension is 2.4/1.12 = 2.14 cm, or about 7% of the length of the tendon at rest.

When a human or a sheep is running fast, each foot is on the ground for about 0.2 s, during which time the tendons of the lower leg are stretched. The energy thus used is stored elastically and released when the tendons recoil to their normal length. Such storage and later release of the elastic strain energy in tendons, ligaments and, to a lesser extent other connective tissues such as articular cartilage (Section 7.4.2), make an important contribution to the energy economy of fast locomotion, as explained in greater detail in Section 8.2. At the stride frequency of running, about 93% of the energy absorbed in stretching the tendons is recovered as recoil; this efficiency of energy storage is as good as that of the best quality industrial rubber. The remaining 7% of the energy used to stretch the tendon is converted into heat. The quantity of heat so generated is small compared to that produced by active contraction of muscles (Section 6.3.1) and it is normally dissipated very quickly, particularly if the tendon is situated just under the skin. Most large tendons, such as the Achilles tendon near the ankle and those in the wrist, are so close to the skin that you can see them as discrete entities in your own limbs. However, if heat dissipation is restricted by bandaging the legs, as is traditionally often done with racehorses, the temperature of the tendons and surrounding tissues can become high enough to cause inflammation during prolonged, strenuous galloping.

7.2.3 How long and how thick should a tendon be?

As explained in Section 6.4.2, the length and insertion points of a muscle–tendon system, and the relative length of the muscle determine the range of movements it can perform. The mechanical properties of the tendon are also important because they determine how the forces generated by the muscle are transmitted to the skeleton. The main functions of tendons that are attached to muscles that are frequently used in the negative work mode (Section 6.2) are energy storage and recoil, so they should be long, thin and stretchy, like an elastic band.

■ Referring back to Section 7.2.2 and to Chapter 6, what reasons could there be for *not* having long, thin tendons?

First, thin tendons would have a lower safety factor and hence would be vulnerable to injury from exceptionally large strains. Second, muscles that normally operate in the positive work mode need tendons that transmit precisely small changes in muscle length: precision movements, such as those of human fingers, would be very difficult to control with sensory input from muscle spindles and tendon organs (Section 6.5.1) if the mechanical properties of their tendons resembled those of elastic bands.

■ What features would you expect in musculo-skeletal systems adapted for precise movement? Can you suggest which group of muscles would have these properties?

Really accurate control of length changes would require minimizing tendon length and maximizing its stiffness. Precision movements are essential (and energy storage unimportant) for the facial muscles that operate the jaws, cheeks and tongue (especially those of humans that are used for speech as well as eating). Feel your own face: it has lots of muscle and very little tendinous material. The thick, powerful muscles are attached to the skeleton by very short, stout aponeuroses. The tendons of the fingers have to be long because their muscles are in the forearm, but, in proportion to the forces that they normally transmit, they are much stiffer than those of the foot. They transmit accurately the length changes applied to them, like the stiff wires of the gears and brakes of a bicycle.

Tendons become stiffer by ossifying into bone. When eating your Christmas dinner, you may have noticed that certain tendons in the lower legs of domestic turkeys are ossified to form thin 'needles' of bone.

■ Under what conditions would ossified tendons be inappropriate?

Where the tendons are required to transmit forces around joints or other curved planes. The other way in which tendons become stiffer is to become thicker, as is the case with the stout, stiff tendons that operate the fingers. The dimensions of tendons, like the physiological properties of muscles, are adapted to particular functions at the expense of maximum efficiency of other properties.

Both the red kangaroo (*Macropus rufus*, body mass about 40 kg) and the smaller and unrelated kangaroo rat (*Dipodomys spectabilis*, a rodent of body mass about 100 g) have similar body proportions: short forelimbs and long, powerful hindlegs. At first glance their posture and locomotory adaptations also appear to be very similar: they usually stand bipedally and, instead of trotting or galloping, they hop using only the hindlegs. The gastrocnemius muscles are large and powerful and they and the attached Achilles tendons extend and recoil at each hop (there are further details of this mechanism in Section 8.3.1). However, studies of the mechanical properties of their muscles and tendons, and the strains they undergo *in vivo*, reveal subtle but ecologically important differences.

The Achilles tendons of *Dipodomys* are relatively thick; their maximum stress during hopping is only 8 MPa and they absorb only 14% of the total mechanical work used for each stride. The gastrocnemius muscle exerts a force equivalent to only 70 kPa, about 35% of its maximum isometric stress (Section 6.2). In comparison, the tendons of *Macropus* are thinner and longer (relative to body mass) and the stress in them is about 55 MPa at maximum; about 62% of the strain energy is recovered. The gastrocnemius muscle exerts a stress of up to 180–240 kPa, close to its maximum possible isometric stress.

■   Under what safety factors (Sections 3.2.2 and 7.2.2) do the Achilles tendons of these species operate?

Tendon is permanently deformed by stresses of 80 MPa (Table 7.1) and breaks at stresses of 100 MPa. So the safety factor for the Achilles tendons of *Dipodomys* is 80/8 = 10 and that for *Macropus* is 80/55 = 1.5.

■   What do these facts imply about activities other than hopping in which the hindlegs of these species might be involved?

These observations show that in hopping, the muscles and tendons of *Macropus* experience forces close to the maximum that their tissues can sustain, but that those of *Dipodomys* are capable of withstanding much higher forces, and do not store strain energy very efficiently. The tendons and muscles of *Dipodomys*, but not those of *Macropus*, are probably used for activities such as jumping that involve much higher accelerations, and hence greater maximum stresses in both muscles and tendons. In fact, observations on *Dipodomys* in its native habitat of deserts and dry scrub in southwestern USA and northern Mexico show that it cannot hop very fast (only about 1.5 m s^{-1}, compared to 3.9 m s^{-1} for *Macropus*) but when pursued by predators such as owls, rattlesnakes and foxes, it jumps to heights of at least 0.5 m (ten times its hip height).

Macropus, being larger and living in Australia where there are very few vertebrate predators, does not jump much, and hops mainly to travel long distances between feeding grounds rather than to escape predators. *Macropus* thus maximizes the efficiency of energy storage and recoil in its tendons during steady, long-distance hopping, while *Dipodomys* retains the ability to leap safely away from predators at the expense of having tendons that store less energy. The importance of energy storage in tendons and other collagenous tissues for the energetic cost of locomotion as a whole is described in Chapter 8.

Similar analysis shows that most mammalian and avian tendons are much thicker than would be necessary for adequate strength. Like muscle, the arrangement and properties of tendons are intricately adapted to their roles in the animal. Thus the long tendons that operate human fingers, which can be felt easily through the skin of the wrist and the back of the hand, are relatively thick compared to those of the ankle, although the muscles in the forearm just below the elbow that move the fingers are much smaller than the gastrocnemius muscle of the lower leg. Most limbs taper towards the ends, with the more massive muscles nearest to the trunk, and lighter tendons extending to the tips of fingers and toes. The ends of the limbs are the fastest moving parts and minimizing their mass reduces the total energetic cost of movement. Thinner tendons would be more stretchy so the muscle fibres would have to be longer to take up the slack, thus increasing the combined mass of the muscle–tendon system.

Although the human hand is capable of a wider range of movements than almost any other limb in the Animal Kingdom, the arrangement and mechanical properties of the muscles and tendons make certain combinations of actions impossible.

■　Grasp the index finger of one hand with the other, and bend the joint between the finger and the hand, and that between the first two segments of the finger into right angles. Now try to flex the finger tip.

The most you can achieve is a shallow, weak movement, although coiling the whole finger towards the palm as a single action is easy. Once the tendon and muscle have been stretched over two of the three bent joints, the muscle, which is located high up the forearm, is incapable of shortening with sufficient force to produce significant flexion of the last joint.

Summary of Section 7.2

Collagen, which consists of a highly ordered assembly of triple-stranded, helical molecules, is the major component of the tendons and aponeuroses by which muscles are attached to the skeleton. In tendons, the collagen molecules are assembled in a parallel array, stabilized by covalent bonds. Tendons are strong in tension and can undergo reversible extension to about 8% of their original length: further extension breaks intermolecular bonds and causes damage that can only be repaired by new growth processes that may take a long time to complete. Up to 93% of the energy absorbed by stretching reappears as recoil shortening when the tendon is released. The rest is dissipated as heat. The length and thickness of tendons are intricately adapted to their roles in the animal's normal actions. Thick, short tendons absorb less energy but are stronger and transmit muscle length changes more exactly than long, thin tendons, which store strain energy more efficiently under the moderate stresses imposed on them in locomotion.

7.3　Hard skeletal tissues

The main stiff components of musculo-skeletal systems are bone and arthropod cuticle. Bone is found only in vertebrates and is the major skeletal material of almost all adult terrestrial vertebrates and most fishes except the chondrichthyans. Its unique mechanical properties and mode of growth (Section 2.3) are believed to be among the main factors that have enabled vertebrates to become large.

7.3.1 Bone structure

The basic framework of bone (and similar tissues such as tooth and antler) is an extracellular matrix of collagen fibres of diameter up to 100 nm, and hydrated crystals of an inorganic salt, **hydroxyapatite**, $3[Ca_3(PO_4)_2]Ca(OH)_2$, in the form of long, thin crystals about 4 nm by 40–400 nm. The hydroxyapatite crystals lie parallel to the collagen fibres, and together they form a composite material. The collagen is strong in tension, and can withstand considerable strain (Section 7.2.2); crystalline materials such as hydroxyapatite are strong under compression, but break at very low strains. Bone is strong in both tension and compression: its high mineral content makes it stiff, but the presence of collagen stops cracks from running through the brittle crystals of hydroxyapatite.

Bone differs from most invertebrate skeletal materials in that, in most but not all forms of bone, the living cells, called osteocytes (Section 2.3), which secrete the precursors of the collagen fibres and the hydroxyapatite, are incorporated into the mineralized skeleton. Like all other living cells, osteocytes require nourishment, and cellular bone is permeated with small channels containing blood vessels, and is surrounded by a soft, metabolically active periosteum. The rich blood supply means that most mammalian bones bleed profusely when bruised or broken.

Both the cellular and the extracellular components of bone are replaced during growth and, particularly in mammals, during adult life; osteoclasts (Section 2.3.1) invade the functional bone through the vascular channels and break it down, thereby making way for the formation of new bone. As the bone is dismantled, calcium and phosphate ions and amino acids are released into the bloodstream; often the new bone is formed from these same mineral and amino acid precursors, but they may also be taken up by other tissues that have a greater affinity for them. If ions of similar shape to calcium, notably barium and strontium, are present in the blood, they are sometimes incorporated in place of calcium. Such substitution distorts the crystal structure of the hydroxyapatite and may make the bone mechanically weaker. Fluoride ions (Fl^-) can replace the OH^- ion in the crystal, distorting the entire structure in a way that (by a mechanism still not completely understood) increases its resistance to bacterial attack. This property has been exploited to protect teeth from decay caused by dental caries.

■   Why is the application of fluoride to teeth particularly beneficial for young children? Why is it of some value even for mature adults?

Ideally, fluoride ions should be incorporated into hydroxyapatite into the entire tooth as it grows, so it should be administered to children aged 4–11 as their adult set of teeth is forming (Section 1.2.3). Secondary dentine forms and a small amount of ion substitution takes place in adults, so fluoride toothpaste can still offer some protection from decay.

The main categories of bone in terrestrial vertebrates are distinguished by their arrangement of osteocytes and blood vessels and their mode of growth. By far the most abundant is **lamellar bone**, so called because it is composed of sheets (lamellae) of collagen and mineral elements a few micrometres in thickness between which are the osteocytes and blood vessels. Within any one lamella, all the collagen fibres are more or less parallel, and the bone is built up of many layers of lamellae, each with a different preferred orientation. Less abundant but more spectacular is **Haversian bone**, named after Clopton Havers, the British anatomist who first described its remarkable microscopic structure early in the 18th century. In Haversian bone, most of the lamellae form concentric cylinders (that appear as rings in sections), called **osteons**, around central canals containing blood vessels.

Haversian bone is always formed as a replacement for a less highly organized and probably flimsier kind of bone, often called woven bone (Section 2.3.1), that forms during periods of rapid growth or repair of fractures. It is therefore found mainly in adult mammals, in which there has been extensive bone remodelling. For reasons that are not understood, much of the bone of adult carnivores and primates (including *Homo*) is Haversian in form, but this type of bone is much rarer in cattle, and almost absent in rodents. Ectopic bones are normally woven bone.

At the macroscopic level, **compact bone** is characterized by the absence of cavities other than those containing the osteocytes and the blood vessels and is up to 90% calcified. In **cancellous bone** the hard tissue is reduced to thin strands called **trabeculae,** interspersed with soft **bone marrow.** In fetal, neonatal and juvenile mammals, the bone marrow is the principal site of synthesis of red and white blood cells; the newly formed blood cells are released into the small blood vessels which permeate the bone and thence travel to the rest of the body. The haemopoietic red marrow is gradually replaced by a fatty tissue called yellow marrow, and in adult terrestrial mammals, including humans, only the cavities in the ribs, vertebrae and skull contain red marrow.

Most trabeculae and some cortical regions of the skeleton are made of lamellar bone, and Haversian bone forms the cortex of many long bones, with the osteons running approximately parallel to their long axes. Figure 7.5 is a section of a dried specimen of a talus, a small weight-bearing bone in the hock (ankle joint) of the hindleg of a cow; the outer cortex consists of compact bone but the interior is filled with cancellous bone organized into trabeculae. The thickest trabeculae appear to be aligned in the direction in which the greatest forces are normally applied. In adult humans, trabecular bone accounts for only about 20% of the mass of the skeleton.

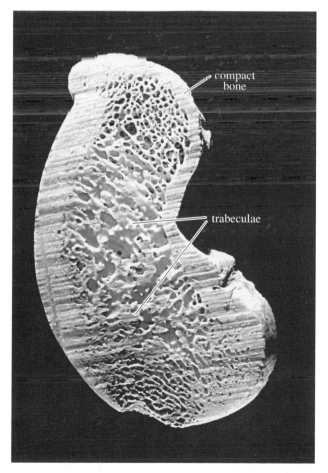

Figure 7.5   Section through a dried specimen of a weight-bearing bone from the hock of the hindleg of a domestic cow, approximately natural size. The regular, almost horizontal, lines are the marks of the saw used to section this piece of bone.

The density of some very stiff skeletal elements (e.g. the ear ossicles) that are composed of compact bone is up to $2.4\,\mathrm{g\,cm^{-3}}$, mainly because of the high density ($3.2\,\mathrm{g\,cm^{-3}}$) of the hydroxyapatite mineral. The mass of the entire skeleton is reduced by replacing compact bone with trabeculae and tissues such as haemopoietic marrow (density about $1.0\,\mathrm{g\,cm^{-3}}$) and adipose tissue (density $0.93\,\mathrm{g\,cm^{-3}}$), in places where the flimsier kind of bone is strong enough to withstand the forces normally applied to it.

The cavities of most long bones of flying birds (and the extinct flying reptiles, e.g. pterodactyls) contain air sacs that reduce the overall density of the skeleton. The limb bones of certain marine mammals and birds such as penguins lack proper marrow cavities. The humerus of the king penguin (*Aptendytes patagonia*) is very dense and stiff, with an exceptionally high Young's modulus (Table 7.1), possibly as an adaptation to the forces it sustains when the animal swims fast using its wings as flippers.

Bone, especially trabecular bone, acts as a reserve of essential metabolites such as calcium ions, which may be present in only small quantities in the diet (Sections 1.2.3 and 2.3). The mammalian skeleton accumulates calcium during pregnancy: herbivores such as rats and deer whose diet is low in calcium may gnaw old dried bones, antlers or even chalky soils. The calcium is released during lactation and secreted in the milk and is thereby incorporated into the skeletons of the growing young. Because of the profuse blood supply, the mineral component of the mother's bone can be withdrawn very rapidly in response to calcium-releasing hormones. As you would expect, alteration of the mineral content of bone profoundly affects its mechanical properties; the bones (and teeth) of lactating female mammals become less dense and much more fragile towards the end of lactation because of calcium depletion.

7.3.2 Mechanical properties of bone

The limb bones of cattle, pigs and sheep slaughtered for meat are a convenient source of material for studies on the mechanical properties of bone. Figure 7.6 shows a typical stress–strain curve for samples of bones prepared from freshly isolated cattle femurs. In the linear region of the curve, the bone behaves elastically; it can be strained to about 0.5% of its original length without damage, and returns to normal when the extending force is removed. Young's modulus for this region is about 20 GPa, almost 10 times greater than that of tendon. Beyond a strain of about 0.5%, the bone is permanently damaged by stretching, and it snaps suddenly when extended by about 3%.

Most components of the skeleton are much more frequently subjected to compression, torsion and bending (see Figure 3.3, Section 3.2.1), than to stretching along the axis. The bone shaft is tubular in shape, like a scaffolding pole, with the densest material around the circumference (Figure 7.5). When the limb is bent, tissue on one side is compressed, while that on the other side is loaded in tension; the bone almost always fails first on the side loaded in tension.

The chemical composition and mechanical properties of different kinds of bones are adapted to particular functions. Deer antlers (Young's modulus 2–12 GPa) are often subjected to bending and to sudden impact forces during fights and when tangled in trees: bone that has a high collagen content is tougher and more compliant and

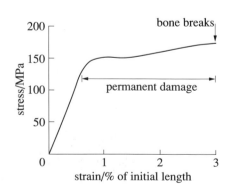

Figure 7.6 The relationship between stretching force applied (stress) and longitudinal extension (strain) for freshly dissected femurs from adult cattle.

hence less likely to break under such forces. High-frequency vibrations are transmitted most efficiently by very stiff materials. Earbones are adapted to this role: their Young's modulus is up to 30 GPa and they have almost twice as much hydroxyapatite as more pliant tissues such as deer antlers. But such bones are much more brittle: the earbone of a whale (among the few that form pieces large enough for mechanical testing) is crushed by stresses of only 33 MPa, compared to 179 MPa for antler, and 247 MPa for cow femurs. Since earbones are never subjected to bending, twisting or crushing forces, the risk of breakage *in situ* is slight.

As explained in Section 7.3.1, there is great variation in the microscopic and gross structure of bone in different regions of the skeleton. It is difficult to relate mechanical properties to microscopic structure because there are very few histologically homogeneous samples of bone that are large enough for mechanical measurements to be made from them. Haversian bone, which always forms as a reconstruction of previously laid down bone, is weaker and has a lower Young's modulus than lamellar bone of similar density: indeed, it is far from clear what mechanical advantages arise from the formation of Haversian bone. Although weaker than lamellar bone, it may be stronger than the material formed when the trabeculae of cancellous bone are filled in to form compact bone. Haversian bone is often found near the points of attachment of large muscles, where cancellous bone has gradually thickened during growth to form compact bone. Cancellous bone is found particularly in the middle of the joint regions of long bones and as the 'filling' between sheets of compact bone in broad flat structures such as the hip, shoulder and ribs. It is much weaker but more compliant than Haversian bone and behaves mechanically rather like a stiff sponge.

The bending and recoil of bones during locomotion can be measured directly by attaching small strain gauges onto the bone shafts and allowing the animal to move normally. Figure 7.7 shows some data on the compressive strain (i.e. the small changes in bone length caused by compression forces) measured from the posterior surface of the radius bone in the upper part of a horse's foreleg. The forces that cause the bending are produced both by the muscles and by the weight of the body when the leg is on the ground. As you would expect, the compression increases sharply with increasing speed in both walking and cantering. You might be surprised, however, that there is no significant difference in the average compression and recoil recorded during walking and during cantering, in spite of the fact that the horse travels more than four times as fast when using the latter gait. The bending of the radius bone is also about 50% greater during the trot than during walking or cantering at the same speed, and does not increase with increasing speed. These observations seem at odds with the elementary laws of mechanics; the change in gait must somehow alter the distribution of forces between the skeleton, muscles and tendons. How these changes might be achieved is discussed in Chapter 8.

For reasons that are not yet fully understood, the bone remains healthy and well mineralized only if frequently subjected to compression and extension (Section 2.3.1). Such forces are easily generated by a few hours of walking or cycling, but they are lacking in a weightless environment such as living in space or submerged in water. The bones of astronauts start to lose mineral and protein after only a few days in space and become fragile and painful when stressed. The effects can be partially counteracted by regular exercise on apparatus such as rowing machines, but most astronauts become too weak to stand up on Earth after a month or more in space. Marine mammals spend a large proportion of their time swimming.

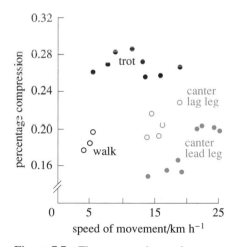

Figure 7.7 The compressive strain measured from the posterior surface of the radius bone of the foreleg of a horse.

7.3.3 Ontogenetic changes in bone structure and properties

Bone plays a central role in growth and ageing: as explained in Chapter 1, growth of skeleton 'sets the pace' for the growth of the soft tissues, and cells of the epiphyses respond readily to growth-regulating hormones. In mammals, closing of the epiphyses is closely linked to the endocrinological changes at puberty (Section 2.3). Among terrestrial species, the skeleton of larger animals is relatively massive compared to smaller ones (Section 3.2.1, Figure 3.5). Ontogenetic changes in the mechanical properties of femurs have been investigated in only a few species, among them humans, a slow-growing relatively light species, and polar bears, a fast-growing, very massive animal.

Femurs (Figure 7.8) are the parts of the skeleton most frequently used for such comparisons as they are large and of a convenient shape for making test pieces. In the sample of polar bear femurs shown in Figure 7.8, the femur of the half-grown male is about the same length as that of the almost fully grown female, but the former is more massive, with larger joints and thicker shafts.

■   Is growth in thickness controlled independently of growth in length?

Yes. Bone thickening is due endosteal and periosteal osteoblasts but growth in length occurs only at the epiphyses, which close around sexual maturity (Section 2.3).

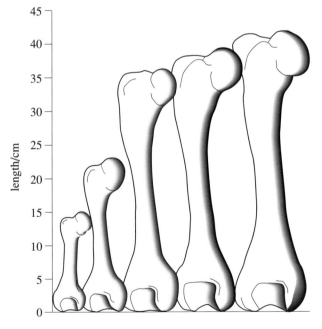

Figure 7.8   Femurs of polar bears of different sizes and ages from which some of the data in Figures 7.9 and 7.10 were obtained. From the left: a 4-month-old male cub, body mass 9.5 kg; a 9-month-old female cub, 58 kg; an almost fully grown but not yet reproductive female, 197 kg; a 4-year-old male, 251 kg (i.e. living independently but sexually immature and still growing) and an 8-year-old male, 407 kg (i.e. almost fully grown and sexually mature). The articulating surfaces of the joints are the ball of the ball-and-socket joint of the hip (top) and the knee (below).

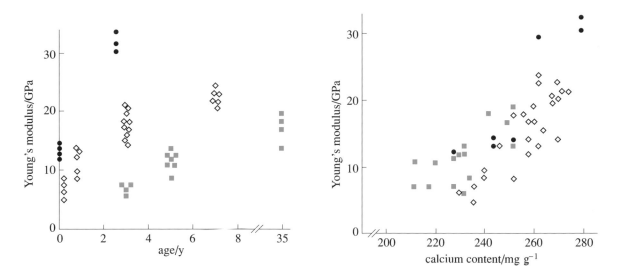

Figure 7.9 Young's modulus for samples of bone from humans (blue squares), a deer (black circles) and polar bears (open diamonds) of different ages.

Figure 7.10 Young's modulus as a function of calcium content for samples of bone from humans (blue squares), a deer (black circles) and polar bears (open diamonds).

Figure 7.9 shows data obtained from bones taken from human cadavers and from wild polar bears whose femurs are shown in Figure 7.8, that range in size from a suckling cub to an adult male. The data for the deer (*Axis axis*) came from an unborn full-term fetus and its 2.5-year-old mother, which weighed 53 kg.

In all three species, Young's modulus increases with age, but it does so much faster in the deer than in bears or humans.

■   How can you explain the species differences in the age changes of Young's modulus?

Like most ruminant mammals, deer fawns at birth are large relative to the size of the mother and grow rapidly to adult size. Growth stops and they become sexually mature at an early age. Bears also grow fast but they are relatively very small at birth. Their adult size is so big that even the females, which as adults are only about half the maximum size of males, do not breed until they are four or five years old. Deer fawns have to run with the herd within a day or two of birth, but polar bear cubs remain in a den for the first three months of life, so they can probably manage with bones of a much lower Young's modulus than the deer. Humans are not particularly large as adults, but they grow very much more slowly than other mammals (Section 1.3.2).

Additional measurements from the same bones shown in Figure 7.10 help to explain these age changes. Young's modulus increases with increasing mineralization in a more or less similar way in all three species.

■   Can you suggest why the bone of the adult female deer has such a high mineral content?

Bones also act as a calcium store, especially for breeding females whose diet provides barely enough calcium. This female was about to give birth and begin lactation, so her calcium stores may have been near maximal (Sections 3.4.2 and

7.3). The high mineralization and Young's modulus may thus be seen as an adaptation to her breeding condition rather than directly related to the mechanical requirements of the bone.

7.3.4 Osteoporosis

Bone is replaced and repaired continually throughout life (Section 2.3). In children, the rate of deposition is faster than the rate of absorption, so the bones grow thicker, longer and stronger. In young adults, the two processes are in equilibrium so the mass of the skeleton remains approximately constant, but in older humans, the activity of osteoclasts exceeds that of osteoblasts so bones become thinner, lighter and weaker. The rate of bone loss is much lower in men, only about 0.4% per year from about the age of 50, so men's skeletons are not greatly weakened until they are about 80 years old. But women lose bone at 0.75–1% per year from age 30, reaching a rate of 2–3% per year during the five years after menopause, so at age 70 years, the mass of women's skeletons are only 60% that of their average mass at age 30. This depletion of bone causes a syndrome of structural and mechanical abnormalities called **osteoporosis**, the most obvious manifestation of which is an increased probability of fractures.

■   What kinds of bone would be most susceptible to reabsorption in osteoporosis?

Osteoclasts attack bone on its surface (Section 2.3.1). Trabecular bone (Section 7.3.1), although very strong, has a larger surface area than cortical bone, and so would incur faster reabsorption. By the age of 90, most women have lost about 35% of their dense bone in the cortices, and about 50% of trabecular bone.

In humans, trabeculae are most abundant in vertebrae, the pelvis and other flat bones, and in the ends of long bones such as the femur, and the radius and ulna in the forearm, so it is these bones that are most frequently weakened by osteoporosis. The vertebrae often collapse as a crush fracture, causing a reduction in standing and sitting height as well as chronic, sometimes severe, backache. Such fractures in several thoracic vertebrae lead to a permanent forward curvature of the upper spine, called a 'dowager's hump' (Figure 7.11). Older readers probably remember when advanced cases of this condition were common among old ladies. These days, treatment with hormones and calcium supplements slows the progress of osteoporosis, and severe, untreated cases are becoming rare.

Fracture of the head of the femur is the most common serious injury among elderly people. It happens nearly five times as often in old women as in men of the same age, although the latter are more likely to engage in strenuous or dangerous activities. During the 1980s, the injury occurred at a rate of nearly 1% per year among women aged 75 years or older, often following only a very minor fall from standing height. Several factors in addition to osteoporosis contribute to the susceptibility of this part of the skeleton to injury. Correct coordination of the activity of the hip muscles is essential to mechanically sound walking. Anomalous forces may be imposed on the skeleton if the muscles become weak in old age (Section 4.3.2), or their neural control is impaired (Section 6.5).

Figure 7.11   An elderly woman with a 'dowager's hump' caused by advanced osteoporosis. Note that she is of quite petite build, and that her posture is so deformed that she is using a child's pushchair as a walking aid.

■   Would fractures in osteoporotic bones heal as fast as similar injuries in younger people unaffected by the disease?

No. Osteoporosis is caused by a disorder of osteoclasts and osteoblasts, the very cells that are essential to bone healing (Section 2.3.1).

Most mammals lose body mass in extreme old age (Section 4.5.1), much of it due to loss of skeleton mass, but osteoporosis in middle age seems to be an exclusively human disease. Indeed, some biologists believe that its origins are inextricably related to the unique features of reproduction in human females: menstruation and menopause. Osteoporosis is less common and less severe among mothers of large families than among childless women, suggesting that depletion of bone calcium during lactation (Section 7.3.3) does not promote it. The decrease in oestrogen at menopause seems to be the root cause of most of the symptoms, and synthetic oestrogens are widely used for treatment and prevention of osteoporosis. Oestrogens promote uptake of calcium from the intestine, and stimulate the thyroid gland to secrete calcitonin, a hormone that inhibits demineralization.

Nutrition is also important. Obviously adequate calcium intake is essential to support bone formation, but a high protein diet, high alcohol consumption and smoking promote calcium excretion, which can lead to net calcium loss, even when intake is high. However, obesity *per se* seems to protect people against osteoporosis (although it increases the risk from many other disorders including heart disease and some forms of cancer): it is thin elderly women, eating a sophisticated Western diet rich in protein and alcohol who are most at risk.

■   Can you suggest how obesity could protect older women from osteoporosis?

The greater body weight imposes more stress on the leg bones and vertebrae during standing and walking. Regular stress promotes the formation of new bone (Section 2.3.1). For the same reason, bones stressed by regular exercise are less likely to become osteoporotic than those of inactive or bedridden people. Adipose tissue also secretes small amounts of oestrogen, formed from androstenedione, even after secretion from the ovaries has stopped, thereby preventing bone loss throughout the skeleton. Well-padded bones may also be less susceptible to fracture.

Regular stress is important for the maintenance of all bones, not just those of the limbs. The classic facial appearance of a stereotyped witch is a long-term consequence of missing or defective teeth combined with osteoporosis in old age. In the absence of the stresses generated by biting and chewing, the jaws gradually shrink, with the lower jaw sometimes being reduced to a thin band of bone in edentulous (toothless) skulls. Consequently, the chin and cheeks are greatly reduced, but, because the nose is mainly cartilage, it is less affected and so appears relatively prominent. This facial structure is much rarer now, thanks to modern dentistry and the wide availability of false teeth that stress the jaws nearly as efficiently as natural teeth.

Summary of Section 7.3

Bone consists of crystals of hydroxyapatite embedded in a matrix of collagen fibres. It also contains numerous living osteocytes which are nourished by blood vessels permeating the bone. The different histological types of bones are distinguished mainly by the arrangement of the osteocytes and blood vessels. The structure and mechanical properties of bone change with age, maturation and, in female mammals, reproductive status, at very different rates in different species. Osteoporosis is a specifically human disorder that affects women more severely and at a younger age than men. Bone, particularly trabecular bone, is eroded away when the activity of osteoclasts is faster than that of the osteoblasts, leading to weakening and greatly increased risk of fracture.

7.4 Joints

Where there is little movement between skeletal elements, bones are usually linked by **suture joints** in which numerous short, stout bands of collagen bind the articulating surfaces together; sutures are usually found where sheets of bones at joined along their edges, as in the skull, the pelvic girdle and the tortoise's shell. In growing animals, the edges of the bones that form the sutures are relatively straight, and there is significant movement at the joint; at many such joints, the bands of collagen gradually ossify and the sutures close as growth ends, but sometimes the capacity for movement is retained throughout life. One of the most thoroughly studied suture joints is that between the two halves of the lower jaw; in many mammals, including humans, elephants and camels, the two jawbones are almost completely fused, but in many carnivores and in kangaroos, the small movements across the suture joint between the two halves of the lower jaw are an integral part of the biting and chewing mechanism.

In many adult vertebrates, movements at suture joints, particularly those of the skull, are greatly limited by the formation of crenulations at the edges of the bones, which interlock tightly like pieces of a jigsaw puzzle. In Figure 7.12, the sutures of the antelope skull are elaborately frilled near the horns where the skullbones risk sudden and uneven impact forces, but they are almost straight around the less vulnerable nasal region. Although there is almost no movement at frilled suture joints, they are very important for limiting the propagation of minor cracks in the bone: homogeneous sheets such as a window pane or a dinner plate usually shatter into several pieces once cracks form, but in a tiled or mosaic floor, cracks in one tile do not spread across the grouting, so adjacent ones remain intact. In this respect, vertebrate skulls resemble a mosaic: instead of splitting like a broken jam jar, weakening the entire structure and causing massive bleeding, cracks remain localized and the broken surfaces well aligned, so healing quickly and often perfectly.

7.4.1 Cartilage

Cartilage ('gristle') is the major skeletal material of all embryonic vertebrates, and of chondrichthyan fishes throughout life. As well as being an essential stage in the growth and healing of bone (Section 2.3), cartilage is also found in parts of the skeleton of adult vertebrates, such as the tip of the nose, the outer ear and the ventral area of the rib cage, where flexibility and toughness are more important than rigidity, and at joints.

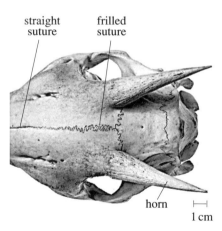

Figure 7.12   Dorsal view of the skull of an adult yellow-backed duiker, *Cephalophus leucogaster* (a small antelope-like mammal), showing the sutures between the skull bones.

The most familiar, and in many ways the most unusual, property of cartilage is the almost complete lack of a blood supply: undamaged cartilage appears greyish-white even in living vertebrates because, unlike bone, it is not permeated by blood vessels.

■   What histological features would you expect in a tissue that lacks a blood supply?

The tissue would consist mostly of metabolically inert, extracellular matrix and contain very few living cells. Stained sections of cartilage show a few small oval cells about 10–30 μm in diameter called **chondrocytes**, embedded in an extensive and apparently homogeneous extracellular matrix. Both the density of chondrocytes and the frequency of their division depends upon their location and the age of the specimen. The density of mitotically dividing chondrocytes is 20 times higher in epiphyseal cartilage (Section 2.3) than in articular cartilage of the same species.

The matrix consists of about equal quantities of collagen and **proteoglycans** to which large quantities of water are bound. Proteoglycans are some of the largest of all biological macromolecules (Section 2.3), consisting of 50–150 carbohydrate molecules, mostly keratan sulphate and chondroitin sulphate, attached to a central core of protein. The M_r of this complex is about 1–3 million, larger than all muscle proteins except perhaps titin (Section 5.2.1).

Up to 100 core proteins (each surrounded by its group of carbohydrate molecules) are linked, probably mainly by hydrogen bonds, to a single unbranched molecule of **hyaluronic acid**. Hyaluronic acid is a polymer of the disaccharide unit (N-acetylglucosamine + glucuronic acid). Both the carbohydrate and the protein components of proteoglycans contain numerous charged sites (for example, the SO_4^{2-} components of the sulphated sugars, and the COO^- groups of some amino acid residues), which exert electrostatic forces on adjacent water molecules. Proteoglycan molecules are therefore able to exert forces that organize large numbers of water molecules around themselves. In a form of cartilage called hyaline cartilage, both the collagen and the proteoglycans are arranged in a three-dimensional network, and the sponge-like properties of the latter are so effective that water is, in fact, by far the largest single component of the cartilage.

■   Can you suggest what role the collagen might play in cartilage?

It confers strength in tension on the tissue. The major components of proteoglycans are held together mainly by hydrogen bonds, and there are large quantities of water between adjacent molecules; without a 'framework' of fibrous, covalently bonded collagen running through it, cartilage would be weak when twisted or stretched. The abundance of fibres and lack of crystalline minerals in cartilage make it much less brittle than bone, and considerable force is needed to break it by twisting or bending.

7.4.2 Lubricated joints

The lubricated joints of terrestrial vertebrates are remarkable in that, although there is often substantial movement between the articulating surfaces, less energy is lost as friction than in most engineering joints; furthermore, they are very hard-wearing, maintaining their superior mechanical performance for more than 70 years in the case of many human joints. The unique properties of hyaline cartilage play an essential role in **synovial joints**, which are found where there is movement through a wide angle, including joints between the limb bones and in the hip and shoulder.

Figure 7.13 shows the general scheme of a typical synovial joint. The ends of the bones are often, but not invariably, expanded in the region of the joint so that the weight-bearing surfaces are enlarged and rounded. The articulating surfaces are lined with a layer of very smooth cartilage about 2 mm thick, and bathed in synovial fluid. This sticky, viscous fluid is secreted by the synovial membrane and is similar in composition to other intercellular fluids except that it contains hyaluronic acid (Section 7.4.1). The entire structure is enclosed within the fibrous joint capsule, which may be continuous with the periosteum surrounding the bone. The hip joint of a large marine turtle shown in Figure 7.14a was photographed in a marketplace in Costa Rica; you can see that the smooth articular cartilage and the tough flexible joint capsule are almost entirely without a blood supply in spite of their massive proportions.

Many synovial joints are subject to stretching and twisting as well as compression and bending; these forces are resisted by ligaments that run between the two bones, either around the outside of the joint or within the synovial capsule. These ligaments usually undergo only small changes in length during normal movements but are arranged so that they restrict movements that would damage the precisely matched articulating surfaces. Figure 7.14b shows the bony elements of the disarticulated hip joint of an adult macaque monkey. The rounded head of the femur fits onto the load-bearing rim of the acetabulum, which in life would be lined with articular cartilage and held in place by a short but very stout ligament. In the intact animal, several other ligaments surround the joint capsule and maintain the correct alignment of the articulating surfaces of the joint during activities such as running, sitting or rolling, that might dislocate the joint.

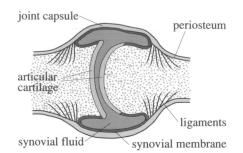

Figure 7.13   Diagram of the principal tissues of a typical synovial joint.

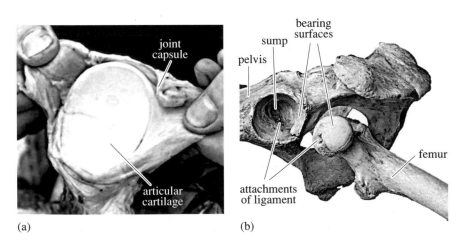

(a)

(b)

Figure 7.14   (a) The acetabulum (hip socket) of a large sea turtle, *Chelonia mydas*. (b) The body components of the left hip joint of a pig-tailed macaque monkey, *Macaca nemestrina*. The femur has been rotated outwards and backwards from its natural position. In life, the bearing surfaces would be lined with articular cartilage. The crown of the acetabulum forms a 'sump' of synovial fluid and also accommodates a ligament which holds the head of the femur into the socket.

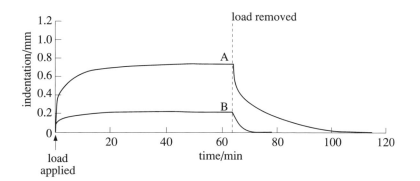

Figure 7.15 The deformation of cartilage following prolonged application of a constant load of 820 kPa. The samples are from human cadavers. Curve A represents articular cartilage from the inner lining of a joint, and curve B the cartilagenous ventral part of a rib.

The synovial fluid and the two surfaces of articular cartilage together form a low-friction, compression-resistant bearing surface. When the two surfaces of the joint are compressed together, the cartilage at the bearing surfaces is deformed, and the water molecules that were ordered around the proteoglycan molecules by the charged sulphate and carboxyl groups are squeezed out of the tissue. However, this squeezing out of the water molecules brings the numerous charged sites on the proteoglycans closer together, and, since like charges repel each other, sets up forces that oppose further compression in the cartilage. At the same time, the water that is squeezed out of the articular cartilage enters the synovial fluid, making it more dilute and hence able to lubricate more efficiently.

There is also a third way in which the cartilage and the synovial fluid are together able to maintain efficient lubrication, even under prolonged compression. Figure 7.15 shows the response of two freshly excised pieces of cartilage to prolonged compression, the probe quickly dents the articular cartilage (A) to a quarter of its total thickness but the cartilage from the ribs (B) responds to similar forces more slowly and the maximum deformation is less. After the first minute, further distortion of both tissues is very slow. After the probe is removed, it takes nearly an hour for the specimens to rebound to their original shape. This slow deformation under prolonged loading is called **creep**; it occurs in all kinds of cartilage but, as you can see from Figure 7.15, it is much more extensive in articular cartilage than in rib cartilage.

In the intact synovial joint, the articular cartilage of the two load-bearing surfaces initially make contact over only a small area, but as they are pressed harder or for a longer time they 'creep', thereby increasing the area of contact between the two surfaces and so decreasing the compression per unit area of articular cartilage. From an engineering point of view, vertebrate synovial joints compare very favourably with artificial systems, both because of their very low friction during movement, and because their low-friction performance is maintained even under prolonged and heavy compression without the need for lubrication under high pressure.

It is important to emphasize that many mammalian joints are much more elaborate than those shown in Figures 7.13 and 7.14. For example, the bones of the wrist, ankle and foot are connected together by numerous synovial joints, many of which bend through only a narrow angle. Correct alignment of all the components of these mechanically intricate structures is important: as most people know from experience, sprains or bruises of the wrist or ankle lead to much swelling, pain and loss of function. Looking closely at Figure 7.14b you can see that the acetabulum is not exactly congruent with the head of the femur; a 'sump' of synovial fluid forms at the back of the joint, which permits synovial fluid to reach the weight-bearing surface from the top of the joint as well as from the joint capsule. The two parts of the joint are held in place by ligaments.

■   Why would a ligament within the hip joint and a sump of synovial fluid be well-developed in the monkey, but absent in the large turtle?

Joint ligaments resist twisting and extension of the joint, and the sump of synovial fluid would be particularly important as a means of maintaining lubrication during prolonged compression, as happens during standing or sitting. Maintaining good lubrication of a joint that is subjected to continuous compression is very difficult. Marine vertebrates such as *Chelonia* (Figure 7.14) are almost neutrally buoyant in the water so their joints would therefore very rarely be subjected to such continuous compressive forces. The joints are compressed by the inertial forces generated by muscular movement, but such forces usually arise from cyclical activities such as swimming so, although transiently highly, they are not as continuous as gravitational forces. Horses that are tied up for long periods, and caged parrots that are unable or unwilling to fly, keep their joints in good condition in spite of standing continuously, by shifting the weight off each leg in turn.

■   From Figure 7.15, how long must the animal rest each leg for the articular cartilage to be almost completely restored to its uncompressed shape?

The body's weight must be off the leg continuously for at least half an hour. You can observe this behaviour for yourself in any stabled horse or caged bird. Regular and strenuous compression and relaxation of the synovial joints is essential to the maintenance of low-friction, painless movement. Dancers and athletes limber up before a performance by bending the arms and legs so that the hip, shoulder and knee joints move through their full range.

Two of the three articulations between the vertebrae of the mammalian spine are synovial joints, albeit of slightly different structure from those of the limb bones. In typical quadrupedal mammals, the intervertebral discs are compressed strongly for only brief periods during fast running or when standing up on the hindlegs. But those of bipedal humans are subjected to almost continuous compression from the moment we get out of bed. Figure 7.16 shows the daily changes in standing height of a normal adult engaged in light work; the body becomes 15 mm shorter within four hours of assuming the upright posture.

This apparent shrinkage is due almost entirely to the expulsion of water from the intervertebral discs, which have been compressed by the weight of the body or by the tensing of the slow postural muscles of the back. When one reclines in an armchair or lies in bed, these postural muscles can relax, and the weight of the upper part of the body is removed from them. The cartilage slowly takes up water from the synovial fluid and expands to its original dimensions. Regular compression and expansion are essential for keeping the intervertebral discs healthy; you may be familiar with the discomfort that arises from interfering with the normal expansion of the intervertebral discs by sitting or standing up all night, or by failing to relax the postural muscles of the back satisfactorily.

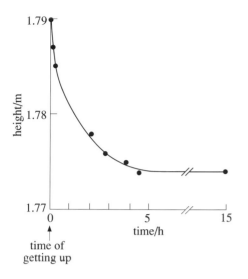

Figure 7.16 The change in standing height of a 29-year-old man from rising in the morning to 5 and 15 hours later. Each point is the mean of observations made on three consecutive days.

Regular compression and extension of both synovial and non-synovial joints are also essential for their long-term health because the flow of fluid between the joint surfaces and the lubricating fluid is the major route for the nutrition of the articular cartilage and internal ligaments; in the absence of a blood supply, oxygen, nutrients, blood-borne hormones and drugs reach cellular components of these tissues via the synovial fluid as well as via the blood vessels in the underlying bone. Small molecules such as glucose diffuse about 40% as fast through cartilage as through water. Since nutrient transfer depends upon diffusion, the nutrition of small joints should be better than that of large ones. However, articular cartilage of small mammals such as mice, and small human joints, has up to 25 times as many chondrocytes per gram as cartilage of large joints and humans so the tissues' supply of nutrients in relation to requirements are about the same.

The cartilage in the joints of paralysed or bedridden people, and that of astronauts, becomes thin and fragile unless the joints are subjected to regular compression and extension. Atrophy of the cartilage in joints and reabsorption of bone from the vertebrae are the main reason why a person's standing height decreases in old age. Normal brisk walking, in which the joints of the legs, hip and spine are compressed and released at about 2 Hz, is almost ideal for the nourishment of cartilage, thereby preventing its atrophy.

Summary of Section 7.4

Cartilage is a matrix of collagen fibres and large highly charged glycoproteins called proteoglycans around which are assembled large quantities of water. It is much tougher and more flexible than bone and 'creeps' when deformed by prolonged application of forces. Synovial joints are lined with articular cartilage and lubricated by synovial fluid secreted from the synovial membrane of the joint capsule. Under prolonged pressure, the water bound to the proteoglycan molecules in articular cartilage is squeezed out into the synovial fluid, thereby preventing the complete elimination of the lubricating fluid from the bearing surfaces. Exchange of extracellular fluid between the cartilage and the joint capsule is also essential for the former's nutrition.

7.5 Conclusion

'Connective' tissues do much more than just connect: they have many subtle and functionally important mechanical properties. Detailed biomechanical studies reveal that apparently similar structures, such as tendons, can have quite different mechanical properties, and hence must perform very different roles in movement. As in the case of muscle, some of these properties change with age and habitual usage. Like muscle, almost all skeletal tissues are living and so need a supply of nutrients. For many such tissues, regular and appropriate usage is essential to keep them mechanically sound. The next chapter is about how these passive mechanical properties of the skeleton and tendinous tissues combine with active contractions in muscle to produce locomotory movements.

Objectives for Chapter 7

When you have completed this chapter, you should be able to:

7.1   Define and use, or recognize definitions and applications of each of the **bold** terms.

7.2   Describe the microscopic and molecular structure of fibrous collagen.

7.3   Outline some concepts and techniques used in the study of the mechanical properties of biological materials.

7.4   Outline the implications of the gross structure of tendons for their functionally important mechanical properties.

7.5   Describe the cytological structure, mechanical properties and anatomical distribution of the principal types of mammalian bone.

7.6   Describe and provide a functional interpretation for some ontogenetic changes in the structure, composition and mechanical properties of bone.

7.7   Outline the structure and composition of the major forms of cartilage.

7.8   Outline the molecular composition and anatomical arrangement of the main tissues in vertebrate synovial joints, and explain how they function together to minimize the energy lost as friction during movement.

Questions for Chapter 7

(*Answers to questions are at the end of the book.*)

Question 7.1 (Objective 7.2)

In what ways do (a) the chemical composition, and (b) the anatomical distribution of collagen differ from that of most other mammalian proteins?

Question 7.2 (Objective 7.3)

Define the following terms and state their scientific units of measurement: stress, strain, Young's modulus.

Question 7.3 (Objective 7.4)

How would the properties of a muscle and tendon system change if the tendon became (a) thicker, (b) longer, (c) ossified?

Classify the following terms depending upon whether they refer to (a) the histological structure of bone, (b) the gross structure of the skeleton, or (c) tissues associated with bone:

trabeculae

compact bone

periosteum

Haversian bone

osteon

cancellous bone

ligament

chondrocyte

lamellar bone

hydroxyapatite

Briefly describe how the structure and composition of the human skeleton changes from birth to old age. Which of these age changes are adaptive and which are non-adaptive?

List three ways in which (a) cartilage and tendon are similar, and (b) the internal organization of cartilage and tendon differ.

Describe the role in vertebrate joints of (a) cartilage, (b) extracellular fluids, and (c) ligaments.

CHAPTER 8   TERRESTRIAL LOCOMOTION

8.1 Introduction

In Chapters 5–7, the structure and properties of each of the major tissues of the musculo-skeletal system were examined separately but, in living systems, the skeleton, muscles, tendons and other connective tissues are always elaborately and intimately associated; coordinated, energetically efficient movements cannot be attributed to any single tissue, but to the integration of properties of all the components of the musculo-skeletal system and its control by the nervous system. The matching of the complementary properties of the different tissues so that they work together efficiently is most clearly demonstrated in natural activities such as locomotion. The additional energy for locomotion is normally the single largest increase of metabolic rate above BMR (Section 3.3). Nearly all animals (other than parasites) have to move to obtain food, to escape from predators and often to migrate as well. Therefore, any change in the energy cost of travel makes a large difference to an animal's total energy budget.

Walking and running seem such natural, straightforward activities but the mechanics are in fact very complicated and have only recently been studied in detail. The physical concepts are not easy to grasp and the theory is complicated and very mathematical: this chapter concentrates on the principles involved, referring wherever possible to common experiences or observations that exemplify the phenomena to be explained. We also return to the theme mentioned earlier: the diversity of structure and function within basic uniformity. If the mechanical principles of locomotion are the same, why do different kinds of animals move in different ways and achieve such different feats? Why do some hop while others trot or gallop, or can only walk, and why can some species climb, or jump, or migrate long distances but very few do all these activities? Answering these questions requires reference to some of the concepts developed in Chapter 3 as well as to Chapters 5–7. This chapter is specifically about how vertebrates with legs travel on land, but many of the same principles also apply to flying and swimming.

8.2 Locomotion on legs

Useful information about the magnitudes and directions of the forces generated during walking can be obtained from the analysis of photographs and records of forces exerted on the ground measured with a force platform. Figure 8.1 (*overleaf*) summarizes calculations based upon such observations.

One use of mechanical energy is obviously for swinging the legs back and forth, but the weight of the body is also raised at each step, as shown in Figure 8.1a, requiring work to be done against gravity, and then allowed to fall back again. On land, body weight in newtons (N) is body mass (kg) × gravity (9.8 m s^{-2}), although of course, in water all organisms weigh much less and many fish are neutrally buoyant (i.e. weightless in water). The vertical movements are much more pronounced at faster gaits, as anyone who has sat on a trotting or galloping horse knows well.

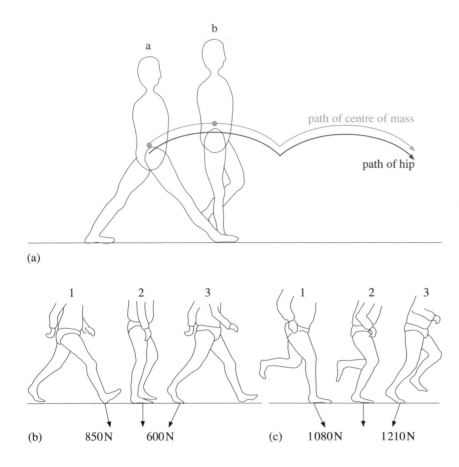

(a)

(b)   850N   600N   (c)   1080N   1210N

Figure 8.1   (a) Diagram of the path of the centre of mass (also called the centre of gravity) of a walking man. (b) and (c) Leg movements and forces in human walking (b) and running (c), based upon films and records from a force platform that measured vertical forces. The arrows show the direction of forces in newtons (N) exerted on the ground by the man's right leg.

The forward velocity of the body is also not constant: at phase 1 of the stride shown in Figure 8.1b, the force exerted between the leg and the ground is directed backwards against the direction of travel. Far from pushing the body forward, this leg is acting as a brake. So, to maintain the average forward velocity, the body has to be accelerated again at each stride, as is happening in phase 3 of the stride shown in Figure 8.1b. As well as moving in the vertical plane (Figure 8.1a), the centre of mass also tilts from side to side, as each foot takes its turn to support the body's weight.

A major advance in our understanding of terrestrial locomotion using legs was the recognition (in the 1970s) that the energy involved in all these different movements alternated between kinetic energy (i.e. motion) and gravitational potential energy, as it does in a pendulum. A swinging pendulum is going fastest at the bottom of its arc of swing, i.e. its kinetic energy is greatest when its potential energy is lowest. At the two extremes of its arc, a swinging pendulum moves more and more slowly, i.e. it loses kinetic energy, but it gains potential energy because its centre of mass is higher, i.e. further away from the Earth. The path of the hip in walking (Figure 8.1a) is like an upside down pendulum. This exchange provides about 60–70% of the energy changes that raise and re-accelerate the centre of mass of the body, so active contraction of the muscles need only contribute the remaining 30–40%.

Quadrupedal walking also involves discontinuous forward movement and vertical and lateral forces although, in ungulates and other large mammals, the rise and fall of the centre of mass and swaying from side to side are small

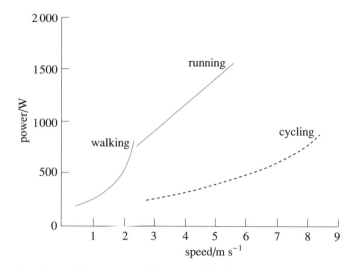

Figure 8.2 The power used by a man while walking, running and cycling on a smooth, level treadmill in still air, based upon measurements of oxygen consumption.

compared to those of humans. Children usually find they need to hang on less tightly when sitting on the back of a walking pony (or cow or elephant) than when on the shoulders of a walking parent.

The comparison in Figure 8.2 of the mechanics of walking (or running, or riding a horse) with riding a bicycle helps to illustrate the importance of these forces in terrestrial locomotion that depends upon legs. When riding a bicycle along a smooth, level road, there are no vertical movements of the body trunk (i.e. one's hip is at a constant height above the Earth's surface), and, if one is pedalling steadily, the velocity of forward movement is nearly constant, i.e. there are no alternating periods of acceleration and braking, and, at least for experienced cyclists, very little wobbling from side to side. You can appreciate the difference by watching the heads of cyclists and runners as they pass a horizontal surface such as window-ledge: the runners' heads bounce up and down but those of the cyclists glide past like ghosts. The elimination of these sources of energy expenditure is the main reason why, as illustrated by the data in Figure 8.2, it is possible to convey one's own mass plus that of the bicycle faster and for less energy by cycling than by walking or running.

■   How do the energetics of cycling change (a) on a bumpy road; (b) when going up hill; (c) in a strong headwind?

(a)   Vertical movements of the body (and bike) are re-introduced, because when the tyre hits a bump, part of the forward kinetic energy is converted into upwards movement, or deflects the vehicle sideways (or both). On a very bumpy road, such energy losses may be so high that cyclists find it is easier to dismount and push than to try to ride.

(b)   Going up hill means doing work against gravity to lift both one's own mass and that of the bicycle. Such work is always directly proportional to the mass that is raised (Section 3.3.3).

(c)   Energy losses from moving into a wind are proportional to the frontal area exposed to the wind, and to the relative velocity of oneself and the wind. The area of exposure is slightly greater for cyclists than for walkers, and cycling is faster, so the combined velocity of the headwind and cyclist is greater, but the main reason why a headwind is a greater impediment to cycling than to walking is that when cycling in still air, one travels much faster for less effort so the reduction in forward velocity (or the increased effort required to maintain normal velocity) is a greater proportion of the total energy expended. Only a small fraction of the energy used for running is work against the environment (i.e. wind, friction on the ground). Most of it is used to lift the body and accelerate the limbs.

Thus, compared to riding bicycles, locomotion using legs seems to use energy extravagantly. The wheel is among the few basic engineering principles of which there is no equivalent among multicellular animals, possibly because of the problems associated with growth and physiological maintenance of structures that rotate on small axles. However, as just mentioned, wheels are efficient only when operated on smooth ground; on rough ground, wheeled vehicles lose energy by doing work against gravity as legged animals do, and they are useless for jumping and climbing. Legs evolved for walking on uneven terrain and can be instantly redeployed for jumping, climbing and many other uses.

Detailed studies of the magnitude and time-course of the forces exerted on the ground during walking and running, combined with measurements of the mechanical and physiological properties of the musculo-skeletal system have revealed several energy-saving mechanisms that make locomotion using legs more efficient. One such mechanism is the principle of the pendulum; another is elastic energy storage (Section 7.2.2), which can also be thought of as an exchange between kinetic and potential energy, but in this case the potential energy is strain energy stored in a stretched tendon, as in a catapult or an elastic band. On release, this energy is transformed into kinetic energy, as in a bouncing ball or an archer's bow. These mechanisms make different contributions to walking and to the various forms of fast locomotion: hopping, running, trotting and galloping.

8.2.1 Walking

For long journeys and when travelling over rough terrain or through dense undergrowth, quadrupeds and bipeds (except very small birds and mammals) prefer to walk. By definition, the **walk** is a gait in which there is no suspended phase: at each stride, the trailing legs do not leave the ground until they have pushed the body forward and its weight has rocked forward onto the other leg or legs. The body is always supported by at least two legs in quadrupedal walking (and crawling of human infants), and by one leg in bipeds, so forward movement can be halted at any stage of the stepping cycle without causing the animal to lose its balance. Walking is therefore a very stable gait, well-suited to locomotion over rough, unfamiliar terrain, and for large animals whose limbs function with a smaller safety factor (Section 3.2.2). Elephants, rhinos and buffalo walk hundreds of kilometres, hardly ever tripping or falling over. They use faster gaits for only a hundred metres or so, and then only when seriously alarmed.

Much information about the roles of the legs in walking can be obtained from the analysis of force platform records such as Figure 8.3 combined with ciné photography. Professor R. McNeill Alexander of the University of Leeds made such measurements of a man walking normally across a platform fitted with stiff springs that measured the forces that he exerted sideways as well as downwards.

The average vertical force exerted over the whole stride is equal to the body weight, but the range changes with speed and gait. In slow walking (Figure 8.3a), the vertical force produced by each leg rises to a maximum within 0.2 s, remains fairly constant then declines only about 0.1 s before the force exerted by the other foot is nearly maximal. At faster speeds (Figure 8.3b and c), the force exerted by each foot becomes more and more biphasic.

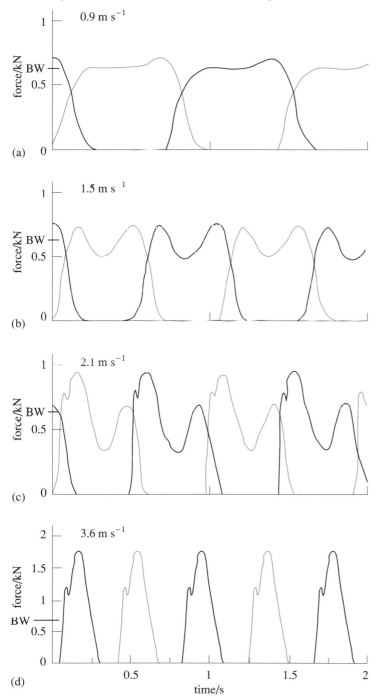

Figure 8.3 The vertical components of forces exerted on the ground by the feet of a man of body mass 68 kg (which exerts a force of 666 N (= 0.67 kN), labelled BW) while he is (a) walking slowly at 0.9 m s^{-1}, (b) walking at 1.5 m s^{-1}, (c) walking briskly at 2.1 m s^{-1}, and (d) running fairly slowly at 3.6 m s^{-1}. Forces generated by the two legs are shown in different colours. (a)–(d) are all drawn to the same horizontal scale, but note the change in the scale of the force axis.

■   How does the peak force exerted on the ground during walking compare with body weight (i.e. the force exerted when standing still)?

At slow and intermediate speeds (Figure 8.3a and b), the peak forces are only about 15% greater than body weight ($770/(68 \times 9.8) = 1.15$) but in brisk walking (Figure 8.3c), forces of up to 45% more than body weight are recorded.

For most mammals and birds, the energy economy of walking is probably just as important as its stability. There are three main reasons why the energetic cost of walking is low. First, the legs are swung, rather than pulled, fowards and backwards at each stride, and folding and extension of the limb joints are minimal. In humans, rotation of the lower back while one leg is swinging forward is counteracted by activity of the slow postural muscles of the other hip, and, particularly when moving fast, by swinging of the arms.

Second, the forward momentum of the body swings it upwards at the end of each stride and the potential energy thus obtained is converted back into kinetic energy, which accelerates the body forwards and downwards for the next stride. Both these mechanisms reduce the need for active contraction of the muscles, although each step requires some active contraction of several muscles, particularly those involved in lifting and bending the legs. During walking, the contribution of gravity acting on the body's mass makes the posture of the trunk, head and, in bipeds, the upper limbs important to its energetic efficiency: for the mechanism to work well, the body's centre of mass must be in the right place.

Third, the stepping frequency is relatively low in walking, so slow contractions, involving the slow phasic muscle fibres, are normally sufficient to power these movements. In fact, only a small minority of the muscle fibres in the large leg muscles are actively contracting during steady walking on level ground; many fibres, particularly the fast glycolytic fibres (Section 5.3.3), are just passengers when the animal is walking steadily. The rate at which muscles use metabolic energy increases sharply with increasing rate of contraction (Section 6.3.2): a gait that involves only slow contractions uses much less energy than one in which the muscles perform cycles of contraction and relaxation at a high frequency.

■   How is swinging the legs affected by (a) moving over irregular terrain such as rocks or boulders; (b) walking over soft sand or sticky mud; (c) ascending a steep hill?

(a) The exact direction and distance of swing has to be adjusted by the muscles at each stride on the basis of feedback from the muscle spindles and tendon organs (Section 6.5.1) and from the eyes and organs of balance, so that each foot lands on a suitable place. Walking over boulders at speed requires both more muscular work, and intense concentration. (b) Walking over soft sand or sticky mud is very hard work because sinking into or sticking to the ground disrupts the pendulum-like swinging of the legs: each leg has to be lifted and placed into position at each stride, instead of being swung there. (c) Lifting rather than swinging each leg is also necessary on a steep hill and when climbing stairs, so these actions depend heavily upon active muscle contraction (Section 6.3.2). Everyone knows how much more tiring it is to walk up a steep hill than to walk at the same speed on level ground.

Disruption of this pendulum-like swinging is the main reason why a minor injury that restricts joint mobility, or a growth defect such as the legs being of unequal mass or length, makes walking so much more tiring as well as slower. Limping means that each leg is placed rather than swung into position at each stride. We manage to use an unnatural gait to go across a room, but it is exhausting for a long hike. Swinging the legs is all but impossible for some highly specialized mammals such as moles (Figure 6.8a), which have short, very muscular limbs. Moles move by shuffling and paddling but they cannot walk in the biomechanical sense of the term.

■   Why is it so much more tiring to walk in a stooping posture (like that of soldiers moving along or between trenches) than to walk upright?

Leaning forward moves the body's centre of mass forward, so the forward momentum of the body is no longer sufficient to swing high enough for the foot to be lifted off the ground in the normal way, and the body tips too far forward over the leading foot, which has to use more muscular energy to prevent falling. We try to minimize this effect by leaning backwards when carrying a heavy parcel with both hands; tall parents find some babies' prams uncomfortable to push because the handles are too low, so they have to lean too far forward.

8.2.2 Walking speed

Measurements such as those in Figure 8.2 show that mammals change from a walk to a faster gait at a consistent speed that depends upon leg length and the action of gravity. The maximum possible walking speed is not limited by power production of muscles or by their maximum shortening velocity, but because the downward acceleration of the body's centre of mass from its highest point in the stride (see Figure 8.1b) cannot exceed the acceleration due to gravity.

Maximum walking speed can be calculated by reference to Figure 8.1a: the leg is pivoted at the hip and moves through an arc of radius l, the length of the leg, about 0.9 m in an average man. A point moving at speed v has an acceleration of v^2/l towards the centre of the circle, which is equivalent to the downwards acceleration at stage 3 of the walking cycle shown in Figure 8.1b. The man's muscles do not pull him down, he 'falls' under gravity. On Earth, gravity (g) is 9.8 m s^{-2}. The acceleration, v^2/l, cannot exceed g, i.e. $v^2/l \leq g$ which, when rearranged, gives: $v \leq (gl)^{1/2}$. From this equation, we can calculate that the maximum possible walking speed for a man of average height is approximately $(9.8 \times 0.9)^{1/2} \approx 3$ m s^{-1}. Most adults walk briskly at about 2.1–2.5 m s^{-1} (Figure 8.3c).

This gait, although slow, requires little muscle energy, so its energetic cost per km per kg body mass is smaller than for the faster gaits and (compared with leaping, galloping or climbing) involves little wear or damage to the musculo-skeletal system. For humans (but not most other animals) the relationship between energetic cost and walking speed is curvilinear, so we would expect the transition to running to take place somewhat below the maximum possible speed, which agrees fairly well with the observations in Figure 8.2. Women and children have shorter legs and so for them, the maximum speed at which walking is the easiest gait is slightly lower than for taller men. The same principle applies to quadrupeds: a Great Dane dog can walk comfortably beside a man, but terrier-size dogs have to trot to keep up with their owners.

■   What is the maximum possible speed for a man of average height walking on the Moon, where acceleration due to gravity is $1.6\,\mathrm{m\,s^{-2}}$?

People could walk at only $(1.6 \times 0.9)^{1/2} = 1.2\,\mathrm{m\,s^{-1}}$ or slower. The astronauts who visited the Moon between 1969 and 1971 chose to hop or skip, for reasons that will be explained in Section 8.3.1.

It is also clear from Figure 8.3 that walking slowly uses nearly as much energy as walking at intermediate speeds. During walking, the body does not move forward steadily but tips forwards and backwards (pitching) and tilts from side to side (rolling), as well as moving up and down at each stride. All these movements use up energy and contribute to the total cost of walking; during brisk walking, the pitching and rolling movements of the body are quite small compared with the forward movement because the swaying of the body in one direction has only just begun before the next step produces forces that swing it in the opposite direction. But in slow walking, there is enough time for the body to sway some distance from the direction of motion at each stride, thereby increasing the total energetic cost of the movement. Thus, for most animals, the energetic cost of walking does not increase linearly with speed (Figure 8.2) and there is an ideal walking speed at which distance travelled per unit of energy used is maximized.

Soldiers at a funeral, cats stalking prey and parents accompanying toddlers have to walk slowly, and the abnormal gait used can be tiring and uncomfortable for more than a short distance. Side-to-side swaying is increased and the pendulum-like motion of the legs is disrupted, so more active muscular contraction is required. When using unnatural slow gaits such as goose-stepping, the total power output of the muscles may be substantially higher than during walking at the optimum, faster speed.

8.2.3 Tortoise walking: adaptation of gait to very slow locomotion

As pointed out in Section 6.4, the strap-like structure and long length of their neck muscles (see Figure 6.5) enable some tortoises, turtles and terrapins to retract the head into the shell with startling speed even when the body is cool, but for other movements, the tortoise's preference for the slow and steady is proverbial. However, unlike moles, these reptiles walk frequently, and often substantial distances. As just explained, it is very difficult to walk both slowly *and* steadily because at low speeds the pitching and rolling movements of the body become more pronounced; such movements may not only cause a significant increase in the total energy used in walking, but would also make it impossible for a short-legged tortoise to hold its shell clear of the ground throughout the stride.

Professor R. McNeill Alexander investigated the gaits used and measured the forces produced by tortoises at low walking speeds. He compared these data with mathematical models of the forces required to produce various gaits. Figure 8.4 shows one of the large tortoises he studied; her short, stout legs (15 cm) are at the corners of her large, almost rectangular shell. During normal walking, each stride lasts more than 2 s, and the body is raised about 4 cm off the ground. A normal tetrapod walking gait would produce too much side-to-side and fore-and-aft rolling when very slow; a tripod gait in which at least three legs were always on the ground would eliminate these unwanted components of the velocity, but would require the muscles to accelerate the limbs abruptly, as anyone who has tried to move a large table or box by 'walking' it from corner to corner knows. Tortoises have perfected a gait that both

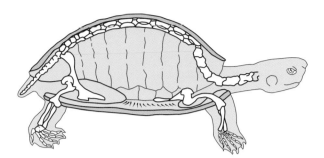

Figure 8.4   An adult female *Geoemyda grandis* of body mass 4.3 kg. The principal bones of the limbs are shown.

minimizes the swaying of the body, and avoids all fast, energetically expensive movements of the limbs: diagonally opposite feet move almost together so that only two feet are on the ground for most of the stride. This gait is less stable than the ideal tripod gait and, in theory, a sudden stop could cause the tortoise to fall forward. In practice, however, the risk of falling is minimized because unscheduled stops are normally accompanied by withdrawing the head and slumping the body onto the ground.

The limb muscles of most tortoises lack fast fibres entirely and tortoises are therefore incapable of moving their legs rapidly. Consequently, the greatest rebuff that sexually mature females can muster to fend off the unwanted attentions of persistent males is to stand on three legs and deliver a slow, deliberate kick. The tactic is not very effective because, for the reasons explained in Section 6.4, a male can withdraw his head to the safety of his shell much faster than a female can kick.

Summary of Section 8.2

All locomotion with legs involves raising and lowering the centre of mass of the body as well as moving the legs relative to the body, so work against gravity is always a large fraction of the total energy expenditure. The maximum speed of walking depends upon how fast the body 'falls' under gravity onto the leading leg. Walking is very stable because the body weight is continuously supported by at least one leg. On a regular surface, legs and body mass are swung forward from stride to stride, so relatively little active contraction of the muscles is required. However, some energy is wasted in swaying of the body out of the line of motion; such energy losses are particularly significant at very low speeds but can be reduced by suitable adjustment of the gait, as happens in tortoises.

8.3 Fast locomotion

Vertebrates use several different gaits when moving fast, the most common of which are bipedal hopping, bipedal running, quadrupedal trotting, ambling,* cantering and galloping. In these fast gaits, the body is suspended during at least one phase of each stride and the amplitudes of vertical movements are much larger. At other phases, the body's weight is briefly supported by one, two or (more rarely) three legs in contact with the ground. Running animals move faster because their strides are both longer and more frequent, but these fast gaits

* In trotting, diagonally opposite legs move almost simultaneously. In ambling (also called 'rack' or 'pace'), legs on the same side move almost together. Horses trot unless trained to amble but camels normally amble.

are much less stable than walking: instant stopping is impossible and tripping or misplacement of the feet is more likely result in a fall. Changes in gait also involve recruitment of different groups of muscles, changes in the way in which muscles and tendons work together to produce movement and alterations in the forces applied to the bones and joints. For nearly all animals, faster travel uses more energy (Figures 3.13 and 8.5).

8.3.1 Hopping

The **hop**, in which the legs are in contact with the ground simultaneously and for only a brief phase of each stride, is the most widely used gait among bipedal vertebrates on land. Most birds can hop; for many small species, it is their most frequently used gait. Various bipedal mammals, including all species of the kangaroo family (Macropodidae) and certain rodents (e.g. the kangaroo rat *Dipodomys spectabilis*, Section 7.2.3) hop at fast and intermediate speeds, as do lemurs and some other small, primitive primates. Higher primates (monkeys, apes and humans) are the only major group in which the bipedal posture *without* hopping has evolved.

The mechanics of mammalian hopping have been most thoroughly investigated in the red kangaroo (*Macropus rufus*) and the wallaby (*Macropus rufogriseus*), which occur in grassland and semi-desert in Australia, and have been bred successfully in zoos all over the world. When moving very slowly, kangaroos and wallabies use an ungainly pentapedal shuffle, in which the stout tail is used as a fifth limb. At all faster speeds, the body is lifted high off the ground for a large fraction of each stride and is propelled by the long hindlegs alone.

■ What role does gravity play in hopping?

Most of the work of hopping is work against gravity at the start of each stride. The body falls under gravity in the second half of each hop, during which time it travels forward through a distance that depends upon its forward momentum and the height of each hop. Force platform measurements show that the maximum force exerted by hopping wallabies is about 65% higher than body weight. In the low gravity environment of the Moon, the astronauts found that hopping was the easiest fast gait, because so little work was needed to jump (in spite of their heavy backpacks and space suits).

Figure 8.5 shows how the energy consumptions of kangaroos and some other mammals change as speed of locomotion increases. You can see that, although the power required to support locomotion increases with speed in the expected way during pentapedal walking, when the gait changes to the bipedal hop, the energetic cost of locomotion actually falls slightly as hopping speed increases. As the kangaroos travel faster, the average distance covered per hop increases but the hopping frequency remains almost constant.

It is possible to explain this apparent paradox by studying the form and frequency of the hopping stride, and examining the muscles and tendons that power it. The most energetically expensive component of the movement is the acceleration of the body upwards at the start of each hop; the other major movement, the backwards and forwards swing of the long hindlegs, involves relatively little muscle power. The body is accelerated upwards by the rapid extension of the ankle joint, but as it hits the ground at the end of each hop, its weight folds the joints of the legs. Flexion of the ankles stretches the Achilles tendons and the gastrocnemius muscles (and other

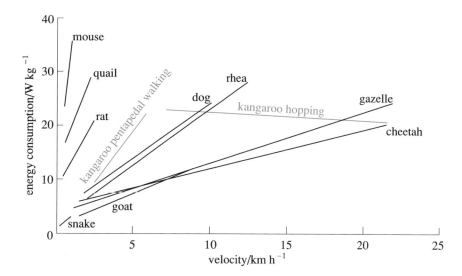

Figure 8.5 The energy consumed by various vertebrates while travelling at various speeds.

parallel muscles and tendons) which run along the posterior surface of the leg from behind the knee to the foot (see Figures 3.7 and 5.2). Calculations from photographs and force platform measurements suggest that muscles and tendons are stretched by about 3%, which is well within the range at which stretch is reversible (see Figure 7.4), so energy can be stored elastically.

As the kangaroo's body moves forwards, its weight ceases to flex the ankle joint; the stretched tendons therefore recoil and the energy so released appears as kinetic energy and contributes to the forwards and upwards movement of the next hop. The animal bounces along on its Achilles tendons, reducing by about one-third the total amount of work that the muscles would have to do if they alone propelled the animal at the same speed.

Muscle activity is usually (but not invariably, as explained in Section 8.3.3) necessary to hold the tendons at the length at which they can act as bouncing springs. Thus, if the gastrocnemius muscle were relaxed, flexion of the kangaroo's ankle would stretch it (Sections 5.3.1 and 5.3.4) more than it stretched the stiffer tendon (see Table 7.1). The tendon would undergo relatively little change in length, most of it in the range of lengths at which little strain energy is absorbed (see Figure 7.4). However, if the muscle were generating forces that actively opposed passive extension, flexion of the ankle would stretch the Achilles tendons in the range of lengths at which the energy absorbed by the tendons as they are stretched is stored elastically (Section 7.2.2) and can be recovered as kinetic energy when they recoil. As explained in Section 7.2.3, the Achilles tendons of wallabies and kangaroos seem to be specifically adapted to function in this way.

■   What arrangement of muscle fibres and tendons would you expect in the gastrocnemius muscles?

The muscles would be expected to be pennate (Section 6.4), because they are adapted to producing large forces, but do not shorten very much. The gastrocnemius muscles are pennate in most mammals (including humans), and in kangaroos and wallabies they and the Achilles tendons are stout and strong. The gastrocnemius muscles would be able to exert high isometric forces on the

Achilles tendons, but during hopping they would undergo little net shortening. In fact, for much of the hopping cycle, their contraction is probably almost isometric; when the ankle joint is flexing as the body hits the ground, the gastrocnemius muscle may be stretched a little and thus may be working in the negative work mode. However, as emphasized in Section 6.2, it is very difficult to obtain precise information about the mechanical conditions under which muscles in intact animals are contracting.

■   Comparing Figure 8.5 with Figure 6.3 (Section 6.3.2), can you suggest an explanation for the fact that the energetic cost of hopping decreases slightly with increasing speed?

If a muscle were stretched while contraction was in progress, the total work output per unit of chemical energy broken down would be greater. The data in Figure 8.5 could be explained in terms of those in Figure 6.3 if it could be shown that the contraction of the muscles became more like that of a negative work contraction at higher hopping speeds; plausible though this suggestion is, it remains to be supported by direct measurements of the mechanical conditions under which the muscles operate in intact kangaroos.

■   Would you expect the gastrocnemius muscle to be contracting in this way during slow walking?

No. Powerful contraction of the gastrocnemius muscle turns the foot and lower leg into a spring, which absorbs, stores and releases energy between hops. These properties would impede activities such as walking and climbing that depend upon swinging or placing the legs into position.

There is direct evidence that the high (0.5 m) escape jumps of the kangaroo rat, *Dipodomys* (Section 7.2.3) can be explained in this way: tiny force transducers fitted to their Achilles tendons record forces of up to 75% greater than the maximum isometric force that can be measured from the gastrocnemius muscle *in vitro*. Such forces could only be achieved by muscles operating in the negative work mode, i.e. the muscle is being stretched while it is fully activated.

The energetic efficiency of kangaroo hopping depends upon the special properties of the leg tendons and muscles described in Section 7.2.3, rather than upon any advantages of the gait itself. Other bipedal mammals, such as the kangaroo rat and the spring hare, *Pedetes capensis* (both rodents so only distantly related to marsupial kangaroos) use as much energy to hop as quadrupedal species of similar size use in trotting or galloping at the same speed. So bipedality in these species must have evolved as an adaptation to habits (such as jumping to escape predators) other than speed or efficiency of long-distance locomotion.

8.3.2 Galloping

Most quadrupedal mammals have two fast gaits: the trot (or amble) at moderate speeds and the **gallop** for maximum speed. In the trot, diagonally opposite pairs of feet are set down almost simultaneously. Galloping and cantering are asymmetrical gaits that are really a series of bounds in which the hindlimbs act more or less synchronously to throw the body upwards and forward. The body is still moving forward fast as it lands, so it rocks forward over first one foreleg, then the other, with small (but never negligible) deceleration.

Cheetahs and hares are some of the fastest of all mammals. They rely upon speed to catch prey (cheetahs) or escape from predators (hares) that are much larger than themselves. Wolves also run down their prey and their domesticated descendants, greyhounds, are bred and trained to gallop almost as fast as cheetahs or hares. Greyhounds are thus a convenient animal in which to study the mechanics of galloping. The hindlegs swing forward to touch the ground near, or sometimes in front of, the forelegs from where they push the body into the next stride (Figure 8.6).

The stride of such specialized gallopers is lengthened by having highly mobile shoulders: in anatomically primitive mammals including ourselves and moles (Figure 6.8a), the clavicle (collar bone) attaches the scapula (shoulder blade) to the sternum, thereby limiting the fore and aft movement of the shoulder. In all fast galloping mammals (e.g. stoats, Figure 6.8b), the clavicle is greatly reduced (you can feel it in dogs and cats as a small sliver of bone embedded in the neck muscles) so the shoulder is free to swing far forward in front of the ribs, thereby lengthening the reach of the forelimbs.

Mammals of similar leg length change gaits at about the same speed regardless of their body mass but since smaller mammals usually have shorter legs, they switch from a trot to a gallop at lower speeds than larger species. Thus galloping is the usual mode of travel for mouse-sized animals, but rhinos and buffalo use the gait very sparingly, and adult elephants not at all (Section 3.2.2).

The change in gait from walking to trotting, running or galloping alters the way in which the muscles and tendons are deployed so that the increase in energy expenditure is minimized. As each foot strikes the ground and takes its turn to support the animal's weight, the joints of the lower leg flex under the body's weight, thereby stretching the tendons and ligaments attached to them. Some of the kinetic energy of the horse's descent is converted into potential energy as the foot strikes the ground, i.e. the energy is stored as strain in the tendons and ligaments and contributes to forward propulsion during the next stride.

Figure 8.7 (overleaf) illustrates how one such structure, the suspensory ligament of the hoof, works. The hoof joints are nearly straight when the leg is not supporting the body (Figure 8.7a), but when the whole weight of the body falls onto this one hoof (Figure 8.7b), the fetlock joint between the carpals and the digit flexes, stretching the ligament and removing some of the load off the bones and joints. The energy thus absorbed reappears as recoil as the horse moves into the next stride (Figure 8.7c). Energy absorption and recoil from alternating flexion and extension of these joints of the lower leg make a significant contribution to energy economy in galloping and trotting. Such mechanisms are particularly important in hoofed mammals such as deer, antelopes and horses: although their legs appear surprisingly slim and dainty, they contain several stout tendons and ligaments that together make them strong enough to withstand the large forces exerted on them during galloping, and make an important contribution to the efficiency of fast locomotion.

■   Why does the fetlock never assume the position shown in Figure 8.7b during walking?

Because the forces applied to the leg are never great enough. In walking, the body weight is always supported by at least two legs, and, as in human locomotion (Figures 8.1b and 8.3), vertical changes in the centre of mass are

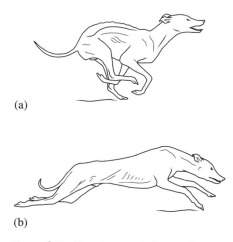
(a)

(b)

Figure 8.6   Drawings made from a film of a racing greyhound galloping at full speed. (a) The hindquarters are bent under the abdomen so that the hindpaws touch the ground after, but in front of, the forepaws leaving the ground. (b) At the end of the suspended phase, the spine flexes the other way, thereby extending the reach of the forepaws.

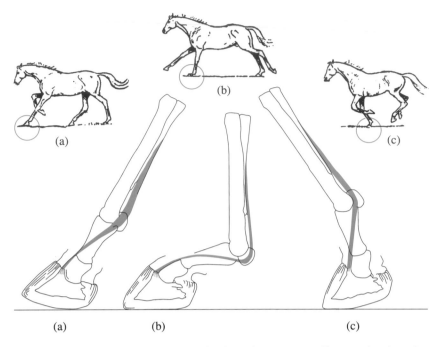

Figure 8.7   A simplified diagram showing how the suspensory ligament in a horse's hoof acts as both a shock-absorber and an energy-saving mechanism.

smaller. In Figure 8.7b, a force of up to three times the body weight of the horse (around 1.5–2.0 kN) is falling on one small hoof. The stresses so generated are momentarily very high: it is no wonder that horses are reluctant to gallop on very hard surfaces such as roads, and that galloping hooves crush plants and soil.

Many of the muscles that move the distal parts of the legs are composed of relatively short fibres and are bunched together around the hip and shoulder, and hence their leg tendons are long. In galloping, these muscles and their tendons act like the gastrocnemius muscle and Achilles tendon of wallabies (Section 8.3.1): the muscles exert an almost continuous isometric force that stresses the tendons to a length at which the energy used for any further stretch as each leg takes its turn to support the body's weight is stored as strain energy and released as recoil in the next stride.

As well as involving long legs and energy-storing tendons, galloping brings into action a whole new set of muscles, those of the back. These muscles bend the spine, bringing the hindquarters under the body just before the hindlegs reach the ground, so that, in greyhounds, the hindpaws touch the ground in front of the point at which the forepaws left the ground (Figure 8.6a). At a later phase of the stride, the spine bends in the other direction while the hindlegs are on the ground, bringing the forelegs as far forward as possible (Figure 8.6b), and thereby increasing the effective length of each stride. In horses and most deer and antelopes, flexion takes place mainly at the joint between the lumbar and sacral vertebrae, but in smaller mammals with more flexible backs such as carnivores (Figure 8.6), there is significant bending between the lumbar vertebrae as well. Mammals such as cheetahs, greyhounds and hares that gallop well have long flexible backs, compact girdles and small, neat abdomens. In contrast, the scapula and pelvis of moles (Figure 6.8a) are so long that they almost meet at the 'waist', thereby precluding the bending of the spine that is so important for fast locomotion in stoats (Figure 6.8b) and other fast running mammals, which have relatively long, narrow backs and shorter girdles.

The recruitment of the muscles and joints of the spine in fast locomotion may help to explain why the compressive forces on the bones of the foreleg are almost the same in cantering as in walking (Section 7.3.2, Figure 7.7): instead of being absorbed by the limb bones, the energy imposed by impact of the leg onto the ground is absorbed by the muscles and joints of the back as flexion of the spine. Recent studies of the extensive aponeurosis over the back of deer and other galloping mammals suggests that it acts as a spring in the back, in much the same way as tendons do in legs. It is, of course, technically much more difficult to measure the mechanical properties of diffuse structures such as aponeuroses than of tendons. Instead, the stress/strain properties (as in Figure 7.4) of the whole back of a 50 kg fallow deer have been studied. From these measurements and observations of the living animal, the investigators calculated that a strain of about 0.04% (about 5 mm) as the back flexed and extended would enable this broad sheet of collagen with the muscle attached to it to store about 40 J if the muscle was contracting while the back was arched as in Figure 8.6a. Such energy storage could make a significant contribution to the energetic efficiency of galloping.

Faster galloping is achieved by both longer and more frequent strides and the energy used rises almost linearly with speed, although the rate of increase differs between species, being generally greater for smaller animals (Figures 3.13 and 8.5). Everyone has noticed that animals (e.g. dogs, horses) become hot and tired more quickly when galloping than when walking. Is galloping an inherently more exhausting gait, or do gallopers tire sooner because they are travelling faster? To investigate this question, Professor Richard Taylor and his colleagues at Harvard University trained a small pony to run on a treadmill while wearing a facemask and to change gaits at a verbal command. Their data are shown in Figure 8.8 (*overleaf*).

■   From Figure 8.8a, which speed and gait are the least efficient (i.e. which uses most energy for each unit of distance travelled)?

At their optimum speeds, the energetic cost of movement per unit of distance is almost the same for all three gaits used by the pony. Efficiency changes with speed for all three gaits, but the optimum for walking is much narrower than that of the faster gaits. The energetic cost of travel is greatest for slow walking, but efficiency increases sharply as the animal accelerates from about 0.5 m s^{-1} to about 1.3 m s^{-1}. Furthermore, the distance travelled while each foot is on the ground, i.e. each foot's contribution to propulsion in each stride, was found to increase only slightly between a slow trot and a fast gallop.

Galloping uses energy at a high rate only because it is faster: strides are longer and slightly more frequent, so more metres are covered per unit time. This conclusion may at first surprise you: it seems obvious that the longer stride and the involvement of the back muscles in galloping would use disproportionately more energy than a gait in which the limbs only moved through a relatively small angle. However, the muscles are deployed in energetically efficient ways and the arrangement of the tendons and ligaments makes maximum use of the conversion of kinetic energy into potential energy stored as strain in the elastic tissues and its re-use as kinetic energy for the next stride.

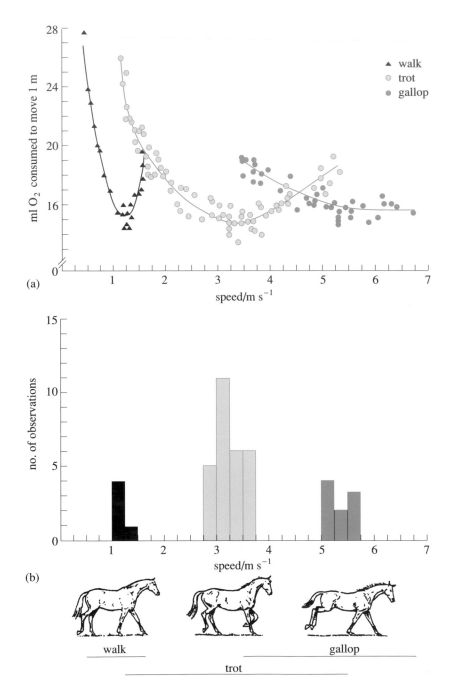

Figure 8.8   (a) The oxygen used by a small pony to travel one metre at various speeds at a walk (triangles), a trot (tone circles) and a gallop (closed circles). The pony was trained to run on a treadmill and to change gaits to a verbal command. (b) The frequency of different speeds chosen by the same pony when moving freely over open ground.

The maximum force that the feet exerted on the ground (measured as in Figure 8.3) and the peak stresses in the muscles that extend the ankle were measured in laboratory rats galloping at about $1.5\,\mathrm{m\,s^{-1}}$, and compared with those of the kangaroo rats, *Dipodomys spectabilis,* whose fastest gait is hopping at about the same speed (Section 7.2.3). Although their gaits were quite different and the kangaroo rat's feet exerted almost twice as much force as those of galloping laboratory rats, the peak stresses in the leg muscles were almost identical in the two species. The peak stresses measured *in vivo* when the animals were moving at their preferred speeds were 34–36% of the maximum isometric stress that the muscles could generate when studied *in vitro*.

■   Why should animals choose gaits and speeds that involve generating stresses of about one-third of the muscle's maximum possible isometric force?

As explained in Section 6.2 (Figure 6.1b), muscles produce the maximum *power* when shortening at about one-third of the maximum possible speed of shortening and producing one-third of the maximum isometric tension.

There are no data similar to those in Figure 8.8a for other species and it is far from certain that all gaits are as nearly equally efficient at their optimum speeds in all kinds of mammals as they are in horses. As in most ungulates, the major cause of death among wild horses (horses are now all but extinct in the wild) was predation from fast-running carnivores such as wolves and cheetahs, so selection for energetic efficiency in galloping would have been strong. The musculo-skeletal system of animals such as elephants, hedgehogs or buffalo that walk long distances and do not run away to avoid predation may be significantly more efficient for walking than for faster gaits.

Taylor and his colleagues also measured the speeds at which their pony chose to travel when roaming freely in a field. As you can see from Figure 8.8b, it almost always moved at speeds that were optimal for one or other gait. Both people and animals avoid very slow running, trotting or galloping and very fast walking because the gaits become inefficient at these extremes of speed. If they want to travel at an average speed that falls between the two gaits, they alternate bouts of moderately fast walking with bouts of moderately slow running. Such alternation only presents problems when two animals with different speeds of transitions between gaits try to travel together, such as a mother hand in hand with a small child.

8.3.3 Muscles and tendons in the legs of camels

The mechanical behaviour of tendons in hopping and galloping is similar in many ways to that shown by muscles contracting in the isometric and negative work modes (Section 6.2). It has probably occurred to you already that a muscle that is never required to shorten could just as well be replaced by a tendon: both tissues are elastic so they recoil when stretched. It is only the abilities to shorten and to control the forces necessary to extend it that are unique properties of muscle.

Camels are renowned for their ability to travel very long distances without food or water. Their fastest gait is the gallop, but at moderate speeds, they usually walk or use the amble (see the beginning of Section 8.3). As in other ungulates, the weight of the body causes the joints of the supporting legs to extend, thereby stretching the ligaments, tendons and muscles around them (Sections 7.2.2 and 8.3.1). When the body weight is transferred to the other legs, these joints return to their resting position; much of the energy used is stored elastically as deformation of the tendons and ligaments, but active muscular contraction is also essential because, as emphasized in Section 8.3.1, the tendons must be stressed to the correct length to function efficiently. Figure 8.9a (*overleaf*) shows some of the muscles that flex the lower part of the foreleg of a one-humped dromedary camel; the ulnaris lateralis is a pennate muscle, and in the camel it consists of a large number of very short fibres each averaging only 3.4 mm in length.

■   What role would you expect a muscle of this anatomical structure to play in movement?

Muscles composed of many short fibres are best suited to exerting large isometric forces (Sections 5.3.2 and 6.4). The ulnaris muscle would be almost useless for flexing the joint between the radius and the lower leg because, even if the fibres contracted to half their resting length, the shortening would still only be 1.7 mm, a negligible fraction of the total length of the ulnaris and its tendon in a camel whose shoulder height might be over 2 m. The ulnaris muscle must therefore act only to stress its tendon during locomotion.

Figure 8.9b shows some of the structures involved in bending the joints of the lower part of the camel hindleg. In most ungulates, the gastrocnemius, digital flexors and plantaris are pennate muscles attached to very long, stout tendons, but in the camel the plantaris 'muscle' is devoid of all contractile tissue: it and its tendon have become a collagenous ligament extending from the femur to the base of the foot. As long as the arrangement of the joints and the line of action of the body weight are correct, the plantaris 'ligament' stretches as the weight of the body falls on each leg at the end of the stride, stores this energy elastically and releases it at the beginning of the next stride as effectively as a normal muscle attached to a long tendon. The plantaris muscle of the hindleg therefore seems to have taken to its logical conclusion the trend towards reduction in muscular components of the leg muscles noticed in the ulnaris of the forelimb.

■   Would replacement of a muscle by tendinous material reduce the total energetic cost of movement?

Yes. Even when contracting in the isometric or negative work modes, muscles are generating active tension and hence consuming more ATP than when relaxed (Section 6.3), but the ability of tendons to stretch, store the energy used in deforming them and to shorten when released is a passive property. The metabolic rate of tendons and ligaments is always low (Section 7.2.3), and there is no evidence that it increases when they are stretched and recoil during locomotion. Locomotion may thus involve little or no increase in energy expenditure by those structures in which muscle has been replaced by tendinous tissue. It has been calculated that the replacement of the plantaris muscle by a 'plantaris ligament' may have cut the energy needed to move the leg during ambling by half. In view of the vast distances that camels travel between their meagre grazing grounds, the advantage of this anatomical adaptation is clear.

8.3.4 Breathing while hopping or galloping

It is clear from Section 8.3.2 that fast locomotion such as galloping involves much more than just the limbs. The viscera (guts, liver, lungs, reproductive organs, etc.) are not rigidly attached to the skeleton, so they shift as the body is accelerated and decelerated in the horizontal and vertical planes. In humans, each foot exerts almost vertical forces of up to 1.7 kN each time it strikes the ground in running (Figure 8.3d). The forces are transmitted through the body and move the internal organs, just as a car passenger's position (relative to the car) is shifted by abrupt acceleration, sharp turns or emergency stops. Flexion and extension of the back (Figure 8.6) alter both the shape and the volume of the

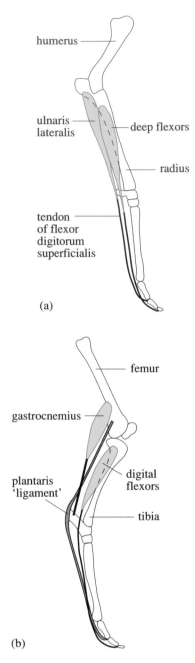

(a)

(b)

Figure 8.9 The principal muscles and tendons in the lower parts of (a) the foreleg, and (b) the hindleg of an adult one-humped camel, *Camelus dromedarius*.

thorax and abdomen, and impose forces on the thoracic and abdominal viscera suspended from it. Sustained exercise always entails increased respiration. How are the forces generated by locomotion integrated with those of lung ventilation?

D. M. Bramble and David Carrier of the University of Utah obtained the records in Figure 8.10 by training a pony to trot or gallop over a force platform like that used for Figure 8.8a while wearing a facemask containing a microphone. Both records (a) and (b) clearly show coupling between footfalls and breaths.

■   How does ventilation change as the pony goes from a trot to a gallop?

Ventilation increases slightly in frequency (from about 91 breaths per minute in trotting to about 112 when galloping) and greatly in amplitude. Similar observations on other mammals that habitually use fast gaits for significant distances, such as dogs, hares and wallabies, showed similar synchronization between ventilation and footfalls.

Professor R. McNeill Alexander investigated the theoretical bases for these phenomena. He concluded that synchronization in wallabies arose mainly from the viscera. As the feet leave the ground and the body is launched into a hop, the loosely suspended viscera 'get left behind', pulling the diaphragm backwards (through a distance of about 1 cm at the centre) thereby expanding the thoracic cavity and facilitating inspiration. As the body decelerates on landing at the end of a hop, the opposite happens and the thorax is compressed, causing expiration. The mass of the viscera acts like a piston, expanding and compressing the lungs. As in the muscles and connective tissue of limbs, some of the energy absorbed by the diaphragm is stored elastically and appears as recoil. In other words, the diaphragm vibrates at hopping frequency. The mechanical properties of the respiratory muscles and their associated connective tissue seem to be 'tuned' to vibrate at about the same frequency as hopping.

■   How would this mechanism change as the speed of travel increases?

It would not. As pointed out in Section 8.3.1, the distance travelled per hop contributes much more to increased speed of travel than the hopping frequency, which changes very little. The ventilation mechanism vibrates passively at the same frequency as hopping, which would reduce significantly the energetic cost of breathing, and hence of locomotion as a whole, over the normal range of hopping speeds.

The pattern of vertical and horizontal forces is much more complicated for trotting or galloping quadrupeds than for bipedal hoppers, so for them, the piston-like mechanism probably makes only a minor contribution to breathing. Calculations suggest that in horses, flexion of the back and vertical compression of the anterior thorax through the forelimbs and shoulders contribute more to changing the volume of the thoracic cavity and hence to powering ventilation.

8.3.5 Human running

If people want to travel faster than 2.3 m s^{-1}, they normally run (see Figure 8.2). As pointed out at the beginning of Section 8.3, humans are unique among bipedal mammals in using running rather than hopping as their principal fast gait. The only other living vertebrates that frequently run bipedally are large birds, particularly flightless species such as ostriches and rheas, but the basic

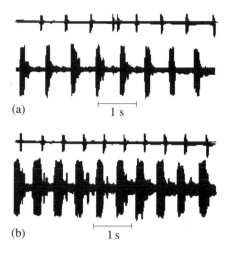

(a)   1 s

(b)   1 s

Figure 8.10   Recordings of the footfall of the right foreleg (upper traces) and breathing, recorded by a microphone in a face mask (lower traces) (prominent bursts are exhalations) of a pony (a) trotting, and (b) galloping over a force platform.

structure of birds' legs, backs and hips is obviously quite different from that of humans. Because of its importance to sports and medicine, the mechanics of human running have been studied in great detail. There is only space here to outline a few principles.

■ From the force platform record in Figures 8.1c and 8.3d, what mechanical features does running share with hopping and galloping?

The peak vertical forces produced are large, nearly twice as great as the maximum observed during walking (Figures 8.3a–c), and more than 2.5 times body weight. Unlike the situation in walking, the body is suspended for about a quarter of the total duration of the stride. In physically fit men running fast and steadily, the body's centre of mass (Figure 8.1a) rises and falls through about 6 cm during each stride. In other words, as in galloping and hopping, much of the work of running is work against gravity, and so, as for other kinds of fast locomotion, efficient exchange between kinetic and gravitational potential energy and the use of passive energy storage in the tendons and ligaments would greatly reduce the energetic cost of running. Measurements of the rate of oxygen uptake during running indicate that fit young people can run fast using energy at only about half the rate that theoretical calculations predicted that they should if all the movements were powered by active contraction of the muscles alone. The unique structure of the human foot is believed to make a major contribution to the energy economy of running.

The human foot, like the brain and the pelvic girdle, has changed greatly in the evolution of savannah-dwelling *Homo* from arboreal ape ancestors. The appearance of adaptations of its structure to walking and running are some of the best clues about when, and in which hominid species, the upright posture and our unique style of locomotion appeared. Most primate feet are flat and the digits are flexible like those of a hand, but the human foot is arched rather than flat as it is in apes. The toes are relatively shorter and more or less parallel, and the bones of the first ('big') toe are stout and strong because most of the weight of the body is carried on this toe. The plantar aponeurosis runs under the main bones, from the heel to the toes, like the bowstring of a 'bow' formed from the arched bones.

To investigate how the passive elastic properties of this aponeurosis and other ligaments in the foot might behave during running, isolated human feet were subjected to compression forces similar in magnitude and frequency to those that occur during running (Figure 8.3d). The investigators found that, at their peak, these forces flattened (and so slightly lengthened) the foot, stretching the plantar aponeurosis. Recoil of the aponeurosis (and other ligaments) restored the foot to its resting shape as soon as the load was removed. This stretching of the plantar aponeurosis would absorb impact energy, cushioning the impact of the foot with the ground, and would release the energy thus absorbed during the following stride. Thus the aponeurosis in the sole of the foot and the ligaments that link its many bones store energy from one stride to the next as ungulates' hooves do.

The longer stride of running also involves much greater excursion of the hip, knee and ankle than happens in walking. As the body's weight falls onto the foot, the ankle joint flexes (Figure 8.1c, phase 2), thereby stretching the Achilles tendon and the gastrocnemius muscle. The ankle extends again as it pushes the body forward into the next stride (Figure 8.1c, phase 3), and is still extended when the foot first touches the ground, but is not yet carrying the body's full weight (Figure 8.1c, phase 1). The large proportion of the energy used to flex the ankle is believed to be stored as elastic strain in the tendons and muscles of the lower leg, and released as recoil in the next stride in human running in much the same way as it is in hopping kangaroos (Section 8.3.1). But, as in kangaroos, the mechanism depends upon the tendons being appropriately stressed by the calf muscles.

■ Why is running in tight-fitting high-heeled shoes so difficult?

Because tight-fitting shoes prevent the normal extension of the feet as the body weight falls onto them, and high heels distort the posture of the ankles so that the Achilles tendons are no longer in a position to absorb energy as the body's weight falls onto the feet. Sports shoes should be flat and loose-fitting.

■ Would you expect breathing and running movements to be coupled in people, as they are in hopping and galloping mammals (Section 8.3.4)?

Possibly not, because running does not entail flexion and extension of the spine, and its vertical forces are not as large as those produced by hopping. Bramble and Carrier studied this question in humans using the same apparatus as that used for horses (Figure 8.11). They found various phase relationships between stride and breathing movements, with the most common pattern for fast, level running being 2 : 1 coupling, as shown in Figure 8.11b. The athletes were often unaware of switching between 2 : 1 (Figure 8.1b) and 4 : 1 (Figure 8.11a) coupling, even though the transition took place within a few strides and involved an abrupt change in breathing frequency.

There was strong evidence that this coupling is learnt, or at least that it is perfected by practice. Marathon runners synchronized their breathing and running within the first four or five strides of starting to run, but less experienced runners took longer. There was little or no tendency towards synchronization of leg and respiratory movements among people who rarely ran, including those who maintained a high level of fitness from other forms of strenuous exercise such as swimming. It was clear from the way in which coupling was established in runners in which it was variable that ventilation was entrained to gait, not the reverse. The mechanics of this coupling have not been worked out, so it is not possible to say how much energy is saved by establishing fixed phase relationships between breathing and running, but acquisition of the habit is almost certainly a significant element in achieving maximum athletic performance.

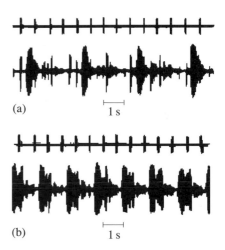

Figure 8.11 Recordings of the footfall of one leg (upper traces) and breathing of an adult human (lower traces) (prominent bursts are exhalations). The coupling between the stride and breathing is 4 : 1 during (a), and 2 : 1 during (b).

Summary of Section 8.3

Fast locomotion involves more work against gravity because the body's centre of mass is raised higher than in walking. The strides are also more frequent and of greater amplitude. Energy storage in tendons is important in fast locomotion; the muscles contract in an almost isometric mode and stress the tendons around the joints to the length at which they can stretch and recoil, and the weight of the body flexes and extends the joints. Mainly because of these effects, the energetic cost of locomotion does not increase as fast with increasing speed as would otherwise be expected, and in kangaroos, the energetic cost of hopping decreases slightly with increasing speed. Flexion and extension of the back increases the effective length of the stride and so increases the maximum possible speed of galloping. In limbs used only for locomotion, muscles may be partially or completely replaced by tendinous material. In mammals that gallop or hop far and fast, breathing is synchronized with stride, which may reduce the total energy expended in fast locomotion. Human running is a unique gait for mammals. Its efficiency is improved by passive elastic storage of energy by the arched foot and the plantar aponeurosis.

8.4 The allometry of locomotion

Body size and body shape are some of the most obvious differences between species. Indeed, these features are the main clues by which we, and most other species, recognize other kinds of animals. The relationships between body mass and the energetic cost of locomotion were described in Section 3.3.2. Some associations between locomotion and aspects of body form, such as the presence of hooves, long, slim legs and the flexibility of the spine were discussed in Section 8.3. This section is a synthesis of this information that tries to explain in anatomical and physiological terms how body size and body composition determine what animals can do and hence their habits and habitats.

8.4.1 Energetic efficiency

Figure 3.12 (in Section 3.3.2), shows that energy used in transporting 1 kg through 1 km decreases by a factor of more than 100 between mouse-sized and elephant-sized mammals. The energetic cost of locomotion also rises faster with increasing speed in small animals (Figure 3.13). Although the picture is very far from complete, detailed study of the physiology of isolated tissues and observations on intact animals suggest an explanation along the following lines.

According to a recent hypothesis from Taylor's group, the main cost of locomotion is supporting the animal's weight (Section 8.2), and the species differences arise from the time course of generating the necessary force, i.e. the frequency and duration of steps, and the length of the legs. Larger mammals generally have longer legs, which enable them to use fewer, longer strides than is possible for smaller animals covering the same distance. Longer legs also enable larger animals to achieve higher speeds with lower stride frequencies than smaller animals (Section 8.3.2).

It was emphasized in Chapters 5 and 6 that the total power output and the energetic efficiency of a muscle depend upon its fibre-type composition, the stimulus regime applied to it and the mechanical conditions under which it contracts. Brief, repetitive contractions involving shortening over a significant distance use more energy than slow, continuous contractions which take place under the isometric or negative work modes. Fewer, slower strides mean both slower muscle contraction, and fewer starts and stops of the contractile cycle. Slower contractions can be achieved with slow fibres (Section 5.3.3) and always use less energy than fast contractions (Section 6.3.2, Table 6.2). So fewer, more prolonged cycles of muscle contraction use less energy than a greater number of brief cycles of contraction and relaxation.

Swinging rather than placing the legs into position reduces the total muscular energy used for locomotion, but it does not work well on steep hills or rough terrain. A pebble landscape that is effectively smooth for a camel would seem like a mountain range for a mouse. Posture and the form of movement of the limbs affects both the energetic cost of running and the range of activities other than running that animals can perform. Large mammals such as horses stand on fairly straight legs but small mammals crouch. This latter posture is efficient for fast acceleration and for leaping (human athletes crouch on starting blocks before a race) but positions of the attachments of the muscles and tendons to the skeleton are not favourable to swinging the legs (Section 6.4.2), so the legs of small mammals are proportionately more muscular than those of large species. The differences also contribute to the relative ease with which small animals jump, climb and run up steep slopes (Sections 3.2.2 and 3.3.3).

The difference between the energetic cost of running or galloping and that of walking is much less for small animals than for larger species, because many of the ways in which energy expenditure is reduced during running depend upon having slower muscles and longer legs (and hence long tendons). So small animals, if they make a journey at all, may as well run, because running involves expending only a little more energy and incurs an only slightly greater risk of injury.

The relationship between body size and maximum speed of locomotion is more complicated and not well understood. As well as the design of the limbs, feet and back, safety factors of the skeleton and maximum sustainable metabolic rate (Sections 3.2.2 and 3.3.2) determine the maximum speed. Most of the fastest mammals on straight runs are of intermediate size (about 10–50 kg), with neither very small nor very large species being particularly fast. Small animals achieve the impression of speed, and many of its objectives (i.e. avoiding predators) by frequent and abrupt changes in direction, made possible by limbs built with high safety factors. Using this strategy, a mouse can easily outwit a human and a squirrel evade a cat.

There also seems to be no general pattern about whether running on two or four legs is faster or more efficient. The efficiency of running birds such as rheas, ostriches and quails compares favourably with that of quadrupedal mammals of similar body mass (see Figure 8.5), although the gait of penguins, whose bodies are adapted primarily to swimming, seems to use more energy. People can run and walk bipedally much faster and more efficiently than any other primate, but compared to quadrupedal locomotion, human running is neither very fast nor very efficient. Racing greyhounds (body mass about 30 kg) can gallop at 15–17 m s^{-1} ($\approx$ 34–38 m.p.h.) for distances of a few hundred metres; the fastest speed achieved by human sprinters (body mass about 70 kg), whose upright posture restricts effective use of the back musculature to increase the stride length or for energy storage, is a little over 10 m s^{-1} ($\approx$ 22 m.p.h.).

8.4.2 Multipurpose limbs

In considering the relationship between an animal's locomotory capacities and its body size and shape, it is important to remember that as well as being able to travel at different speeds, animals also have to be able to do other things with their limbs, such as lying down, scratching themselves and more elaborate activities.

■   Referring to Section 8.3.3, can you suggest any disadvantages that may result from the replacement of muscles by tendinous tissue?

The camel's plantaris 'muscle' would be almost useless for other gaits, climbing trees and for non-locomotory actions such as digging, scratching, handling food items and lying down or getting up, because without any contractile material, the 'muscle' cannot actively generate tension so its length can be changed only from stretching by external forces. Camels use their legs in general, and these 'muscles' in particular, almost exclusively for locomotion; they do not build nests for their offspring nor do they dig for food. Adult camels are much larger than nearly all the predators that inhabit the deserts in which they mainly live, so in the wild they rarely have to gallop. Camels do lie down to rest but lying down and standing up are notoriously slow actions. Replacement of limb muscles by tendinous material is much less extensive in animals such as squirrels, bears, badgers, monkeys and humans, which use their relatively thick, meaty limbs for all the non-locomotory actions just mentioned, plus a great many more.

Detailed investigations of forces generated and muscle and tendon function are feasible for only a few kinds of animals, mostly domesticated species. Allometric studies (see Chapter 3) of animals of different sizes and shapes can help us infer from their structure the action, or range of actions, to which muscles and tendons are adapted. To investigate how the relative masses of different muscles differ in animals that use their limbs for different kinds of actions, Professor R. McNeill Alexander went to East Africa and enlisted the help of colleagues at the University of Nairobi to compare the dimensions of various homologous muscles and their tendons in a wide variety of wild and domesticated mammals of different sizes and habits.

Figure 8.12 shows some of their data for the muscles that flex the anterior joints (wrist and digits) of the forelimbs (Figure 8.9a) of three groups of animals that have very different habits. The relative mass of these muscles (Figure 8.12a) increases slightly with increasing body mass in all three groups, approximately in proportion to $M^{1.1}$. Although heavier, and thus (since the density is constant), of greater volume, the muscle fibres of larger animals were only a little longer than those of much smaller species in all three taxonomic groups, scaling approximately to $M^{0.3}$ (Figure 8.12b). Thus larger animals must have forelimb muscles of greater cross-sectional area.

■   How do muscle length and muscle cross-sectional area determine the maximum force and maximum velocity of contraction?

The velocity of contraction is determined mainly by muscle length, and the maximum force by the area of sarcomeres acting in parallel (Section 6.4). If the muscles featured in Figure 8.12 exert equal stresses, the forces they can produce are proportional to $M^{1.1}/M^{0.3} = M^{0.8}$.

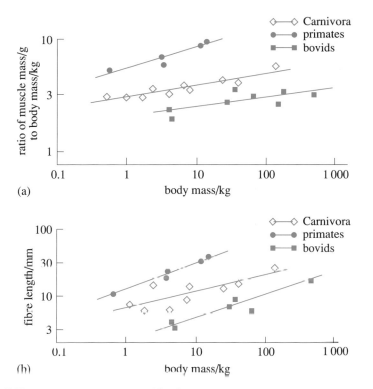

Figure 8.12 The allometric relationship plotted on logarithmic scales between body mass and some features of the muscles that flex the wrist and digits of the forelimb for various bovids (antelope, gazelle, sheep, buffalo), solid squares; Carnivora (ferret, mongoose, fox, jackal, lion, hyena, etc.), diamonds; and primates, solid circles. (a) The ratio of the mass of the forelimb flexor muscles to body mass. (b) The mean length of the muscle fibres in the flexor muscles of the forelimb.

■ How does this exponent compare to that which you would expect if small animals were geometrically similar to large ones?

The exponent expected from geometrical similarity is $M^{2/3} = M^{0.67}$, which is smaller than the exponent calculated from the actual measurements.

■ What can you conclude from this discrepancy about the way tendons and muscle work in large and small mammals?

The limb muscles of large animals are proportionately stronger than those of smaller ones, so they can apply greater stresses to the long, stout tendons to which they are attached. Tendons stressed in this way can store elastic strain energy well, and enable the muscle to work in the negative work mode (Sections 8.3.1 and 8.3.2). In other words, energy saving by elastic storage in tendons seems to contribute more to the energy economy of locomotion in large mammals than in related smaller ones of similar body form. So, as well as using their muscles less frequently and in a more efficient way, larger animals also make greater use of energy storage in tendons and muscle to supplement active force generation in muscles. The greater contribution of elastic energy storage is probably an important reason why the energetic cost of travel, and the rate of increase of energy expenditure with increasing speed of travel are lower for larger animals than for smaller ones (see Figure 8.5 and Figures 3.12 and 3.13).

Figure 8.12 also illustrates large differences between taxa in the dimensions of these muscles. The flexor muscles are only about 0.3% of the body mass in fast-moving bovids whose forelimbs end in hooves, but up to 1% of the body mass of primates that use their hands for climbing and manipulating food. The muscle fibres of primates were also nearly ten times longer than those of the homologous muscles of bovids of similar body mass. As explained in Section 6.4, longer muscle fibres can shorten through greater distances than short fibres and so limbs that are used for a variety of actions have longer muscles and shorter tendons (Section 6.4.2). The pennate structure of these muscles in bovids also indicates that their main function in hoofed mammals is stressing tendons rather than shortening sufficiently to be able to flex the distal joints. The opposite situation has evolved in moles, whose skeleton and musculature are so specialized to digging that they are all but useless for walking or running: the massive forelimb muscles are attached directly to the skeleton (Figure 6.8a) with minimal tendons.

Other adaptations of multipurpose limbs include having several muscles attached at different points along the bone (see Figure 6.7), and several different types of fibre in each muscle (Section 5.3.3). Differences in the relative masses of muscles and tendons in humans and their domesticated livestock comparable to those documented in Figure 8.12 have developed, through genetic selection or physical training, in people and animals that excel at particular artistic skills or sports.

The ability of ballet dancers and gymnasts to assume a variety of (mostly unnatural) postures and of musicians to perform fast, intricate finger movements derives directly from our arboreal ancestors in whom numerous, finely controlled (Section 6.5.1) relatively long muscle fibres were essential for locomotion and feeding.

■   Are human hands and feet more or less specialized for a single kind of activity (e.g. locomotion) than those of chimpanzees?

Human hands are specialized for manipulating objects, and human feet are thoroughly adapted to walking and running (Section 8.3.5). Chimps can grasp branches and hold food items in their feet as well as their hands, but their ability to manipulate small objects in their fingers is inferior to people's. Our feet are specialized for running on open ground at the expense of other functions. Our toes are relatively short and parallel, and only with much practice can we learn to move the toes independently or hold things securely with the foot. But by abandoning the arboreal habit and adopting the erect posture, humans have the best of both worlds: our feet are specialized for running, but our hands have retained and improved upon their basic primate roles of grasping and manipulation.

Summary of Section 8.4

The energetic cost per unit distance of terrestrial locomotion decreases with increasing body mass mainly because larger animals need to move their longer limbs, and hence contract their muscles, more slowly and less frequently than smaller animals. Allometric comparison of the relative masses of muscles that stress the long leg tendons indicates that energy storage in tendons makes a greater contribution to locomotion in larger mammals, especially when they are travelling fast. Limbs that perform a wide range of different movements have more muscle and less tendon, and their muscles are capable of more shortening than those specialized to a single activity. Thus, camels and horses can perform a limited range of gaits very efficiently; although the energetic cost of human locomotion is relatively high, people's limbs enable them to be ballet dancers, pianists and gymnasts as well as long-distance athletes.

8.5 Conclusion

Studies of isolated tissues (Chapters 5–7) can reveal a great deal about their mechanical properties, microscopic structure and chemical composition, but to understand which of these properties are crucial to the tissue's role in normal movement, its responses to the forces applied to it in the intact animal must be measured. Measuring mechanical or biochemical processes in intact animals moving at high speed is extremely difficult, because the phenomena under investigation are changing rapidly in time, and also because monitoring apparatus and invasive techniques can cause discomfort or injuries, which may in turn alter the way the animal uses its tissues. Among the most successful techniques are high-speed photography (Figures 8.1b, c and 8.6), measurement of the forces generated by the limbs during movements in unrestrained animals (Figure 8.1b, c), measurement of energy consumption during locomotion at controlled velocities and gaits (Figures 8.2, 8.5 and 8.8), and applying monitoring apparatus directly to the skeletal tissues *in situ* (Figure 7.7). Each of these techniques has yielded data that were not precisely predicted from studies of the isolated tissues; properties such as negative work contractions in muscle, once thought to be just an anomalous phenomenon demonstrable in excised tissues, are now believed to play a major role in normal locomotion.

In spite of many years of intensive study of the structures and properties of isolated tissues, much work remains to be done to clarify how muscles, tendons, bones and joints normally work together to produce movement in intact animals. As illustrated in Section 8.3.3, specialization of the skeleton, muscles or tendons to one habit or activity, such as climbing or galloping, restricts the range or power of other possible movements. There is also much to be learnt about how such compromises between anatomically and physiologically incompatible activities determine small but crucial differences in the locomotory capacities in apparently similar species.

Objectives for Chapter 8

When you have completed this chapter, you should be able to:

8.1   Define and use, or recognize definitions and applications of each of the **bold** terms.

8.2   Outline the mechanics of normal walking, and explain how quadrupedal animals that walk very slowly minimize the energy lost in lateral and vertical movements of the body.

8.3   Describe the form and major mechanisms of hopping and galloping and list some major differences between these fast gaits and walking.

8.4   Describe the roles of muscles, tendons and ligaments in the legs and trunk in fast locomotion of large mammals.

8.5   Outline the major mechanical features of human running and describe some specializations of the feet and legs to running.

8.6   Outline possible explanations for the effect of body size on the energetic cost of transportation in terms of changes in the way locomotory muscles and their tendons are deployed during locomotion.

8.7   Explain how allometric studies and comparisons between taxa can show how muscles and tendons are deployed in mammals of different size and body form.

Questions for Chapter 8

(*Answers to questions are at the end of the book.*)

Question 8.1 (Objective 8.2)

Which of the following processes (a–e) are characteristic of slow locomotion?

(a)   Energy is stored from stride to stride in the tendons of the foot and lower leg.

(b)   Most of the energy is dissipated in fore-and-aft and side-to-side swaying of the body.

(c)   Most of the locomotory muscles are in continuous tetanic contraction while the body is moving.

(d)   Most of the locomotory muscles are not actively contracting while the body is moving.

(e)   The compression forces exerted on the limb bones are minimized.

Question 8.2 (Objective 8.2)

Explain briefly why a person can travel further and faster by riding a bicycle than by walking or running.

Question 8.3 (Objective 8.3)

(a)   Why are people much more likely to fall if they trip over objects when running than when walking?

(b)   Why are structures such as floor boards much more likely to be broken by people running across them than by similar people walking across them?

Describe the roles in fast locomotion in large terrestrial mammals of (a) the tendons of the legs and feet, (b) the joints between the bones of the legs, and (c) the aponeuroses and muscles of the spinal column.

Question 8.5 (Objective 8.4)

In one or two sentences, suggest mechanical or physiological explanations for the following observation:

(a)   Ponies and donkeys can carry very heavy loads on their backs without injuring their legs as long as they are not forced to go faster than a slow trot.

(b)   Coachmen choose to assemble teams of horses of similar size and build for pulling carriages and carts.

(c)   Skilled riders maintain their seats on galloping horses but inexperienced riders or heavy packs are easily thrown off.

(d)   Horses gallop surprisingly well with a girth fastened tightly around their ribs.

Question 8.6 (Objective 8.5)

Outline the roles in human running of the (a) foot, (b) ankle and calf, (c) back.

Question 8.7 (Objective 8.6)

Which of the following statements (a–f) may be valid explanations for the decrease in the energetic cost of locomotion with increasing body size?

(a)   The stepping frequency of larger animals is lower than that of smaller animals.

(b)   Larger animals have proportionately less muscle tissue.

(c)   Larger animals walk and run more slowly.

(d)   Larger animals have longer legs and so can cover a greater distance per stride.

(e)   Larger animals are able to make greater use of energy storage in their tendons.

(f)   The muscles of larger animals are more likely to be able to metabolize fatty acids instead of glucose as a fuel for contraction.

Question 8.8 (Objective 8.7)

Explain in a few sentences the evidence for the conclusion that storage and release of elastic strain energy in tendons is more important in locomotion of large mammals than in small species.

Question 8.9 (Objective 8.7)

Describe some properties of the skeleton, musculature and general body form that you would expect to find in typical champions of (a) weight-lifting, (b) marathon running, and (c) basketball playing.

EPILOGUE

'Size' and 'Action' might at first have struck you as a curious mixture of topics. The reasons for discussing them together should have become clear: size is an important determinant of what animals can do, and, especially in adults, the dimensions and properties of tissues depend upon how much and how often they are used. The study of movement provides one of the most meaningful and convincing answers to the basic question: all animals develop from a single small zygote, so why do some species spend a larger fraction of their lifespan growing larger (e.g. elephants and crocodiles) while others (e.g. owls and parrots) become full-size in the first few months of life, and stay that size for the next half-century? In essence: why bother to grow larger?

The answer is not because animals can live in and go to a wider range of places (Section 3.4), or have a lower risk of injuries and accidents (Section 3.2.2), or live longer (Section 4.4) or even because they run faster (Section 3.3.2). It is true that sexual selection, in the forms of male–male rivalry and female preference for larger males, often promotes large adult body size, but the most generally applicable explanation is that larger animals can move more efficiently. They can travel further for less energy (Sections 3.3.2 and 8.4), and they incur a lower risk of predation, so they need to run away less often.

The study of size began as a theoretical concept (Section 3.1.1) and formulating an appropriate predictive theory is still an important part of the investigation of size, growth and many aspects of movement. The theoretical backgrounds to these topics are far from fully worked out: biologists are still uncertain about how to measure lines and areas accurately in real tissues (Sections 3.1.1 and 3.3.4) and how to interpret the mechanical properties of tissues in multi-purpose limbs (Section 8.4.2). In spite of these limitations, a few general biological principles emerge from the topics discussed in this book.

Integration and control

Both the first half of the book about growth and lifespan, and the second half about locomotion, point to the same basic principle: the central role of coordination, synchronization and matching between different tissues. Athletic feats such as jumping, climbing and sustained running are only possible when all the muscles and skeleton, and support tissues such as lungs and liver, are 'matched' to each other. Minor discrepancies in the dimensions or properties of skeletal tissues, or injuries that cause limping or loss of synchronization between breathing and locomotory movements (Section 8.3.4) substantially increase the energetic cost of motion, so the animal tires much more quickly. Ageing also involves progressive failure of coordination between organ systems, less prompt and less effective response to minor damage and thus increasing risk of mismatch between tissues and organs.

Senescence and fast locomotion both involve pushing metabolism and structural tissues to their limits. Minor defects are exposed and can lead to catastrophic failures that would not happen if the animal was young and 'taking it easy'. The safety factors decline with age as skeletons and muscles weaken and the metabolic capacity for prolonged or transiently strenuous activities declines. Serious mismatch between tissues and organs impairs locomotion to the point that escaping predators becomes more a matter of luck than of speed, stamina or agility, greatly increasing the risk of predation (Section 4.3.1).

In terms of the economy of the whole body, locomotion is an expensive business, especially for large animals. The muscles, skeleton and tendons account for a large fraction of the total body mass (Sections 3.2 and 3.3) and the muscles use a large proportion of the available metabolic energy (Section 3.3.3). Muscle and skeletal tissues are subjected to large, abruptly changing forces and are constantly under repair; their mass and shape are continuously remodelled as functional demands change (Sections 2.1.1 and 5.3.4). A large proportion of the body's intake of both protein and energy is deployed to keep the locomotory system in trim: too much such tissue is energetically wasteful, but too little could lead to disaster.

A similar principle applies to regulation of the size of viscera such as the liver, kidneys and gut. The fact that rats (and humans) survive major operations such as those mentioned in Section 2.2 without serious disruption of metabolic homeostasis shows that the organs are normally maintained with quite large safety factors (Section 3.2.2). Enzyme activities can be increased or additional enzymes induced almost instantly to compensate for the loss of up to half the tissue. The surviving tissue is able to increase its metabolic functions and activate its growth processes at the same time. Such a feat is not as difficult as it may seem if, as is the case with viscera such as the liver, the chief mechanism of growth is curtailing the breakdown stage of a very high rate of protein turnover (Section 2.1.2). Of course, such 'emergency' provision is not without its costs: relative to their mass, the liver and kidneys make a disproportionately large contribution to BMR (Figure 3.11 and Section 3.3.1), a significant part of it due to protein turnover.

Growth and repair are potentially dangerous processes: cells that proliferate unchecked can invade other tissues and being too large can be disadvantageous. Genetic make-up, nutrition, age, habitual use of the tissue or organ and an array of hormones and growth factors interact to regulate each step of the process. The rate of accumulation of new tissue is matched to apoptosis and protein turnover. In spite of all these checks and balances, rogue lineages of cells sometimes escape the network of regulators and proliferate out of control, forming tumours that eventually lead to the death of organism that has supported their growth.

The study of chronic diseases such as Duchenne muscular dystrophy has shown that it is impossible to make a firm distinction between growth and physiological function. In this case, it is not obvious whether the diseased state is due to a defect in the structure of the mature muscle, or inadequate repair, or to both. A relatively minor defect in cell structure does not greatly impair normal function, but it increases the need for repair. In humans and certain animals with similar defects, the healing mechanisms cannot keep up with the demand, and the tissue ages and weakens prematurely.

Efficiency

Using energy efficiently is particularly important to the study of growth and movement because these processes account for a large proportion of the organism's total energy budget. As already mentioned, improvements in energetic efficiency may be one of the main reasons for growing larger. However, progress in understanding and measuring the efficiency of biological processes has not always been straightforward.

For a long time, it was customary for muscle physiologists to study isolated muscles in apparatus that imposed on them very different mechanical constraints from those normally applied *in vivo* (Sections 6.2 and 6.3). Consequently, physiologists measured the oxygen utilization, heat production and performance of mechanical work of muscles that were working under artificial stimulus regimes in mechanically abnormal, energetically inefficient ways. The figures thus obtained, although accurate for the (non-physiological) experimental conditions, misled studies of locomotory mechanics for decades. More measurements from the musculo-skeletal system *in vivo* have radically altered our understanding of what muscles, tendons and bones actually do. The many ways in which the musculo-skeletal system is adapted to maximize efficiency are now quite well understood: the mechanical properties of the muscles are matched to those of their tendons, and their neural control and arrangement in the body normally preclude their being used very inefficiently.

At present, many aspects of growth are studied *in vitro*, which may be producing inaccurate or misleading values as the early studies of isolated muscles did. It remains to be seen whether a similar revolution in our concept of energetic efficiency in growth takes place when biologists are able to measure accurately the processes of growth and repair *in vivo*.

Species diversity

A great many different species have been mentioned in this book, ranging in size from *Drosophila* to elephants, and in lifespan from *Caenorhabditis* to humans. In growth processes, senescence or muscle contraction, and many other topics, the principles are the same but the details are immensely diverse. Muscle is among the few tissues for which there is enough detailed information to demonstrate this point clearly. The molecular biology of the proteins, the fine structure and the mechanical performance have been studied in muscles of a wide variety of species. Qualitative differences are always found to accompany quantitative differences: even if adjusted for body size, a horse could not use a fly's muscles and the converse (Sections 5.2 and 5.3.4). Although Kleiber's rule (Section 3.3.1) can be partially explained as arising from differences in the proportions of tissues with widely different rates of energy utilization, that is not the whole story. There are intrinsic differences in the metabolism of apparently similar tissues from different species.

Detailed study of the structure and physiology of muscle (Chapter 5) in a wide range of animals reveals a huge array of variations on the same basic theme. A similar wide range of differences between species would probably be found in other tissues, if enough species were studied in sufficient detail. Are these differences minor, trivial, or even an artefact of tissue preparation, or are they the key to the species' success? The fascination of comparative physiology is the emergence of broad, general principles from a mass of species-specific detail, and the demonstration of how minor differences in structure or function confer unique adaptations on particular species.

REFERENCES AND FURTHER READING

Chapter 1

Pond, C.M. (1977) The significance of lactation in the evolution of mammals, *Evolution*, **31**, pp. 177–199.

Schofield, P. N. (ed.) (1992) *The Insulin-like Growth Factors: Structure and Biological Functions*, Oxford University Press, Oxford.

Tanner, J. M. (1978) *Foetus into Man, Physical Growth from Conception to Maturity*, Open Books, London.

Chapter 2

Goss, R. J. (ed.) (1972) *The Regulation of Organ and Tissue Growth,* Academic Press, New York.

Doherty, F. J. and Mayer, R. J. (1992) *Intracellular Protein Degradation*, IRL Press, Oxford.

Favus, M. J. (1993) *Primer on the Metabolic Bone Diseases and Disorders of Mineral Metabolism*, 2nd edn, Raven Press, New York.

Mastaglia, F. L. and Walton, J. N. (1992) *Skeletal Muscle Pathology*, 2nd edn, Churchill Livingstone, Edinburgh.

Chapter 3

Biewener, A. A. (1989) Scaling body support in mammals: limb posture and muscle mechanics, *Science,* **245**, pp. 45–48.

Elia, M. (1992) Organ and tissue contribution to metabolic rate, in Kinney, J. M. and Tucker, H. N. (eds), *Energy Metabolism: Tissue Determinants and Cellular Corollaries,* Raven Press, New York, pp. 61–79.

Pennycuick, C. J. (1992) *Newton Rules Biology: a Physical Approach to Biological Problems,* Oxford University Press, Oxford.

Schmidt-Nielsen, K. (1984) *Scaling: Why is Animal Size So Important?* Cambridge University Press, Cambridge.

Taylor, C. R., Weibel, E. R. *et al.* (1980) Design of the mammalian respiratory system, *Respiration Physiology,* **44**.

Chapter 4

Comfort, A. (1979) *The Biology of Senescence,* 3rd edn, Churchill Livingstone, Edinburgh.

Douglas, K. (1994) Making friends with death-wish genes, *New Scientist,* **143**, pp. 31–34 (30 July 1994).

Evans, G. (1994) Old cells never die: they just apoptose, *Trends in Cell Biology,* **4**, pp. 191–192.

Perls, T. T. (1995) The oldest old, *Scientific American*, **272**, pp. 50–55 (January).

Raff, M. C., Barres, B. A., Burne, J. F., Coles, H. S., Ishizaki, Y. and Jacobson, M. D. (1993) Programmed cell death and the control of cell survival: lessons from the nervous system, *Science,* **262**, pp. 695–700.

Sinclair, D. (1989) *Human Growth After Birth,* Oxford Medical Publications, Oxford University Press, Oxford.

Chapters 5 and 6

Bagshaw, C. R. (1993) *Muscle Contraction*, 2nd edn, Chapman & Hall, London.

Beall, C. J., Sepanski, M. A. and Fyrberg, E. A. (1989) Genetic dissection of *Drosophila* myofibril formation: effects of actin and myosin heavy chain null alleles, *Genes & Development,* **3**, pp. 131–140.

Brown, S. C. and Lucy, J. A. (1993) Dystrophin as a mechanochemical transducer in skeletal muscle, *BioEssays,* **15**, pp. 413–419.

Cullen, M. J. and Watkins, S. C. (1993) Ultrastructure of muscular dystrophy: new aspects, *Micron,* **24**, pp. 287–307.

Currey, J. D. (1984) *The Mechanical Adaptations of Bone,* Princeton University Press, Princeton.

Curtin, N. A. and Davis, R. E. (1975) Very high tension with little ATP breakdown by active skeletal muscles, *Journal of Mechanochemistry and Cell Motility,* **3**, pp. 147–154.

Finer, J. T., Simmons, R. M. and Spudich, J. A. (1994) Single myosin molecule mechanics: piconewton forces and nanometre steps, *Nature, London,* **368**, pp. 113–119.

Goll, D. E., Thompson, V. F., Taylor, R. G. and Zalewska, T. (1992) Is calpain activity regulated by membranes and autolysis or calcium and calpastatin? *BioEssays,* **14**, pp. 549–555.

Harris, J. B. and Cullen, M. J. (1992) Ultrastructural localization and the possible role of dystrophin, in Kakulas, B. A., Howell, J. M. and Roses, A. D. (eds), *Duchenne Muscular Dystrophy: Animal Models and Genetic Manipulation*, Raven Press, New York.

Josephson, R. K. (1993) Contraction dynamics and power output of skeletal muscle, *Annual Review of Physiology*, **55**, pp. 527–546.

Rojas, C. V. and Hoffman, E. P. (1991) Recent advances in dystrophin research, *Current Opinion in Neurobiology,* **1**, pp. 420–429.

Squire, J. M. (1986) *Muscle: Design, Diversity and Disease,* Benjamin/ Cummings Publishing Co., Menlo Park, California.

Trinick, J. (1991) Elastic filaments and giant proteins in muscle, *Current Opinion in Cell Biology,* **3**, pp. 112–119.

Chapter 7

Alexander, R. McN. (1984) Elastic energy stores in running vertebrates, *American Zoologist*, **24**, pp. 85–94.

Biewener, A. A. and Blickhan, R. (1988) Kangaroo rat locomotion: design for elastic energy storage or acceleration? *Journal of Experimental Biology*, **140**, pp. 243–255.

Brear, K., Currey, J. D. and Pond, C. M. (1990) Ontogenetic changes in the mechanical properties of the femur of the polar bear *Ursus maritimus*, *Journal of Zoology, London*, **222**, pp. 49–58.

Currey, J. D. (1984) *The Mechanical Adaptations of Bone*, Princeton University Press, Princeton.

Currey, J. D. and Pond, C. M. (1989) Mechanical properties of very young bone in the Axis deer (*Axis axis*) and humans, *Journal of Zoology, London*, **218**, pp. 69–85.

Ker, R. F., Alexander, R. McN. and Bennett, M. B. (1988) Why are mammalian tendons so thick? *Journal of Zoology, London*, **216**, pp. 309–324.

Vaughan, J. (1981) *The Physiology of Bone*, 3rd edn, Clarendon Press, Oxford.

Vincent, J. F. V. (1982) *Structural Biomaterials*, John Wiley & Sons, New York.

Chapter 8

Alexander, R. McN. (1984a) Human walking and running, *Journal of Biological Education*, **18**, pp. 135–140.

Alexander, R. McN. (1984b) Walking and running, *American Scientist*, **72**, pp. 348–354.

Alexander, R. McN. (1987) Wallabies vibrate to breathe, *Nature, London*, **328**, p. 477.

Alexander, R. McN. (1988) Why mammals gallop, *American Zoologist*, **28**, pp. 237–245.

Alexander, R. McN. (1989) On the synchronization of breathing with running in wallabies (*Macropus* spp.) and horses (*Equus caballus*), *Journal of Zoology, London*, **218**, pp. 69–85.

Alexander, R. McN., Jayes, A. S., Maloiy, G. M. O. and Wathuta, E. M. (1981) Allometry of the leg muscles of mammals, *Journal of Zoology, London*, **194**, pp. 539–552.

Alexander, R. McN., Maloiy, G. M. O., Ker, R. F., Hayes, A. S. and Warui, C. N. (1982) The role of tendon elasticity in the locomotion of the camel (*Camelus dromedarius*), *Journal of Zoology, London*, **198**, pp. 293–313.

Bramble, D. M. and Carrier, D. R. (1983) Running and breathing in mammals, *Science*, **219**, pp. 251–256.

Dimery, N. J., Alexander, R. McN. and Ker, R. F. (1986) Elastic extension of leg tendons in the locomotion of horses (*Equus caballus*), *Journal of Zoology, London*, **210**, pp. 415–425.

Dimery, N. J., Ker, R. F. and Alexander, R. McN. (1986) Elastic properties of the feet of deer (Cervidae), *Journal of Zoology, London,* **208**, pp. 161–169.

Hoyt, D. F. and Taylor, C. R. (1981) Gait and the energetics of locomotion in horses, *Nature, London,* **292**, pp. 239–240.

Jayes, A. S. and Alexander, R. McN. (1980) The gaits of chelonians: walking techniques for very low speeds, *Journal of Zoology, London,* **191**, pp. 353–378.

Ker, R. F., Bennett, M. B., Bibby, S. R., Kester, R. C. and Alexander, R. McN. (1987) The spring in the arch of the human foot, *Nature, London,* **325**, pp. 147–149.

Kram, R. & Taylor, C. R. (1990) Energetics of running: a new perspective, *Nature, London,* **346**, pp. 265–267.

Perry, A. K., Blickhan, R., Biewener, A. A., Heglund, N. C. and Taylor, C. R. (1988) Preferred speeds in terrestrial vertebrates: are they equivalent? *Journal of Experimental Biology,* **137**, pp. 207–219.

Taylor, C. R., Schmidt-Nielsen, K. and Rabb, J. L. (1970) Scaling of energetic cost of running to body size in mammals, *American Journal of Physiology,* **219**, pp. 1104–1107.

ANSWERS TO QUESTIONS
Chapter 1

(a)   Growth velocity is measured as the annual increment of height.

(b)   Growth in body mass can be measured directly, or calculated from the linear dimensions such as height. However, this latter method assumes that body proportions and body density are constant; if the shape or composition of the body changes, a change in body height is not necessarily accompanied by a commensurate increase in body mass. Growth rates should also be seen in relation to the quantity of tissue contributing to the increase in body mass.

(a)   Deficiencies of growth caused by undernutrition can be rectified in full if:

(i)   The improved diet is available before the age at which cell division in the particular tissue can take place has passed.

(ii)   Cell division of the tissue was complete before undernutrition started.

(iii)   The tissue enjoys 'priority' in access to nutrients for growth and has hence been unaffected by the period of undernutrition.

(iv)   Growth follows that of another tissue, e.g. growth of muscles and tendons follows the growth of bones.

(b)   Permanent deformation occurs if:

(i)   There is a limited period during which cell proliferation can occur.

(ii)   Undernutrition strikes during that period.

(iii)   The period of cell division is not extended as a result of the slower growth rate.

(iv)   Anatomically adjacent or functionally interrelated parts are differently affected by the period of undernutrition, so that the growth of the parts gets 'out of step'.

(a)   A calcium-deficient diet first slows the growth of bones, thus delaying attainment of full stature generally, and then promotes the formation of abnormal bone. This abnormal bone is often too weak to withstand the normal forces applied to it and may be deformed. Because they support the weight of the body, the leg bones are particularly likely to bend with normal use, resulting in bowed legs. The timing of eruption of the teeth is almost unaffected. The bite may be impaired if the jaw is too small to accommodate the teeth.

(b)   The growth of uncalcified tissues is relatively unaffected. The tendons and muscles grow to the lengths appropriate to the size of the skeleton.

Only (d) is true. Growth in *utero is* slower than growth after birth for most of gestation. Although nutrition, constant temperature, etc., may permit fast growth, there is no evidence that these factors can by themselves cause maximum rates of growth.

Question 1.5

Only (b) is true. There is no evidence quoted in the text that any of the other statements could be true.

Question 1.6

(a)   The thyroxin is a peptide that contains an iodine atom, but GH is simply a peptide. Iodine may be absent from certain water supplies or foods produced in such areas, and people and animals raised in such places may be unable to obtain enough iodine to synthesize thyroxin.

(b)   When dietary iodine is low, the thyroid gland hypertrophies as an adaptation to scavenging iodine ions from the blood as efficiently as possible. Lack of GH could not be caused only by lack of precursors for its synthesis (it is more likely to be due to failure of gene activation) so there would be no reason for similar hypertrophy of the nutrient uptake mechanisms in the pituitary.

(c)   Thyroxin affects basal metabolic rate as well as influencing growth, but most known effects of GH concern growth. Lack of thyroxin produces low BMR, and hence lethargy.

Question 1.7

Only (c) is true; human GH, produced by hGH genes, artificially introduced into mouse genomes promotes faster growth of the mouse's tissues.

(a) is false, because a lack of GH has no detectable effect on fetal growth. GH is most concentrated in the pituitary but it has no effect on the growth of this structure (or any other part of the brain).

(b) is false, because GH from mice and humans (and other species) have slightly different amino acid sequences so can be distinguished using antibodies.

(d) is false, because individual differences in growth rate and adult height cannot be related to GH concentration in normal populations of rats or humans.

(e) is false. GH exerts its effects on growth only through stimulating the production of IGFs. It has never been demonstrated to act directly on growing tissues.

Question 1.8

(a)   The synthesis of the hormone is controlled by GH. Its effective concentration in the blood depends upon the abundance of binding proteins. Its action on cells depends upon their production of IGF I receptors.

(b)   IGF II regulates growth *in utero* while IGF I determines the rate of post-natal growth. IGF II production is not affected by the serum concentration of GH but that of IGF I is GH-dependent. The IGF II gene is imprintable but that for IGF I is not known to be imprintable.

(c)   The IGF and insulin molecules are about the same size and are peptides of similar structure. They both control energy utilization and sequestration, especially in adipose tissue and muscle.

(d)   Insulin is produced only by the β-cells in the pancreas but many different tissues produce IGFs. Insulin circulates in the blood, acting as an endocrine hormone, but much of the body's IGFs acts in a paracrine or autocrine manner.

(a)   (i) The parents either provide all the food for the nestlings, or aid in food gathering by escorting the young.

(ii) Energy expenditure of the young on non-growth activities is reduced by brooding them, keeping them inactive in a nest, or by escorting them to feeding grounds and protecting them from predators.

(iii) Growth rate slows greatly at about the time that the hatchling or weanling is abandoned to forage for itself.

(b)   Poikilothermic vertebrates do not follow this pattern because, in the great majority of species, the parents do not secrete or acquire food for the newly-hatched young. The young have to find their own food, even if they are escorted by the parents for a period after hatching. The uncertain food supply is compatible with slower growth, the rate of which is less firmly determined by the animal's age.

Chapter 2

Question 2.1

(a), (b) and (e) are features of organisms that show indeterminate growth. (c) and (d) are characteristic of organisms with determinate growth.

Question 2.2

(a)   Proteins that attach to ubiquitin are quickly degraded. Certain sequences of amino acids and/or certain chemical modifications of amino acids may predispose the protein to combine with ubiquitin.

(b)   All growth and regeneration is accompanied by faster turnover of protein. The process is always higher in young animals and increases abruptly at the onset of tissue repair following injury. Tissues grow when protein synthesis increases more than protein degradation.

(c)   Several widely different hormones adjust the rate of protein turnover, usually by modulating the rate of degradation. In starvation, they also mediate the rapid release of amino acids from muscle and liver proteins for gluconeogenesis.

Question 2.3

The immediate response of the kidney and liver is greater protein turnover and cell enlargement. In both liver and kidney, DNA synthesis leading to a greatly increased rate of mitosis begins about 15 h after removal of tissue and continues for several days. Cell enlargement makes a greater contribution to growth in older rats, and cell proliferation in young animals.

Question 2.4

(a)   Protein, RNA and DNA synthesis all increase rapidly, shortly after surgical removal of part of the tissue, but essential functions continue at the same time. A single kidney from a weanling rat can sustain an entire adult (see Figure 2.6c) while that kidney is growing rapidly.

(b)   The data in Figures 2.4 and 2.5 show that remaining kidneys enlarge following removal of one organ; transplanted organs grow to normal or greater than normal size depending upon whether one or both of the host's original organs are removed at the same time.

(c)   If an additional kidney is transplanted from a weanling rat to another weanling rat, all three kidneys grow about equally. An additional kidney transplanted into an adult rat fails to grow or atrophies unless one or more of the host's kidneys are removed.

The growth of the skeleton has been studied in detail because:

(a)   Its growth in length is the main determinant of height, which is the easiest of all aspects of growth to measure.

(b)   The site of division and maturation of bone-forming cells is well known and easily located, at least in the case of mammalian long bones.

(c)   The structure of the growth zones can be easily studied by non-invasive techniques such as X-rays.

Three control mechanisms are:

(i)   The rate of formation and maturation of bone cells at the epiphyseal plate during the juvenile growth period may depend upon the action of growth factors and hormones, and upon the availability of nutrients, especially calcium.

(ii)   In mammals, the growth rate slows and may stop when epiphyses begin to close with the onset of sexual maturity.

(iii)   The rate of growth at the epiphysis at the other end of the same bone can, at least in experimental situations, affect bone growth at the other end. If growth is restricted at one end, the epiphysis at the other end grows more.

Satellite cells are essential for (b) and (g).

(a)   Myoblasts form the basic complement of muscle fibres in the fetus.

(c)   Satellite cells are attached to the plasmalemma but are not essential to its maintenance (there are many fewer satellite cells on the plasmalemma of adult muscles).

(d)   Protein turnover is rapid and extensive in muscle but does not involve satellite cells.

(e)   Genes within the nuclei of the muscle fibres control the synthesis of different kinds of myosin produced as adaptations to changes in exercise regime.

(f)   Satellite cells are specific to muscle formation and do not affect tendons.

Question 2.8

(a)   Immobility leads, starting within a few days, to atrophy of both bone and muscle. Bone loses its mineral content and becomes lighter and weaker. Muscle loses protein and becomes less capable of producing large sustained forces or prolonged exercise.

(b)   Bones remain stout and strong, and muscles develop and retain their capacity for powerful, energetically efficient contractions.

(c)   Abrupt application of large forces leads to breakage of bones, especially if they have previously been immobilized, and to strains or tears in muscle.

Question 2.9

(a)   In muscle, proliferation of muscle-forming cells (myoblasts) ends at or shortly after birth. Satellite cells retain the ability to divide well into adult life, but this capacity wanes with age. Proliferation of pre-adipocytes is minimal until birth, proceeds rapidly during suckling and, at least in large, slow-growing species, can continue at a variable rate in weaned animals.

(b)   Muscle-forming cells fuse to form muscle fibres, which enlarge greatly by incorporation of satellite cells as the animal grows. However, the maximum size of a whole muscle fibre is fixed by an upper limit on the ratio of nuclei to cytoplasm. Adipocytes can change in volume by up to 100-fold, and become both larger and smaller at any time of life according to nutritional status.

(c)   Muscle fibres can hypertrophy or atrophy at any time of life in response to exercise or disuse, changing in mass and protein content by as much as 50%. The mass of adipose tissue changes according to fattening or starvation but its basic cellular structure or distribution are not necessarily altered. One or a very few generations of cell division, doubling or quadrupling the number of adipocytes, can underlie massive obesity in humans.

Chapter 3

Question 3.1

(b), (d) and (e) are correct. Allometry deals with empirical data, so (a) must be wrong, and is not concerned with establishing morphological similarity, so (c) is wrong.

Question 3.2

(a), (b), (c), (d) and (f) are correct. Larger animals have proportionately lighter, and hence more fragile skeletons, but they avoid injury by moving more sedately. The work required to fracture bones from larger animals is slightly greater (see Figure 3.4). (e) is wrong because the skeleton is relatively slightly larger in larger animals (Figure 3.5). (f) is correct because larger animals have a smaller ratio of surface area to volume. However, the skin is likely to be thicker, and therefore heavier, in larger species

Question 3.3

Safety factor is the ratio of the force required to break a structure to the maximum forces that it normally experiences. The concept can be used to estimate (a) because it sets limits on the maximum forces the skeleton can sustain during movement. An animal with a relatively fragile skeleton must have avoided strenuous activity if its skeleton is found undamaged.

(b)   Assuming that the safety factors are similar in both cases, animals living on a rough terrain would be expected to have proportionately stronger skeletons than those adapted to living in a level, smooth area.

(c)   If the locomotory habits and dimensions of the skeleton of normal individuals are known, a specimen from the same area which is found to have a much weaker musculo-skeletal system (i.e. to be operating with a lower than expected safety factor) is likely to be deformed through abnormal growth or injury.

Question 3.4

Only (d) is correct. Measurements (e.g. leg length, stride length) must be made; the skeleton is only the most widely studied organ because it is the easiest for which to obtain data. Small animals are usually easy to obtain and examine in the laboratory, so allometry is less necessary as a tool for study. Allometry is a technique that describes mathematical relationships between elements; it is not necessarily derived from any engineering or biological principles.

Question 3.5

In large animals, the maximum forces exerted on the skeleton can be reduced by changes in habits, such as avoiding jumping and climbing. But an increase in the stresses applied to internal organs cannot necessarily be reduced in the same way, so their structural tissues should increase in mass in the way predicted by the geometrical analysis.

Question 3.6

(a), (d), (f) and (g) are correct. (b) is false because Kleiber's rule cannot be explained in terms of simple geometrical principles. The scatter of points on Figure 3.10 shows that the BMR of many organisms deviates to some extent from that predicted from Kleiber's rule, so (c) is false. Body shape does not directly determine BMR, so (e) is false.

Question 3.7

The rabbit should run up the nearest steep slope. The gradient increases the energy needed for locomotion for both animals, but the increase is proportionately less for the rabbit, which therefore has a better chance of sustaining a running speed close to its maximum. The dog has to slow down because its muscles are unable to produce sufficient power to enable it to run uphill at full speed. The steeper the gradient, the greater the difference in the maximum sustainable speed of the two animals; on any slope above about 10°, the rabbit has a good chance of escaping unharmed.

Question 3.8

The anatomical dimensions and physiological performance of the lungs do not scale with body mass in the same way as $\dot{V}_{O_2\,max}$ scales with body mass. But the proportion of the muscles occupied by mitochondria increases in smaller animals with the same allometric relationship to body mass as the increase in $\dot{V}_{O_2\,max}$.

Question 3.9

(a)   Growing mammals obtain a continuous supply of nourishing food from the mother's body, which enables them to grow rapidly, thus shortening the juvenile phase of even very large species.

(b)   The young are large enough to eat the same diet as their parents by the time they become nutritionally independent, thus eliminating the need for a special food supply for the juveniles.

(c)   Large reptiles can only breed in habitats where there is food suitable for all growth stages, but mammals can breed anywhere where there is enough suitable food to sustain a population of adults.

Question 3.10

Size-related effects would be expected in all these aspects of biology, except in (h), crystallography and some other areas of molecular biology. All the other fields of study involve the metabolism in whole organisms, cells or organelles, and hence would be expected to be quantitatively different, depending upon the body size of the organism from which the living material is derived.

Chapter 4

Question 4.1

The age of a horse can be estimated by examining the teeth because, in a young animal, there is a close correlation between the individual's age and the appearance of the permanent set of teeth. The teeth are worn continuously through contact with fodder, but wear is to some extent offset by the slow continuous eruption of the very long thin molar teeth. In mature animals the approximate age can be estimated from the extent of tooth wear and compensatory eruption. However, the rate of wear depends greatly upon the animal's diet, and may not correspond closely to the chronological age if the diet has been very soft or very abrasive.

Question 4.2

(a)   It must show easily detectable changes that occur at a fixed time in relation to age (e.g. closing the epiphyses of long bones).

(b)   It must be non-renewable or, if renewed, renewal must involve a time-related sequence of events, so that age-related wear and degeneration can be detected.

(c)   Growth rings or lines must be laid down at regular time intervals as a result of seasonal changes in the rate or form of a continuously growing tissue.

Question 4.3

(a)   Senescence plays a major role in determining the age at death in populations living in natural or artificial environments, where predators are few or absent, or are normally only able to take weak individuals.

(b)   Senescence plays a minor part as a cause of death in populations subjected to heavy mortality from other causes, such as predators, severe weather or pathogens, which strike individuals of all ages almost equally.

Question 4.4

Only (d) and (f) are true.

(a)   False, because senescence appears at very different ages in different species, regardless of whether they share the same habitat.

(b)   False, because juvenile and young adults can also die from predation, etc.

(c)   False, because senescence affects tissues such as sense organs, failure of which only indirectly causes death.

(e)   False, because very few individuals of species such as lapwings (Figure 4.9) live long enough to become elderly in the wild.

Question 4.5

None of these statements is consistent with all the data presented in Chapter 4.

Question 4.6

(a), (b) and (e) are true. The interval between divisions is longer in older animals (Section 4.5.1) and regeneration slower (see also Sections 2.2.1 and 2.4). (c) and (d) are false. The longevity of erythrocytes does not change during the human lifespan and transfusing them from old to young people makes no difference to how long they remain in circulation.

Question 4.7

Weight loss occurs in elderly animals because the rate of replacement and regeneration of cells and cell components fails to keep pace with the rate of cell death and protein loss.

Question 4.8

(a)   Two of the most consistent features of senescence are slower and less extensive DNA synthesis, and a longer interval between cell divisions. Certain agents which cause mutations in germ cells also cause sickness in non-reproducing organisms, and the ailments have some features in common with normal senescence.

(b)   Attempts to accelerate normal senescence by moderate doses of radiation actually prolong the lifespan. The mechanism of DNA repair appears to be adapted to function efficiently for as long as is necessary, because longer-lived species have more extensive DNA repair mechanisms.

(i)   An external agent is necessary for necrosis but apoptosis can occur spontaneously.

(ii)   Cells swell in necrosis but shrink in apoptosis.

(iii)   Apoptosis sometimes requires the synthesis of new proteins but necrosis never does.

(iv)   The presence of many necrotic cells causes tissue inflammation.

(v)   Apoptosis is extensive in the protective environment of fetal development, but necrosis occurs most in free-living animals that are exposed to injury and infection.

Question 4.10

Misalignment of skeletal elements may prevent wear from matching growth, and the converse; excesses or deficiencies of enzymes may cause accumulation or lack of metabolites; inaccurate sensation (e.g. temperature sensors) generates inappropriate, possibly harmful responses.

Question 4.11

Constant turnover of cells (e.g. erythrocytes, intestinal cells, immune cells, etc.) is necessary to protect organisms from damage and disease and to provide a prompt response to injury. Apoptosis balances continuous cell proliferation. The prompt elimination of slightly abnormal or substandard cells maintains high standards of cell function and prevents the formation of tumours and other defective lineages of cells.

Chapter 5

Question 5.1

In order of increasing size, the structures are: myoglobin, crossbridge, myosin, nebulin, titin, Z-line, T-tubule, sarcomere, sarcolemma, myofibril, muscle fibre.

Question 5.2

The following features are present in all striated muscle: actin, ATPase, I-bands, sarcolemma, sarcomeres, sarcoplasmic reticulum, sliding filaments. The following are variable features of muscle: M-lines (differ in different types of fibres), myosin (several different isoforms), titin (the form in vertebrate muscles is larger than that in invertebrates), troponin (different subunits occur in different types of fibres), T-tubules (only seen in highly ordered, fast muscles).

Question 5.3

(a)   The sarcomeres of muscles such as insect flight muscles have very short I-bands (so they cannot shorten far). Insects also have three thin filaments to each thick filament, compared to a 2 : 1 ratio in vertebrates. The thick filaments also contain paramyosin.

(b)   Such muscles have relatively long I-bands and thus proportionately more actin.

Question 5.4

All movement, whether passive or caused by contraction of certain muscles, involves stretching other muscles. In cyclical activities such as walking or swimming, muscles alternate between active contraction and passive stretching while they are relaxed. Much energy would be wasted if relaxed muscle were not readily extensible. If all the muscles became inextensible, the body would be rigid, as happens in a state called *rigor mortis* that develops several hours after death. In the absence of oxygen, the crossbridges cannot break contact with the thin filaments so all the muscles become stiff and the limbs cannot easily be moved.

Question 5.5

Only (c) and (e) are correct. The internal elastic components must be stretched before force appears as external work, but the muscle fibres quickly fatigue if stimulated repeatedly. Contraction is initiated by depolarization of the plasmalemma, but once started it cannot be terminated by electrical events on the plasmalemma so (a) is false. All, or at least a large proportion of, muscle fibres are stimulated to contract, so (b) is false (although the rates of rise of the twitch may be very different in different kinds of fibres). (d) is false because the differences in maximum rates of contraction are intrinsic to each type of fibre and cannot be modified by the stimulus regime.

Question 5.6

Oxidative fibres are usually slightly larger than glycolytic fibres and have more myoglobin and mitochondria and a richer blood supply. They use lipids as well as glucose as fuel. Oxidative fibres help maintain posture and power repetitive movements. Glycolytic fibres can briefly produce fast, powerful movements but they fatigue quickly as their glycogen supplies are depleted.

Question 5.7

(a)   (i) Glucose is taken into the muscle from the blood via transporters in the plasmalemma. (ii) Glucose is oxidized in the formation of the large quantities of ATP used to fuel muscle contraction. (iii) Glucose is polymerized to form glycogen, which is sequestered in numerous granules in the myofibrils.

(b)   (i) Glutamine is far more abundant as a free amino acid than as a constituent of muscle proteins. (ii) Muscles release glutamine into the circulation. (iii) The rate of release of glutamine from muscle is greater in the presence of disease-causing bacteria.

A lack of dystrophin in the muscle plasmalemma has appeared independently in several kinds of laboratory and domestic animals, but the long-term effects of the deficiency for the structure and mechanical performance of the muscles are very different. For example, the muscles of affected dogs and humans become weak early in life, but some dystrophin-deficient animals such as *mdx*-mice are bigger and stronger than normal individuals. However, in all dystrophin-deficient mammals, there is always histological evidence of breakdown and regeneration of muscle fibres. In *mdx*-mice and cats, the rate of repair of the muscle fibres equals, or even exceeds that of their rate of breakdown, leading to muscle hypertrophy. But in boys and puppies, the repair mechanisms cannot keep pace with the breakdown of muscle that is stimulated by the leaking in of calcium ions through dystrophin-deficient membranes so muscle is gradually replaced by scar tissue and fat, leading to functional impairment. The processes of breakdown and repair become more nearly equal in adult dogs, so the progress of the disease is slowed or even reversed.

Chapter 6

Only (e) is true. Some ATP continues to be broken down (see Figure 6.3), and heat production is increased by shortening, which does not take place during isometric or 'negative work' contractions, so (a) and (c) are false. (b) is clearly nonsense because the muscle is being stretched, and there is no indication in the text that (d) or (f) could be true.

Tension (measured in Figure 6.2b) is maximal in situations 2 and 3 of Figure 6.2c when the thick filaments lie adjacent to thin filaments in an ordered array. Tension is less if opposing thin filaments partially overlap each other in the middle of the sarcomere, thus reducing contact with the adjacent thick filament (situation 4 of Figure 6.2c), or the thick filaments abut onto the Z-lines (situation 5). No tension is generated if the thick and thin filaments do not overlap (situation 1), although the structure of the filaments themselves is unimpaired.

(a)   More heat is produced when muscles are allowed to shorten (heat of shortening) than when shortening is prevented; therefore, contractions involving shortening are less energetically efficient than isometric or negative work contractions.

(b)   The highest heat production is at the beginning of each contraction, and fast fibres, which convert metabolic energy into work less efficiently than slow fibres, are used for frequently repeated actions. Sustained actions have fewer starts and stops and can involve slow muscle fibres.

All the statements are true except for (e) and (f). (e) is false because pennate muscles produce high isometric tension, and their maximum velocity of shortening is lower than that of strap-like muscles of similar fibre-type composition and working at the same temperature. (f) is false because, in most mammalian muscles, the fibres do not run exactly parallel to the long axis of the muscle, i.e. most are pennate to some degree.

Question 6.5

(a)   The rate of shortening varies greatly between muscles. It depends upon the type of fibre (and thus upon the isoforms of myosin and M- and Z-line proteins present, see Section 5.3.3) and upon their temperature and the mechanical conditions under which the muscle is contracting. In general, muscles contract faster when warmer, when lightly loaded and when contraction begins at or near their normal resting length.

(b)   The maximum distance of shortening depends upon the size of its sarcomeres, particularly the length of the I-band. Sarcomeres with very short I-bands can contract by only a few per cent of their initial length, and even those of more typical proportions cannot shorten to less than about half their resting length. Strap-like muscles in which many sarcomeres are arranged end to end can usually shorten through a greater distance than pennate muscles.

(c)   The initial length at which efficient shortening can begin depends upon the length of the sarcomeres and the ability of the passive elastic components other than the sarcomeres to absorb stretch so that the sarcomeres are not extended beyond the point at which there is substantial overlap between the thick and thin filaments.

Question 6.6

(a)   On rough ground, the muscular forces required to move the limbs change from one stride to the next. Such adjustments are based mainly upon sensory feedback from the muscle spindles and tendon organs.

(b)   Contractility enables muscle spindles to shorten, or be extended passively, so they are almost exactly the same length as the surrounding fibres. They can then detect small deviations from the 'set' length, whether by fatiguing of some fibres or following the imposition of external forces.

(c)   The integration of sensory feedback from the muscle spindles takes time. Where haste is essential, sensory feedback may be bypassed, but the resulting movements are poorly controlled.

Chapter 7

Question 7.1

(a)   Collagen contains a much higher proportion of the imino acids proline and hydroxyproline than most other proteins.

(b)   Mature collagen is almost entirely extracellular, while most enzymatic and many structural proteins, e.g. those of muscle, are intracellular. It is one of the most widespread and abundant proteins in the vertebrate body.

Question 7.2

Stress is force exerted (or experienced) per unit area in $N\,m^{-2}$ or Pa (pascals).

Strain is the extension by means of a mechanical force, expressed as a percentage of the unstretched length. Because it is a ratio of similar measurements it does not have units.

Young's modulus is the ratio of stress to strain calculated from the linear region of the stress/strain curve. It has the same units as stress.

Question 7.3

(a)   Thicker tendons are stiffer and so are tougher under injury and transmit the length changes imposed on them by muscles more exactly, but, because they are less stretchy, they can store less energy elastically.

(b)   Longer tendons can store more strain energy but, since muscles cannot shorten beyond a certain minimum length, certain movements may become impossible if the tendons are too long.

(c)   Ossified tendons are much stiffer than unossified ones, so they transmit the length changes accurately but they cannot store much elastic energy and cannot transmit forces around corners.

Question 7.4

(a)   Haversian bone, osteon, chondrocyte, lamellar bone, hydroxyapatite.

(b)   Trabeculae, compact bone, cancellous bone.

(c)   Periosteum, ligament.

Question 7.5

The skeleton of infants and children contains more cartilage and less bone than that of adults. Epiphyseal cartilage disappears after puberty when growth in the long bones ends, but that of the nose, external ears, etc., remains throughout life. In childhood, woven bone is replaced by Haversian bone and bones become thicker and hence stronger as the person becomes heavier. Young's modulus of bone increases with age, although relatively slowly in humans. The skeleton is heaviest and toughest in early adulthood. From middle life onwards, several decades earlier in women than in men, the rate of erosion of bone exceeds that of its deposition, so the skeleton becomes lighter and weaker. Trabecular bone is affected more severely than compact and lamellar bone, so parts of the skeleton containing such bone are weakened sooner, and hence are the most common sites of fractures. These changes are non-adaptive, but since they take place after reproduction is over, they cannot be eliminated by natural selection.

Question 7.6

(a)   Both tissues contain very few cells, have a poor blood supply and a low metabolic rate; fibrous collagen is an important structural material in both tissues; both tissues usually lack impregnation with inorganic minerals.

(b)   Proteoglycans and the carbohydrate, hyaluronic acid, are important components of cartilage (see Section 7.4), but not of tendons; the collagen in tendons is arranged in parallel fibres, but, in cartilage, the fibrils form a felt-like mat. Tendons are strong in tension but weak when torsion or compression forces are applied. The mechanical strength of cartilage is more nearly equal in all directions.

Question 7.7

(a)   Articular cartilage forms a smooth bearing surface; it creeps in response to prolonged stress, so increasing the area of the bearing surface. It also promotes efficient lubrication by releasing water into the synovial fluid when compressed.

(b)   The synovial fluid is an extracellular fluid that interacts with the articular cartilage to provide smooth lubrication even when the joint surfaces are compressed for long periods. It also nourishes the cartilage by conveying nutrients from the joint capsule to the inner part of the joint.

(c)   The ligaments are flexible and can resist tensile stresses. They maintain the correct alignment of the articulating surfaces and so prevent damage to the joint and its capsule.

Chapter 8

Question 8.1

Only statement (d) is true of slow locomotion: the majority of muscle fibres are inactive during steady, level walking. (a) Energy storage in tendons is a major form of energy saving only in running and galloping. (b) Vertical movements of the body are the major energetic cost of walking. (c) Contraction is not continuous in those muscles that are contracting. (e) The compression measured from the radius of a horse was as high during walking as it was during cantering (see Figure 7.7).

Question 8.2

It is possible to travel faster for less power output when cycling than when walking (Figure 8.2) because forward motion is continuous in cycling but in walking, the body is slowed and re-accelerated at each stride. Cycling on level ground involves no vertical movements and minimal lateral swaying of the body's centre of mass, which are major causes of energy expenditure in walking and running (see Figure 8.1).

Question 8.3

(a)   Walking is a stable gait because at least one foot is always in contact with the ground, but each stride of running involves at least one suspended phase. The body's centre of mass is raised higher in running than in walking and it 'falls' onto each foot in turn. If the foot is not in the right place to support the body when its turn comes, there is nothing to stop runners falling flat onto their faces.

(b)   In fast walking, the feet exert forces on the ground of up to 45% more than body weight, but in running, such forces may transiently be up to 2.5 times body weight (see Figures 8.1b and c and 8.3).

Question 8.4

(a)   The tendons are stressed by the muscles attached to them, and are further extended when the joints are flexed by the weight of the body on the ground. When the force stretching them is removed, they recoil, releasing about 93% of the energy used to stretch them (Section 7.2.2); this energy is used to accelerate the animal forwards and upwards during the next stride.

(b)   Most of the joints bend through a much greater angle during fast running; the flexion of joints in the legs and feet absorbs the impact of the feet and the ground, and also permits the tendons and ligaments around the joint to be stretched.

(c)   In quadrupeds, the muscles of the spinal column actively produce forces that flex and extend the spine, thereby increasing the effective length of each stride; the muscles of the back may also absorb some of the energy released when the limbs hit the ground at the end of each stride. Such movements also help to ventilate the lungs if breathing and stride movements are coupled.

Question 8.5

(a)   As explained in Section 8.3.2, hooves are adapted to withstand the very large forces imposed upon them in galloping (see Figure 8.7), up to three times the body weight. At slower speeds, the maximum forces are less than twice body weight (Figure 8.3), so the safety factor is not exceeded even if the animal is carrying a load equal to its body weight.

(b)   Horses of similar size and build are able to move greater loads further because they walk or trot most efficiently at almost exactly the same speed (see Figure 8.8) and change gaits at the same speed.

(c)   Galloping involves large changes in kinetic energy in both the vertical and horizontal directions. Skilled riders adjust their posture to accommodate these forces, but the forces generated by the galloping horses act to eject 'passive' riders and loads.

(d)   Horses can gallop well with a girth fastened tightly around their ribs because the lungs are ventilated mainly by locomotory movements including flexion and extension of the back. Expansion of the ribs contributes little.

Question 8.6

(a)   The arched foot is compressed by the weight of the body during the support phase of each stride, stretching the plantar aponeurosis. Much of the energy involved is stored and released when the body's weight is removed from the foot.

(b)   The weight of the body also flexes the ankle, stretching the tendons and muscles of the calf. If the muscles contract to stress the tendons appropriately, much of this energy is stored as elastic strain and released to power the next stride.

(c)   The upright posture of humans restricts the use of the back musculature to increase the stride length or for energy storage, as happens in quadrupedal galloping. But many of the muscles that extend the leg insert onto the pelvis and lower back, and of course all are controlled by spinal nerves.

Question 8.7

Only (a), (d) and (e) are correct (Section 8.4.1). (b) Large animals do not have proportionately less muscle as a whole (Section 3.2) and in the distal flexor muscle of the forelimb they have slightly more than small species of similar body form and locomotory habits (see Figure 8.12a). (c) The relationship between speed and body size is complicated and non-linear, but as a generalization, this statement is false. There is nothing in Sections 5.3.3 and 5.4.1 to suggest that (f) could be true.

Question 8.8

For tendons of similar mechanical properties, the quantity of elastic strain energy that can be stored in tendons depends upon their length. Large animals have longer legs and so their limb muscles can have longer tendons. Allometric comparison also shows that the distal limb muscles of large mammals are proportionately stronger than those of smaller ones, so they can probably apply greater stresses to the long, stout tendons to which they are attached, enabling them to work more efficiently as energy stores.

Question 8.9

(a)   The muscles of weight-lifters produce large forces while contracting almost isometrically. The skeleton is strong with stout flanges for muscle attachment and the muscles hypertrophy to become very massive. The shoulders and hips are broad but the limbs may be relatively short. Since weight-lifters do not run or jump, obesity presents little mechanical disadvantage and some are quite fat.

(b)   Long-distance running involves generating moderate forces at moderate speeds of contraction, but the muscles must be able to use fatty acids as fuel; therefore the fast oxidative fibres are well-developed and other types of fibres may acquire the ability to use fatty acids as fuel. The total energetic cost of travel is greater for heavier athletes, so marathon runners tend to have moderately massive muscles but to be lean, sometimes even slight, people.

(c)   Basketball players have to jump and run very fast for short distances. They tend to be tall people with long legs and hence long muscles with long tendons attached to them, in which both kinds of fast phasic fibres are well-developed. The maximum height to which a person can jump is limited by the total body mass, so basketball players do not have excess fat and their skeletons are long and slender, not massive.

ACKNOWLEDGEMENTS

The Course Team thank Dr Belina Bullard, European Molecular Biology Laboratory, Heidelberg, Germany, for helpful advice on recent developments in muscle research and on Chapters 5 and 6, and for the provision of dead moles for Figure 6.8a, and Dr D. J. Law, School of Biological Sciences, University of Kansas, Kansas City, Mo., USA, for providing the electron micrograph in Figure 6.6; also: Dr Alicia El Haj, University of Birmingham, Birmingham, England, for advice on Chapters 1 and 2; Dr Michael J. Cullen, Muscular Dystrophy Laboratories, School of Neuroscience, Newcastle General Hospital, Newcastle-upon-Tyne, for providing Figure 2.13 and the electron micrographs in Chapter 5, and much useful advice on Chapters 5 and 6; and Professor John D. Currey for advice on Chapters 7 and 8.

Grateful acknowledgement is made to the following sources for permission to reproduce material in this book:

Figures 1.1, 1.2, 1.3, 1.4, 1.7, 2.7: Tanner, J. M. (1978) *Foetus Into Man: Physical Growth From Conception To Maturity*, 2nd edn, Castlemead Publications; *Figure 1.5:* UNICEF copyright Arild Vollan (photographer); *Figure 1.6:* Courtesy Dr Basiro Davey; *Figure 1.8:* Bryden, M. M. (1969) 'Growth of the southern elephant seal', *Growth*, **33**, p. 72, Growth Publishing Co. Inc.; *Figures 1.10(a), 4.2, 5.13, 7.5, 7.12:* Copyright Dr C. Pond; *Figures 1.10(b) and (c), 2.8, 2.9, 2.12, 3.8, 4.1, 6.8, 7.14(b)*: Mike Levers/Open University; *Figure 2.1:* Reprinted with permission from Goss, R. J. 'Hypertrophy versus hyperplasia', *Science*, **153**, pp. 1615–1620. Copyright 1966 American Association for the Advancement of Science; *Figures 2.2, 4.4, 4.6, 4.7, 4.8, 4.9:* Lamb, M. J. (1977) *Biology of Ageing*, Chapman and Hall; *Figures 2.3, 2.4, 2.5, 2.6, 2.10, 2.14:* Goss, R. J. (1978) *The Physiology of Growth*, Academic Press Inc.; *Figure 2.11:* Courtesy Dr Alica El Haj; *Figures 2.13, 5.2, 5.3, 5.4, 5.5, 5.6, 5.8, 5.10, 5.14, 5.15, 5.16:* Courtesy Dr M. J. Cullen; *Figure 2.15:* Pond, C. M. (1994) 'The structure and organization of adipose tissue in naturally obese non-hibernating mammals', in *Obesity in Europe '93*, ed. Ditschuneit, H., Gries, F. A., Hauner, H., Schusdziarra, V. and Wechsler, J. G., *Proc. 5th European Congress of Obesity*, J. Libbey & Co.; *Figures 3.1 and 3.2:* Davis, D. D. (1962) 'Allometric relationships in lions versus domestic cats', *Evolution*, **16**, pp. 509–510, Society for the Study of Evolution; *Figure 3.4:* Currey, J. D. (1977) 'Problems of scaling in the skeleton', in Pedley T. J. (ed.), *Scale Effects in Animal Locomotion*, Academic Press Ltd; *Figure 3.5:* Schmidt-Nielsen, K. (1977) 'Problems of scaling, locomotion and physiological correlates' in Pedley T. J. (ed.), *Scale Effects in Animal Locomotion,* Academic Press Ltd; *Figure 3.6:* Alexander, R. McN. (1974) 'The mechanics of jumping by a dog', *Journal of Zoology*, **173**, p. 559, by permission of Oxford University Press; *Figure 3.7:* 'Factors of safety in the structure of animals', *Science Progress*, **67**, p. 113, Science and Technology Letters; *Figure 3.9:* Harkness, R. D. (1968) 'Mechanical properties of collagenous tissue', in Gould B. S. (ed.), *Treatise On Collagen*, 2A, Academic Press Ltd; *Figure 3.10:* Wilkie, D. R. (1977) 'Metabolism and body size', in Pedley T. J. (ed.), *Scale Effects in Animal Locomotion*, Academic Press Ltd; Elia, M. (1992) 'Organ and tissue contribution to metabolic rate', in Kinney, J. M. and Tucker, H. N. (eds), *Energy Metabolism: Tissue Determinants and Cellular Corollaries*, Raven Press, New York, pp. 61–79; *Figure 3.12:* Reprinted with permission from Schmidt-Nielsen,

K. 'Locomotion: energy cost of swimming, flying and running', *Science*, **177**, p. 223, Copyright 1972 American Association for the Advancement of Science; *Figure 3.13:* Taylor, C. R. *et al.* (1970) 'Scaling of the energetic cost of running to body size in mammals', *American Journal of Physiology*, **219**, The American Physiological Society; *Figure 3.14:* Taylor C. R. *et al.* (1981) 'Design of the mammalian respiratory system', *Respiration Physiology*, **144**, Elsevier Science BV; *Figure 3.15:* Mathieu-Costello, O. *et al.* (1981) 'Design of the mammalian respiratory system VII', *Respiration Physiology*, **144**, Elsevier Science BV; *Figure 3.16:* Cott, H. B. (1961) 'Scientific results of an enquiry into the ecology and economic status of the Nile crocodile (*Crocodylus niloticus*) in Uganda and Southern Rhodesia', *Transactions of the Zoological Society of London*, **29**, Zoological Society of London; *Figure 4.3:* Courtesy Mrs Christina Lockyer; *Figures 4.5 and 4.18:* From *Cancer, Science and Society*, by Cairns. Copyright © 1978 by W. H. Freeman and Company. Used with permission; *Figures 4.10, 4.11:* Comfort, A. (1979) *The Biology of Senescence*, 3rd edn, Churchill Livingstone; *Figure 4.12:* Reprinted with permission from *Nature*, **181**, p. 787, Copyright 1958 Macmillan Magazines Ltd; *Figure 4.13:* Shock, N. (1956) 'Some physiological aspects of ageing in man', *Bulletin of the New York Academy of Medicine*, **32**, 1956; *Figure 4.14:* Davies, I. (1983) *Ageing:Studies In Biology No 151*, Edward Arnold; *Figure 4.15:* Strehler, B. (1962) *Time, Cells and Ageing*, Academic Press Inc.; *Figure 4.16:* Courtesy Dr Julia Burne an Professor Martin Raff; *Figure 4.17:* Keith Howard/Open University; *Figure 5.1:* Offer, G. (1973) 'The molecular basis of muscular contraction', in Bull *et al.* (eds), *Companion to Biochemistry*, Longman Group Ltd; *Figure 5.5:* adapted from Trinick, J. (1991), *Current Opinion in Cell Biology*, **2**, pp. 112–119, Current Science; *Figure 5.8:* Courtesy Dr E. Fyrberg; *Figure 5.9:* Lowry, J. (1960) *Structure and Function of Muscle*, **1**, Academic Press Inc.; *Figure 5.12:* Courtesy M. C. Thompson; *Figure 6.2:* Huxley, A. F. *et al.* (1966) *Journal of Physiology*, **184**, The Physiological Society; *Figure 6.3:* Curtin, N. A. and Davies, R. E. (1975) 'Very high tension with very little ATP breakdown by active skeletal muscle', *Journal of Mechanochemistry and Cell Motility*, **3**, Gordon and Breach Science Publishers; *Figure 6.6:* Courtesy Dr D. J. Law; *Figure 6.7:* Currey, J. D., *The Mechanical Adaptations of Bone*. Copyright © 1984 by Princeton University Press. Reproduced by permission of Princeton University Press; *Figures 7.1, 7.4:* Courtesy Dr R. F. Ker; *Figure 7.2:* Courtesy Dr J. Woodhead-Galloway; *Figure 7.3:* Courtesy Professor Andrew Miller; *Figure 7.6:* Courtesy Professor J. D. Currey; *Figure 7.7:* Rubin C. T. and Lanyon L. E. (1982) 'Limb mechanics as a function of speed and gait', *Journal of Experimental Biology*, **101**, Company of Biologists Ltd; *Figures 7.9 and 7.10:* Brear, K., Currey, J. D. and Pond, C. M. (1990) 'Ontogenetic changes in the mechanical properties of the polar bear *Ursus maritimus*, *Journal of Zoology*, **222**, by permission of Oxford University Press; *Figure 7.11:* Courtesy Sally and Richard Greenhill; *Figure 7.14(a):* Courtesy Dr D. H. Janzen; *Figures 8.1a, 8.2, 8.3:* From 'Walking and running', *American Scientist*, **72**, Sigma XI; *Figures 8.1b, 8.1c:* Redrawn from *Journal of Biological Education*, (1984) **18**, p. 136, Institute of Biology; *Figure 8.5:* Alexander, R. McN. and Goldspink, G. (1977) *Mechanics and Energetics of Animal Locomotion*, Chapman and Hall, © Alexander, R. McN. and Goldspink, G; *Figure 8.7:* Hildebrand, M. (1974) *Analysis of Vertebrate Structure*, Copyright © 1974 by John Wiley and Sons Inc. Reprinted by permission of John Wiley and Sons Inc.; *Figure 8.8:* Reprinted with permission from *Nature*, **292**, p. 240, Copyright 1981 Macmillan Magazines Ltd; *Figure 8.9:* adapted from Alexander, R. McN. *et al.*

(1982) 'The role of tendon elasticity in the locomotion of the camel (*Camelus dromedarius*)', *Journal of Zoology*, **198**, p. 297, Academic Press Ltd; *Figures 8.10 and 8.11:* Reprinted with permission from Bramble, D. M. and Carrier, D. R. (1983) 'Running and breathing in mammals', *Science*, **219**, p. 253, Copyright 1983 American Association for the Advancement of Science; *Figure 8.12:* adapted from Alexander, R. McN., Jayes, A. S., Maloiy, G. M. O. and Wathuta, E. M. (1981) *J. Zool. Lond.*, **194**, pp. 539–552, by permission of Oxford University Press.

INDEX

SR *see* sarcoplasmic reticulum
starvation, 38, 57
Steatornis caripensis see Venezuelan oil
  bird
stem cell, 36
sternum, *193*, 194
stoat (*Mustela erminea*), musculo-
  skeletal system, 193–4
strap-like muscle, 188
structural allometry, 74–81
subscapularis muscle, 188
succinate dehydrogenase, 157
suckling, growth while, 17–19
suni antelope, *89*, 90, *91*
superoxide dismutase (SOD), 125
surface area (organisms), 70
suture joint, 218
swan, black, healed fracture, 54
synovial joint, 220

T-tubule, 140, 143–4
    abnormal, in muscular dystrophy,
      167, 168
Talpa europaea see mole
Tanner, J., 6
Taylor, R., 88–92, 241, 243
teeth
    defective, cause of death, 129–30
    eruption, 12–13
    protection by fluoride, 210
    wear, indicator of age, 102–5
tendons, 201, 202
    heat production in, 206
    in legs of camels, 243–4
    length and thickness, 206–9
    mechanical properties, 203, 204–6
    and muscles, 136, 187–94
    proprioreceptors in, 196
    safety factors, 77
teres minor muscle, 188
terrapin
    head retractor muscles, 188
    red-eared terrapin (*Trachemys
      scripta elegans*), effect of iodine
      deficiency, 25–7
tetanus (muscle contraction), *154*, **155**
TGF-ß *see* transforming growth factor
thyroxin, 24–7, 85

tiger, allometric relationship, 73
tissue growth, effect of undernutrition,
  10–11
tissue regeneration *see* regeneration
  (tissue)
titin, 147, 150, 152, 165
toes, 252
tonic fibres (muscle), **156**, 159, 192
tortoise (*Geoemyda grandis*)
    efficiency of muscles, 185
    longevity, 112, *113*
    walking, 234–5
trabeculae, 211, 216
Trachemys scripta elegans see terrapin,
  red-eared
transforming growth factor (TGF-ß), 27,
  48
transverse tubule *see* T-tubule
triad (muscle), 144
tricarboxylic acid cycle enzymes, 58,
  157
tropomyosin, 146, 153
troponin, 146, 153, 165–6
trot, 235n.
    oxygen use in, 242
tsetse fly, flight muscles, 141, *142*, 154n.
tumour formation, 40, 128, 130–1
turtle
    sea (*Chelonia mydas*), hip joint, 220,
      222
    wood turtle (*Clemmys insculpta*),
      head retractor muscles, *188*
twitch (muscle contraction),
    154–5

ubiquitin, 37–8
undernutrition
    and delayed senescence, 116, 122,
      123
    effect on adipose tissue formation,
      62
    effect on tissue growth, 10–11

Venezuelan oil bird (*Steatornis
  caripensis*), nutrition of young, 95
viruses, apoptosis inhibitors, 128
vitamin A, effects of deficiency on
  growth, 12

vitamin D, effects of deficiency on
  growth, 12

walk, walking, 228–9, **230**–3
    forces generated in, 227–8, 230–2
    speed, 233–4
    tortoises, 234–5
wallaby (*Macropus rufogriseus*)
    breathing while hopping, 245
    locomotion, 236–7
wasp
    digger, 193
    longevity, 112, *113*
water bug, giant (*Lethocerus*), 136–7
Weibel, E., 88–92
weightlessness, 213
weight-lifter, 57, 197
whale
    blue, growth while suckling, 16
    fin (*Balaenoptera physalus*),
      intermuscular adipose tissue, 158
wolf
    epiphyses, 50
    running, 239, 243
wolverine, adipocytes and body
  composition, 62–4
work (muscle) *see* negative work;
  positive work
woven bone, 210
wrestler, 197

Young, T., 205n.
Young's modulus, 205
    bone, 212, 213
    ontogenetic changes, 215
    tendon, 205, 206

Z-line, *138*, **139**, 140, *141*, 143, *144*, *145*
    abnormal, in muscular dystrophy,
      167, 168, 169
    attacked by calpain, 165–6
    components, 147–8
    in different fibre types, 159
    internal structure, 143
    in mutant flies, *149*, 150
    in overshortened muscle, 180
    role, 144
    and sarcomere assembly, 148